THE NOBEL PRIZE WINNERS

Chemistry

THE NOBEL PRIZE WINNERS

Chemistry

Volume 2
1938 – 1968

Edited by
FRANK N. MAGILL

SALEM PRESS
Pasadena, California   Englewood Cliffs, New Jersey

∞ The paper used in these volumes conforms to the
American National Standard for Permanence of Paper
for Printed Library Materials, Z39.48-1984.

Library of Congress Cataloging-in-Publication Data
The Nobel Prize winners: chemistry/edited by Frank N.
Magill. p. cm.
Includes bibliographical references.
Contents: v. 1. 1901-1937—v. 2. 1938-1968—v. 3. 1969-
1989.
1. Chemists—Biography. 2. Nobel prizes.
I. Magill, Frank Northen, 1907-
QD21.N64   1990   90-8092
540'.79—dc20   CIP
ISBN 0-89356-561-x (set)
ISBN 0-89356-563-6 (volume 2)

PRINTED IN THE UNITED STATES OF AMERICA

CONTENTS

THE NOBEL PRIZE WINNERS

ALPHABETICAL LIST OF PRIZE WINNERS

THE NOBEL PRIZE WINNERS

THE NOBEL PRIZE WINNERS

THE NOBEL PRIZE WINNERS

THE NOBEL PRIZE WINNERS

Chemistry

1938

Chemistry
Richard Kuhn, Germany

Physics
Enrico Fermi, Italy

Physiology or Medicine
Corneille Heymans, Belgium

Literature
Pearl S. Buck, United States

Peace
Nansen International Office for Refugees

RICHARD KUHN
1938

Born: Vienna-Döbling, Austro-Hungarian Empire; December 3, 1900
Died: Heidelberg, West Germany; July 31, 1967
Nationality: German
Areas of concentration: Vitamin synthesis and stereochemistry

Kuhn structurally identified and synthesized lactoflavin (vitamin B_2), pyridoxine (vitamin B_6), p-aminobenzoic acid, and pantothenic acid. He was also able to synthesize many analogues and reversibly competitive inhibitors of these substances, which he called "antivitamins"

The Award

Presentation

Richard Kuhn declined to accept the 1938 Nobel Prize in Chemistry. In 1949, he accepted the gold medal and diploma that accompanied the award without ceremony.

Nobel lecture

Because Kuhn refused the prize, he did not deliver a Nobel lecture.

Critical reception

The Nobel Prize Committees faced a considerable dilemma after 1935 because of the increasingly tense political situation in Europe. The selection of Carl von Ossietzky to be the 1935 recipient of the Nobel Peace Prize had so angered Adolf Hitler that he ordered German scientists to refuse the Nobel Prize thereafter. At the time of his selection, Ossietzky, a pacifist, resided in a concentration camp for the "antisocial" activity of opposing German rearmament.

The Nobel Committee for Chemistry withheld the prize for 1938 but decided to award it belatedly the next year. Consequently, they announced its recipient, Kuhn, concurrently with their announcement of the 1939 recipients, one of whom (Adolf Butenandt) was also a German citizen. The announcement came on November 9, 1939, about two months after the outbreak of World War II, which further added to the confusion surrounding the 1938 prize for chemistry.

American and European newspapers virtually ignored Kuhn's belated selection as the 1938 Nobel laureate in chemistry. A brief notice in *The New York Times* announced the selection of the two Germans by the Nobel Committees for Chemistry and speculated that they would honor Hitler's wishes by declining the awards. An equally brief notice two days later in the *Times* confirmed that both men had refused their awards.

The Times of London and *Le Temps* (Paris) also carried brief announcements of the awards on November 9 and predictably (since their countries were at war with Germany) sarcastic announcements of their rejection on November 11. Along with the announcement that both men had declined to accept the Nobel Prize, German newspapers, including the *Deutsche Rundschau* and the official Nazi organ, the *Völkischer Beobachter*, included statements from both Kuhn and Butenandt supporting Hitler's decision to discourage Germans from accepting Nobel awards. Given the political situation in Germany at the time, they could hardly have done otherwise and remained in their own country. The German newspapers also announced that Kuhn and Butenandt were the recipients of special awards created in 1937 by the German government.

Biography

Richard Kuhn, the only child of Richard Clemens and Angelika Rodler Kuhn, was born on December 3, 1900, at Vienna-Döbling in the Austro-Hungarian Empire. His mother conducted his education at home until he was nine years old, at which time he entered Döbling Gymnasium. At Döbling he was for eight years a schoolmate of Wolfgang Pauli, the 1945 Nobel laureate in physics. In January, 1918, the Austro-Hungarian government conscripted Kuhn, along with the rest of his age group, into the army. He served honorably until his discharge after World War I on November 18, 1918.

Four days after his discharge, Kuhn matriculated at the University of Vienna and studied there for three semesters. In 1920, he transferred to the University of Munich, arriving there just at the time that Adolf Hitler was beginning his meteoric career in Bavarian right-wing politics that culminated with Hitler's arrest and imprisonment after the Beer-Hall Putsch in 1923. Kuhn avoided the political turmoil, rampant not only on the streets of Munich but also on the university campus itself, and concentrated instead on his studies. He completed his Ph.D. in 1922 under the direction of Richard Willstätter, with a dissertation entitled "Zur Spezifität von Enzymen im Kohlenhydratstoff wechsel" (on the specificity of enzymes in carbohydrate metabolism). Shortly thereafter he received his docentship and lectured in chemistry at the University of Munich until 1926, at which time he moved to Zurich, Switzerland, as professor of chemistry at the Eidgenössische Technische Hochschule. In 1928, he married Daisy Hartmann, who eventually bore him two sons and four daughters. In 1929, he became director of the new Chemistry Institute of the Kaiser Wilhelm Institute for Medical Research at Heidelberg and professor of chemistry at Heidelberg University. He occupied those positions until his death in 1967. During his long and productive career he published more than seven hundred scientific papers and won more than fifty major scientific awards, including the 1938 Nobel Prize in Chemistry.

Scientific Career

Kuhn demonstrated his genius for experiment early in his career in the Munich laboratory of Willstätter. Willstätter nurtured and encouraged the characteristics that distinguished Kuhn's later scientific achievements: meticulous precision and discipline in the conception and conduct of experiments, enhanced by an imaginative willingness to depart from widely accepted chemical concepts. Kuhn demonstrated these characteristics in his doctoral dissertation and in his *Habilitation* thesis, "Der Wirkungsmechanismus der Amylassen: Ein Beitrag zum Konfigurations-Problem der Starke" (mechanism of the action of amylases), while still at the University of Munich, both works being expansions of experiments begun by Willstätter.

This early research led him into the problems of optical stereochemistry, the solutions to which he sought for the remainder of his life. While in Zurich, he made several discoveries concerning benzidine, which refuted previously held scientific opinions concerning that important substance. These discoveries resulted from Kuhn's investigation of additions on ethylene bonds. He and his coworkers first demonstrated that the addition of hypochlorous acid to fumaric or maleic acid produces chloromalic acid. The combination also results in ring closure to form ethylene oxide dicarboxylic acid. The work on additions led Kuhn and his team directly into the study of inhibited rotation in diphenyls, particularly ortho-substituted derivatives. This study allowed Kuhn to demonstrate that benzidine is not angled and spaced 1.5 angstroms apart, as chemists had previously believed, but instead is stretched out on a plane with the two NH_2- groups about 10 angstroms apart.

These and subsequent studies defining the level of activation provoked by the rotation of ortho-substituted diphenyls allowed Kuhn and his staff to formulate several new concepts that quantitatively defined the spatial characteristics of particular groups of compounds. Thus the concepts "constellation," "atropisomerism," and "conformation," coined by Kuhn, became familiar and valuable terms in organic chemistry. Kuhn and his coworkers in Zurich also definitively established the existence of colored hydrocarbons and defined the structure of carotenoids.

Upon moving to Heidelberg, Kuhn began an investigation of water-soluable vitamins with his colleagues. His ingeniously devised and precisely conducted experiments first isolated and crystallized vitamin B_2 (lactoflavin or riboflavin) and then effected its synthesis by 1935. In one of these curious and frequent coincidences of science, a chemist working in Zurich, Paul Karrer, achieved the same results in a different way. The two scientists announced their discoveries almost simultaneously. Karrer shared the 1937 Nobel Prize in Chemistry for his work.

Subsequent experiments in 1939 led Kuhn and his assistants to the identification of vitamin B_6 (adermin or pyridoxine) and to its synthesis, and then to the discovery of p-aminobenzoic acid and pantothenic acid. These proved to be especially efficacious agents in preventing dermatitis. He and his laboratory workers then successfully synthesized numerous analogues and reversibly competitive inhibitors ("antivitamins," substances that render vitamins ineffective). It was this work on carotenoids and vitamins that won for Kuhn the 1938 Nobel Prize. All these substances have proved to be of considerable medicinal value, particularly in combating skin diseases.

During World War II, Kuhn worked on several projects concerning the prevention of skin diseases among front-line soldiers. Kuhn's wartime activities have led some of his critics to charge him with supporting the Nazis, an accusation that is unfair and misleading. Kuhn never joined the Nazi Party, even though it would have been expedient for him to have done so and might have advanced his career. It is true that he and the Nazis held similar views on several matters, including German nationalism. Kuhn, like many Auslanddeutscher (Germans born outside the territorial boundaries of Germany), was intensely patriotic. This patriotism did not, however, make him a supporter of the Nazis; Kuhn's scientific research during the war showed a desire to help people, not to support the Nazi regime.

When American troops occupied Heidelberg in 1945, Kuhn managed to ingratiate himself with the wife of a military commander of the city by showing her how to turn green plants into red plants by adding triphenyltetrazolium chloride to fertilizer. Through her intervention, his laboratories were not dismantled during the deindustrialization and "denazification" phase of the American occupation, and Kuhn was allowed to continue in his position. Between 1946 and 1948 Kuhn participated in the transformation of the Kaiser Wilhelm Society for Scientific Research into the politically more acceptable Max Planck Society for the Advancement of Science, thus preserving the endowment of the original society. He served on the new society's senate and later as its vice president. In 1948, he became the editor of the journal *Justus Liebigs Annalen der Chemie* (Justus Liebig's chemistry annual), a position he held until his death in 1967.

In 1949, Kuhn resumed his scientific experiments in biochemistry. His interests had apparently shifted by this time to medical and agricultural applications of his discoveries. He became particularly interested in the identification of factors or substances that allowed organisms, particularly human organisms, to resist infection and diseases. Among other substances, Kuhn and his associates isolated nitrogenous oligosaccharides from human milk and brain gangliosides, both particularly effective in combating bacterial infection. He and his colleagues also identified and synthesized potato alkaloid-glycoside (demissin), which effectively resists the larvae of the potato beetle.

Kuhn conducted important experiments in the 1960's concerning human resistance to influenza viruses. He found that a component of human milk, lactaminyl oligosaccharide, resists the spread of the influenza viruses. Kuhn's laboratory developed methods for the isolation and synthesis of amino-sugar split products of N-oligosaccharides as specifics against influenza. Kuhn was still at work on this project when he died in 1967.

In addition to the 1938 Nobel Prize, Kuhn received the prestigious Louis Pasteur Prize, the Paterno Medal, and the Goethe Prize, among many other honors. He was a member of numerous academic societies and scientific academies in many different countries.

Bibliography

Primary
CHEMISTRY: *Die Fermente und ihre Wirkungen*, 1924 (with Carl Oppenheimer);

Lehrbuch der Enzyme: Chemie, physikalische Chemie und Biologie, 1927 (with Carl Oppenheimer); "Conjugated Double Bonds," *Helvetica Chimica Acta*, vol. 12, 1929 (with Alfred Winterstein and László Karlovitz); "Catalytic Microhydrogenation of Organic Compounds," *Zeitschrift für angewissenschaften Chemie*, vol. 47, 1934 (with Ernest Möller); *Untersuchungen über Enzyme*, 1936 (with R. Willstätter); "Synthesis of Adermine," *Naturwissenschaften*, vol. 27, 1939 (with Gerhard Wendt, Kurt Westphal, and Otto Westphal); *Biochemistry*, 1947 (with H. Fischer et al.); "Synthesis of *meso*-inositol," *Justus Liebigs Annalen der Chemie*, vol. 565, 1949 (with Günter Quadbeck and Erich Rohm); *The Problem of Self-Sterility, and Physical Properties and Chemical Reactions of Zwitterions*, 1951.

Secondary
Baer, Hans H. "Richard Kuhn." *Advances in Carbohydrate Chemistry and Biochemistry* 24 (1969): 1-12. Baer's brief biographical sketch of Kuhn is sympathetic and accurate. The author includes the best account available in English of Kuhn's postwar research. Recommended.
Carmon, Arye. "The Impact of the Nazi Racial Decrees on the University of Heidelberg: A Case Study." *Yad Vashem Studies* 11 (1968): 131-163. Contains little information on Kuhn specifically, but does give a good overview of the milieu in which he worked during the Nazi era.
Dorn, Karl. *Werkstoffe: Miracles of German Chemistry*. New York: German Library of Information, 1941. This work is of limited value because of its obvious propaganda intent. It contains some information about Kuhn's work with vitamins and carotenoids but virtually nothing about his personal life.
Farber, Eduard. *Nobel Prize Winners in Chemistry, 1901-1961*. Rev. ed. New York: Abelard-Schuman, 1963. Includes brief accounts of Kuhn's life and work up to 1938, but virtually nothing about later career. Suitable for all readers.
Montefiore, Leonard G. *The Spirit of German Universities*. London: St. Clements, 1936. Uses Heidelberg as an example of the national socialist spirit of the German universities in the 1930's. Does not mention Kuhn specifically, but will perhaps help in understanding his failure to come to the aid of his "non-Aryan" colleagues during the Nazi era.

Paul Madden

1939

Chemistry
Adolf Butenandt, Germany
Leopold Stephen Ružička, Croatia and Switzerland

Physics
Ernest Orlando Lawrence, United States

Physiology or Medicine
Gerhard Domagk, Germany

Literature
Frans Eemil Sillanpää, Finland

Peace
no award

ADOLF BUTENANDT
1939

Born: Bremerhaven-Lehe, Germany; March 24, 1903

Nationality: German
Areas of concentration: Hormones and attractants, viruses, and carcinogenesis

Butenandt's research concerned biologically active substances present in minute quantities. He isolated the human hormones estrone, androsterone, and progesterone. He also studied animal hormones, including sex attractants (pheromones) in invertebrates

The Award

Presentation

The Nobel Prize in Chemistry in 1939 was awarded jointly to Adolf Butenandt of Germany and Leopold Ružička of Switzerland. The award to Butenandt was in recognition of his work on the sex hormones. Because of the hysteria that gripped Nazi Germany in the 1930's, Butenandt, like Richard Kuhn the year before, was forbidden to accept the award. Although the award was not officially presented, the Nobel Foundation subsequently provided a brief description of his work.

The sex hormones belong to a general class of compounds known as the steroids. The steroid molecule consists of four rings fused together; thus, it is a tetracyclic substance. Three of the rings are composed of six carbon atoms, and the fourth is made up of only five atoms (a "ring" is a group of three or more atoms bound together to produce a form that approximates a polygon or a circle). Estrone, which produces estrus changes in females, was isolated independently by Butenandt and Edward A. Doisy in 1929. Progesterone, the hormone that is responsible for the maintenance of pregnancy, was isolated by Butenandt, Ulrich Westphal, and Walter Hohlweg in 1934. In the same year, three other groups, one in Germany, another in the United States, and the third in Switzerland, also reported the isolation of this hormone. The male sex hormone was first isolated in 1931 by Butenandt and Kurt Tscherning.

Following the initial isolation of estrone, George F. Marrian in London reported the isolation of estriol, another estrogen, from human pregnancy urine. Although estriol is less potent than estrone when given intravenously, it is more potent when taken orally. Butenandt demonstrated that estriol can be converted into estrone with the elimination of water. When two additional hydrogen atoms were added to estrone, a product more potent than estrone was obtained. This proved to be estradiol, an estrogen subsequently isolated by Doisy and his associates in the United States from ovarian tissue.

That the sex hormones are steroids was established by Butenandt and other investigators through both chemical degradation and synthesis. Both estrone and estriol were degraded by Butenandt and his collaborators to the same tricyclic compound that was obtained from cholesterol and the bile acids. Conversion of cholesterol into progesterone was achieved by Butenandt's group in 1939. The structure of androsterone was inferred by Butenandt in 1932 with only 25 milligrams of this hormone on hand. The correctness of the structure was established by Ružička in 1934, when he converted cholesterol into androsterone. Although denied the opportunity to accept the Nobel Prize in 1939, Butenandt received the gold medal and the diploma associated with the prize in 1949.

Nobel lecture
   Because of the political conditions in Germany and the threat of war in Europe, Butenandt did not deliver a Nobel lecture.

Critical reception
   Butenandt, together with Ružička, was awarded the Nobel Prize in Chemistry shortly after Germany invaded Poland. As a result of the public outcry over the invasion and international concern over the situation, the award to Butenandt did not receive the attention that it deserved. Butenandt had already attracted worldwide attention, however, when he isolated estrone at the age of twenty-six in 1929. In 1935, he visited the United States and Canada, lecturing in numerous universities at the invitation of the Rockefeller Foundation. In 1961, he delivered the Windaus Memorial Lecture, which was sponsored by the Chemical Society of London. In this lecture, he expressed his feelings, as well as those of fellow German chemist Adolf Windaus, toward the political regime that allowed him to pursue his scientific activities and yet would not permit him to accept the coveted Nobel Prize.

Biography
   Butenandt was born on March 24, 1903, at Bremerhaven-Lehe in Germany. His parents were Otto Louis Max and Wilhelmine Thomfohrde Butenandt. His father was a businessman whose fortune rose and fell with the political fortunes of Germany. In his lifetime, Adolf Butenandt witnessed the demise of the German empire, the collapse of the Weimar Republic, the resurgence of nationalism, and the destruction of the Third Reich. In his youth, he set his heart on being a scientist, and to this end he devoted his efforts. At the University of Marburg, which he attended from 1921 to 1925, he concentrated on both chemistry and biology. Competitive and outgoing, he also took up the hazardous sport of dueling, a favorite pastime among university students in Germany prior to its being outlawed because of the frequency of injuries and deaths.
   Upon completion of his studies at Marburg, Butenandt was accepted as a graduate student in Adolf Windaus' institute at the University of Göttingen. Professor Windaus was one of the titans of natural product chemistry in Germany in the 1920's. Among Butenandt's contemporaries were Richard Willstätter, Heinrich Wieland, and Hans Fischer. Willstätter was awarded the Nobel Prize in 1915, while

Windaus won the 1927 and Wieland the 1928 prize, and Fischer would receive the prize in 1930. After a relatively brief period of two years, Butenandt was granted the Ph.D. degree, whereupon he began his swift rise in the scientific world.

In 1931, Butenandt married his laboratory assistant, Erika von Ziegner. They became parents of seven children, Ina, Otfrid, Heide, Eckart, Anke, Imme, and Maike. His goal of helping others to understand the chemistry of the living system was attained, and his achievements have been amply recognized by his peers.

Scientific Career

Butenandt began his research career in Professor Adolf Windaus' laboratory at the University of Göttingen in the autumn of 1925. At that time, Windaus was deeply immersed in studies on vitamin D. He had also been involved in steroid research since 1903, and for this work he would receive the Nobel Prize in Chemistry in 1928. Windaus initially assigned to Butenandt the problem of isolating and determining the structures of the iodine-containing hormones in the thyroid. This problem was set aside six months later, however, when it was learned that George Barger and Charles Harrington in England had solved the problem. Butenandt was then requested to elucidate the structure of rotenone, a substance that is toxic to fish and insects. As a result of his investigation, he was awarded a doctorate in 1927. Butenandt continued his studies on rotenone and related compounds until 1933.

In 1927, at the suggestion of Windaus, he also began to investigate the hormones present in the ovarian follicles. This work was carried out in collaboration with Germany's leading pharmaceutical firm, Schering-Kahlbaum AG of Berlin. Concentrated extracts of pregnancy urine collected by Schering were sent to the Chemistry Institute of Göttingen for processing. Initially, Butenandt worked with extracts of placenta, but by 1929 he had switched to the brown, syrupy urinary extracts of Schering. With the use of acid, alkali, and selective solvents, he was able to obtain fractions which exhibited increasing potency in the estrogen assay devised by Edgar Allen and Edward A. Doisy. This bioassay was performed in Butenandt's laboratory by his assistant, Erika von Ziegner.

In mid-September, 1929, Butenandt submitted the more potent oily fractions to sublimation in high vacuum. The product collected was estrone, which was obtained as beautiful white crystals. By the end of September, Butenandt had obtained 20 milligrams of crystalline estrone. His elation was short-lived, however, for he soon learned that a month earlier, when the Chemistry Institute in Göttingen had been closed for cleaning, Doisy and his associates in the United States reported that they had independently isolated estrone and had displayed the first photographs of this crystalline hormone at the International Physiology Congress in Boston.

On the basis of his work on estrone, Butenandt was appointed *Privatdozent* at the University of Göttingen in 1931. The faculty appointment enabled him to attract more students to his research. With one of them, Tscherning, he isolated the first male sex hormone, androsterone. Isolation of androsterone was greatly facilitated by the experience Butenandt had acquired from the isolation of estrone and by the application of a quantitative bioassay for the detection of androgenicity (the male characteristics) developed and refined by other investigators.

Early in 1934, Butenandt, Westphal, and Hohlweg reported the isolation of progesterone. During the next five years, Butenandt and his students developed a variety of approaches to the synthesis of progesterone from readily available steroids. The knowledge acquired proved invaluable to subsequent investigators in the synthesis of cortisone, a steroid hormone found in the adrenal gland. In 1950, Philip S. Hench and Edward C. Kendall of the Mayo Clinic received the Nobel Prize in Physiology or Medicine for discovering the beneficial effects produced by cortisone in patients afflicted with arthritis. The resultant publicity created a great demand for the hormone. Chemists were inspired to modify the cortisone structure to increase its therapeutic potency and to minimize its side effects. Many of the chemical transformations employed to achieve this goal were patterned after those developed initially by Butenandt and his associates.

In addition to the human hormones, Butenandt studied the hormones of invertebrates. Together with Peter Karlson, he isolated the molting hormone, ecdysone, and established its structure as that of a steroid. Ecdysone is responsible for the caterpillar-pupa-butterfly transformation. This hormone, produced in the prothorax gland of the insect, was found to activate a particular gene site, resulting in the induction of a specific enzyme.

The sex attractants constitute another class of insect hormones which Butenandt and his coworkers investigated for many years. Known also as pheromones, they are emitted by female insects and attract male members of the same species. Because of the possible health hazards posed by insecticides, the use of pheromones has been considered as an alternative means to control the population of insects. In 1959, Butenandt and Erich Hecker reported the first isolation of a pheromone, bombykol, which was extracted from the scent glands of the silk moth, *Bombyx mori*. Butenandt's group determined that bombykol was a long-chain alcohol having two double bonds in the molecule.

Because the dimensions of the steroid nucleus approximate the dimensions of some cancer-producing substances (carcinogens), fears were expressed that a steroid hormone may either be converted directly into a carcinogen in the body or that it may produce uncontrolled cellular proliferation as a result of its activity on the genetic apparatus. In the research institute that he headed, Butenandt directed a group that studied the effects of the sex hormones in producing cancer and their relationship to the polycyclic unsaturated hydrocarbons. The latter compounds are composed of only carbon and hydrogen atoms, with many double bonds in their rings. Some of these compounds were found to be extremely carcinogenic.

During the era following the end of World War II, Butenandt was intensely involved in viral research and in the field of chemical genetics. He and his collaborators sought to delineate the complex relationship among hormone, gene, mutation, enzyme, chemical transformation, and biological response. Their work on the biosynthesis of the insect eye pigments revealed the elaborate chain of genetic and chemical events which occurs in the elicitation of a biological response. Viruses and genes share the common properties of replication, expression, and mutation. Because they can be readily obtained, viruses were effectively used as models for genes in some of Butenandt's studies.

Butenandt's brilliance and abilities were recognized early in his scientific career. After he received the Ph.D. degree, he was appointed scientific assistant in the Chemistry Institute of the University of Göttingen. His work on the sex hormones qualified him for the position of *Privatdozent* in biochemistry at Göttingen. Concurrently, he was appointed head of the organic and biochemistry laboratories. He stayed at Göttingen until 1933, when he was called to the Institute of Technology in Danzig to accept the position of professor and director of the Institute for Organic Chemistry. In 1936, the venerable Max Planck, the noted physicist, persuaded Butenandt to accept the directorship of the Kaiser Wilhelm Institute for Biochemistry in Berlin-Dahlem. He was also appointed an honorary professor at the University of Berlin. In 1945, the institute was moved to Tübingen and renamed the Max Planck Institute for Biochemistry. Butenandt continued as director of the institute and also became professor of physiological chemistry at the University of Tübingen. The institute was moved once again in 1956, this time to Munich. Butenandt was director of the Max Planck Institute for Biochemistry in Munich from 1956 to 1960. During this period he was also professor and director of the Institute for Physiological Chemistry at the University of Munich. In 1960, he succeeded Otto Hahn, the discoverer of the fission of uranium, as president of the Max Planck Society for the Advancement of Science.

Butenandt was awarded the Nobel Prize in 1939 and the Paul Ehrlich Prize in 1953. Besides the Ph.D. degree awarded him by the University of Göttingen in 1927, he received honorary doctorates from the Universities of Graz, Tübingen, Munich, Leeds, Cambridge, Thessalonica, Vienna, Madrid, St. Louis, and Berlin. He was granted membership in numerous scientific societies, among which were the Göttingen Academy of Science, Bavaria Academy of Science, New York Academy of Sciences, Japanese Chemical Society, Japanese Biochemical Society, Spanish Research Council, Austria Academy of Science, and Germany Academy for Nature Research.

Bibliography

Primary
CHEMISTRY: "Progynon, a Crystalline Female Sex Hormone," *Naturwissenschaften*, vol. 17, 1929; "Chemical Investigation of the Sex Hormones," *Angewandte Chemie*, vol. 44, 1931; "Androsterone. I. Isolation and Purification from Male Urine," *Hoppe-Seyler's Zeitschrift für physiologische Chemie*, vol. 229, 1934 (with K. Tscherning); "Conversion of Pregnandiol into the Corpus Luteum Hormone," *Berichte der deutschen chemischen Gesellschaft*, vol. 67B, 1934 (with J. Schmidt); "Lumiestrone," *Berichte der deutschen chemischen Gesellschaft*, vol. 74B, 1941 (with A. Wolff and P. Karlson); "Constitution of Kynurenine," *Naturwissenschaften*,

vol. 30, 1942 (with W. Weidel and W. von Derjugen); "The Isolation in Crystalline Form of a Metamorphosis Hormone of Insects," *Zeitschrift für Naturforschung*, vol. 9B, 1944 (with P. Karlson); "Ommochromes. V. Xanthommatin, an Ocular Pigment Found in Blowflies (*Calliphora erythrocephala*)," *Hoppe-Seyler's Zeitschrift für physiologische Chemie*, vol. 301, 1955 (with G. Neubert); "Windaus Memorial Lecture," *Journal of the Chemical Society*, 1961; *Constitution and Development of the Red Coloring Matter, a Problem of Molecular Biology*, 1968; "History of the Evolution of the Hemoglobin Molecules. Introduction to the Fundamentals and Significance of Molecular Biology," *Stahl Eisen*, vol. 88, 1968; "Isolation of Progesterone. Forty Years Ago," *American Journal of Obstetrics and Gynecology*, vol. 120, 1974 (with U. Westphal); "Fifty Years Ago. The Discovery of Oestrone," *Trends in Biochemical Sciences*, vol. 4, 1979.

Secondary

Brues, Austin M., and Barrón Guzman. "Biochemistry of Cancer." *Annual Review of Biochemistry* 20 (1951): 343-366. In this article, the question of whether estrone is a carcinogen is considered. Based on the work of Butenandt, it was concluded that estrone may be regarded as a cocarcinogen.

Doisy, Edward A. "An Autobiography." *Annual Review of Biochemistry* 45 (1976): 1-9. Nobel laureate Doisy describes his own isolation of estrone at the time that Butenandt was also trying to isolate this hormone.

Fieser, Louis F., and Mary Fieser. *Steroids*. New York: Reinhold, 1959. This book is a classic on steroid chemistry. Butenandt's work in the field is covered in detail. In addition, an account is given by Butenandt (in German) on the background of his work.

Karlson, Peter. "Chemistry and Biochemistry of Insect Hormones." *Angewandte Chemie, International Edition: English* 75 (1963): 257-265. The author, a colleague and former student of Butenandt, describes the chemistry and biochemistry of insect hormones in the light of his work with Butenandt.

───────────. "Why Are So Many Hormones Steroids?" *Hoppe-Seyler's Zeitschrift für physiologische Chemie* 364 (1983): 1067. The author delivered the eighth Adolf Butenandt lecture at the University of Göttingen in honor of Butenandt on his eightieth birthday. He argues that cholesterol was the first steroid formed and that the estrogens represent the most recent stage in the evolutionary process.

Wigglesworth, V. B. "Insect Biochemistry." *Annual Review of Biochemistry* 18 (1949): 595-614. Written by an authority in the field, this article describes the state of knowledge of insect biochemistry before the isolation of the molting hormone, ecdysone, by Butenandt and Karlson.

Leland J. Chinn

1939

Chemistry
Adolf Butenandt, Germany
Leopold Stephen Ružička, Croatia and Switzerland

Physics
Ernest Orlando Lawrence, United States

Physiology or Medicine
Gerhard Domagk, Germany

Literature
Frans Eemil Sillanpää, Finland

Peace
no award

LEOPOLD STEPHEN RUŽIČKA
1939

Born: Vukovar, Croatia; September 13, 1887
Died: Zurich, Switzerland; September 26, 1976
Nationality: Croatian; after 1917, Swiss
Areas of concentration: Terpenes and natural product synthesis

Ružička synthesized the odorant musk compounds civetone and muscone and proved that they are large ring ketones. He analyzed and synthesized medicinally important polyterpenes, among them sterols and sex hormones, and achieved the first synthesis of a sex hormone, androsterone

The Award

Presentation

Leopold Ružička was awarded half the 1939 Nobel Prize in Chemistry for his work in polymethylenes and higher terpenes; the other half went to Adolf Butenandt. Because of World War II, the Nobel Foundation found itself forced to postpone the traditional ceremony in Stockholm for six years. In Zurich, Switzerland, however, Baron H. G. Beck-Friis, the Swedish ambassador, presented the prize to Ružička at a special ceremony of the Royal Swedish Academy of Sciences, when he called Ružička one of the most successful creators of new synthetic methods in the field of organic chemistry.

A skilled experimental researcher, Ružička managed to elucidate the difficult structure of higher terpenes in plants and the arrangement of atoms within their molecules. In both muscone and civetone, which are important perfume constituents, Ružička found that the molecules consist of single rings that are much larger than had previously been thought possible. He then synthesized a number of such compounds and concluded that they are formed in nature from fatty acids. Beck-Friis went on to explain that Ružička also showed the relationship between the polyterpenes and groups of medicinally important compounds—the steroids, bile acids, and sex hormones. His most important contribution in the field of sex hormones, Beck-Friis said, was his work on the male hormones androsterone and testosterone, which led to increased understanding of these physiologically important compounds and ultimately to their technical synthesis.

In his short reply, Ružička acknowledged his debt to an eminent member of the Royal Swedish Academy of Sciences, Jöns Jakob Berzelius, who, in the nineteenth century, had placed experimentation above theory. Berzelius gave chemistry its symbolic language, wrote the first chemical textbook, and, Ružička said, was the cofounder of the first chemical theory, the radical theory. He paved the way for the high standard of science in Sweden and the technological achievements of Alfred Nobel, whose invention of modern explosives technology revolutionized the field of civil engineering for railroads, roads, and mining. In spite of the unforgivable misuse of Nobel's inventions, Ružička expressed the hope that the forces Nobel unleashed would turn into benefits for mankind, according to his vision.

Nobel lecture

Almost six years later, on December 12, 1945, Ružička was finally able to deliver his Nobel lecture in Stockholm, entitled "Multimembered Rings, Higher Terpene Compounds and Male Sex Hormones." Starting with a historical introduction, Ružička revealed his deep roots in the philosophy of "classical" nineteenth century chemists August Kekulé, Adolf von Baeyer, and Sir William Perkin. In 1865, Kekulé proposed a six-membered carbon ring containing three double bonds as the structure of the benzene molecule, an idea that maintained its unique position in organic chemistry for several decades. Von Baeyer, in 1870, found a five-membered heterocyclic ring in indigo which contained not only carbon but also nitrogen. Perkin subsequently synthesized small rings but expressed serious doubt about the possible existence of rings with either fewer or more than five or six members. Von Baeyer supported this view in his strain theory, which said that such rings, in which all ring members lie in one plane, are not stable (because their valency angles deviate from their normal position). When, in 1922, Ružička began to investigate the constitution of the natural musk perfumes, civetone and muscone, he was able to show conclusively that they were cyclic ketones with seventeen and fifteen members respectively, but he found it hard to accept this fact, which went against the strain theory. Ružička said that his prejudice led him at first to propose a number of incorrect formulas, but when he broke the molecules into fragments and studied their building blocks, he was able to confirm the presence of large rings in civetone and muscone. He thus challenged von Baeyer's rule and started a new chapter in alicyclic chemistry. He confirmed the constitution of these compounds by synthesis and proposed that they originated from fatty acids in the civet cat. By cleverly modifying existing methods, he prepared an entire series of cyclic ketones, from rings with nine members to rings with thirty members and beyond. He then explained these compounds' deviation from the strain theory by the fact that multimembered rings are basically two parallel chains of methylene groups, closed at each end, and therefore they are not more reactive than open-chain compounds. Of further interest was the relationship between odor and ring size in ring ketones. Compounds producing the familiar mixed odor between bitter almond, caraway, and peppermint have five- to eight-membered rings. Ten- to twelve-membered compounds smell of camphor, and fourteen- to eighteen-membered rings are characterized by their musk odor.

In the second part of his lecture, Ružička explained the work on higher terpenes, or polyterpenes, that he and his laboratory started in 1920. To find the constitution of these compounds, he used a simple working hypothesis, the isoprene rule, which said that the carbon skeleton of the higher terpenes is built up of isoprene units, each containing five carbon atoms. He then partly stripped the compounds of their hydrogen—a process called dehydrogenation—thereby converting them into simpler aromatic compounds that were better known and could be more easily analyzed. To organize the great number of compounds, he proposed a system for higher terpenes: Monoterpenes contain two isoprene units; sesquiterpenes, three; diterpenes, four; triterpenes, six. Among the numerous terpenes occurring in nature are farnesol, nerol, camphor, and vitamin A.

Finally, Ružička described compounds that are related to terpenes but whose number of carbon atoms is not divisible by five. Their carbon skeleton, however, can be completed by adding one or two atoms to give them a structure that obeys the isoprene rule. He called them terpinoids. Cholesterol is such a compound, as are the sex hormones, the first of which was isolated in 1929 by Butenandt. Ružička set out to prove their relationship to cholesterol by the partial synthesis of androsterone, the first synthesis of a sex hormone and the first proof for its structure. He prepared a series of related compounds that also exhibited male hormone activity, and he finally proposed the formula for testosterone, which proved to be identical with the hormone isolated from the testes of bulls.

At the end of his lecture, Ružička came full circle by suggesting a relationship between the molecular structure of another compound with a musk odor—a relative of androsterone—and that of large-ring civetone, the object of his early studies.

Critical reception

Leopold Ružička's Nobel Prize came at a critical time during the start of World War II. *The New York Times*, November 10, 1939, devoted only a short section to Butenandt and Ružička, the joint winners of the chemistry prize. It mentioned Ružička's international reputation in the field of sex hormones, particularly the synthesis of androsterone from cholesterol, and his contact with the scientific community in the United States. In 1935, Ružička had addressed a meeting of the American Chemical Society at San Francisco about his discovery and isolation of the male sex hormone, androsterone, which, with its subsequent synthesis, became one of the milestones of his Nobel Prize-winning work. At that occasion, *The New York Times* of August 20, 1935, had called it "one of the great triumphs of modern chemistry," hailed by chemists in the United States as a magnificent achievement. A year later, Ružička received the honorary degree of Doctor of Science at the Harvard Tercentenary Conference of Arts and Sciences. The enthusiastic reception that Ružička received in the United States shortly before he won the Nobel Prize warrants the assumption that chemists in the United States thought it was well deserved.

If the flow of scientific information across the Atlantic was scarce during the war, the flow to Switzerland was affected even more. There the chemical community was largely cut off from the world's chemical literature; seldom did they receive, for example, the *Journal of the American Chemical Society*. Even from nearby Germany, the journals were often lost. In this vacuum, the Nobel Prize for Ružička was welcome news, yet it was not totally unexpected. He was the fourth successive director of the Laboratory for Organic Chemistry at the Swiss Federal Institute of Technology to win the Nobel Prize, his predecessors being Richard Willstätter, Hermann Staudinger, and Richard Kuhn. Ružička's telephone rang in the middle of the night, when he gruffly picked up the receiver and, to his great surprise, learned that he had won half of the Nobel Prize.

Biography

Leopold Stephen Ružička was born on September 13, 1887, in Vukovar, a small township in Croatia, one of the provinces of the Austro-Hungarian monarchy. His ancestors were artisans and farmers. His father Stjepan, a cooper, was Czech and Croat, and his mother Amalija was of Croat and Swabian extraction. His father died when he was four, and he moved to Osijek with his mother, where he attended public school and the classical *Gymnasium*. At first he wanted to be a priest, but then he came to the conclusion that his future life's work should be organic chemistry of natural products.

To get a better education, he planned to study at the Polytechnic Institute in Zurich, but he was discouraged by the stringent entrance exam. Instead he chose the Technical University of Karlsruhe, where he could enroll without an examination. There he studied chemistry under Hermann Staudinger from 1906 to 1910, earning his diploma and a doctorate in only four years. He stayed on as Staudinger's assistant and followed him to Zurich in 1912 to what was now called the Swiss Federal Institute of Technology (ETH). Before leaving for Zurich, he married Anna Hausmann. In 1917 he became a Swiss citizen.

In Zurich, Ružička was Staudinger's assistant until 1916. In 1918, he was awarded a position as unpaid lecturer at the ETH. He was given a position in 1920 at the University of Zurich for his work in the terpene field. In 1923 he was appointed "courtesy professor," but when Staudinger accepted a position in Freiburg, Germany, Richard Kuhn got the position of full professor that Ružička had hoped to gain. He was forced to look elsewhere, and his interest in terpenes made him join the perfume factory M. Naef (later Firmenich) in Geneva. After only one year, however, he accepted the chair of organic chemistry at the University of Utrecht to be in the mainstream of the academic life again. Two years later, Kuhn was called to the Kaiser Wilhelm Institute (for medical chemistry) in Heidelberg, and Ružička was offered the chair of inorganic and organic chemistry at the ETH, which he accepted. The return to Zurich as Kuhn's successor marks the start of his most fruitful period.

Not content with his demanding professional career, he also supported refugees from the Nazi regime during the war, making it possible for them to study in Switzerland and work in his laboratories. It was a strange sight to see uniformed officers of the Polish Army working alongside Swiss students. His humanitarian efforts did not stop when the war was over. He became a fervent supporter of aid to Slavic countries even after they turned to Communism, which brought him some criticism. Moreover, he was simultaneously a member of the Papal Academy of

Sciences and the Soviet Academy. At that time his interest in chemistry decreased somewhat, and he left much of the work to his assistants and coworkers, among them Vladimir Prelog, who was to become his successor in 1957. During the war, a large sum of money had accumulated from royalties generated by his patents in the United States, money he used to build an extraordinary collection of seventeenth century Dutch paintings. He later presented the collection to the Zurich Museum of Paintings. In the early 1950's, he divorced and remarried. He retired in 1957 and died in 1976 in the clinic Mammern in Zurich, Switzerland.

Scientific Career

Ružička's decision to pursue the chemistry of natural products dated from his high school days. The opportunity came in his postdoctoral work with Staudinger, at Karlsruhe, when he was invited to work with him on the unknown constituents of *Chrysanthemum cinerariifolium*, a plant which had been widely used since the middle of the nineteenth century as an effective insecticide. They isolated the active ingredients, alicyclic compounds, which they called pyrethrins. When Staudinger moved to the ETH in Zurich, Ružička followed him and thus finally came to this institution as he had originally planned—without an entrance exam. There he continued work on pyrethrins; by this time he was convinced that he would "make his mark" in natural-product chemistry. The novel structure of the pyrethrins led him to guess that the hitherto neglected alicyclic field—non-aromatic ring compounds with only carbon in the ring skeleton—would disclose surprising secrets.

This proved to be true, and it led him into his other field of lifelong interest, the terpenes. He started with the simplest group, the monoterpenes, and from 1917 to 1919 he achieved the total synthesis of fenchon and linalool.

Ružička's desire to pursue his interests in terpene chemistry was frowned upon by Staudinger; he lost his assistantship but was allowed to continue using the research facilities. Since terpenes are important constituents of perfumes, he decided to accept financial support for his laboratory from the perfume industry. Other alicyclic perfume constituents, the ring-ketones muscone and civetone, soon captured his interest because of their structure, and he was able to prove that they are large-ring ketones. This opened a completely new chapter in the chemistry of natural products and indeed of general organic chemistry: the multimembered rings. He began by studying muscone from musk, a material secreted in a sac by the male musk deer, and civetone, excreted by both male and female civet cats. Ružička's civetone work was a classic example of his approach. Civetone is unsaturated, and thus it could be chemically attached at the double bonds as well as at the ketone group by potassium permanganate, which was able to split it into two fragments of crystallized carboxylic acids. This allowed him to determine not only the size of the ring but also the position of the double bonds.

His successful work on monoterpenes led him to the study of higher terpenes. He and his team synthesized the sesquiterpene perfumes farnesol and nerolidol in 1923. The isoprene rule—stating that the units in the carbon skeletons of higher terpenes each contain five carbon atoms—became of prime importance for the analysis of terpene structure. This rule had been proposed by the German Professor Otto Wallach in 1887, but nobody paid it much attention until Ružička recognized its great importance for finding the carbon skeleton of terpenes. He designed a plan to penetrate systematically the immense multiplicity of higher terpenes, which no one so far had dared to do, using dehydrogenation as his primary method. "No one," he wrote, "had been presented by fate with the clear conviction of how important was a combination of dehydrogenation with the isoprene hypothesis." Using sulfur, and later, selenium, as the agent for dehydrogenation, he was able to reveal the structure of a great number of diterpenes.

Ružička had started to work on the triterpene group at Utrecht in 1929 and continued in Zurich until 1955. It proved to be a more difficult task than the mono-, sesqui-, and diterpenes, mainly because he had no access to infrared spectroscopy until 1948. The only instrumental aids available were microanalysis and ultraviolet spectroscopy. To solve the puzzles of increasingly complex structures, he had to rely again on the "classical methods" of chemical analysis—dehydrogenation and oxidative degradation at the double bonds; he gained valuable information from intercorrelation of the reduction and oxidation products. Important in this group are the tetracyclic compounds lanosterol and cholesterol. He and his team worked on the constitution of lanosterol and recognized the relationship between lanosterol and cholesterol. At this point, Ružička realized that the structure of lanosterol contradicted the isoprene rule, and he warned that "there is no rule governing the architecture of natural compounds which is valid without exception."

Cholesterol, to which Ružička devoted many years, proved to be more difficult. Cholesterol is a white, fatty substance found in numerous animal products and tissues and also in plants. Its structure, including its stereochemistry, led to much controversy between noted chemists, and the puzzle was not solved for many years.

Cholesterol, however, led Ružička toward the pinnacle of his career, the male sex hormones, when he proposed the structure of androsterone and performed its partial synthesis in 1934 from cholesterol. It was not only the first synthesis of a sex hormone but also the first exact proof of the relationship between a sex hormone and a sterol. In this field Ružička competed with Adolf Butenandt, with whom he shared the Nobel Prize. Butenandt had isolated androsterone from urine in 1932 and proposed its formula—which Ružička proved to be wrong.

He was not so lucky with another male hormone, testosterone, which he also planned to synthesize. He lost that race, while traveling in the United States, to a chemist in the laboratories of CIBA in Basel, Switzerland. Meanwhile, in the United States, he was hailed for the synthetic production of a hormone which previously could be extracted only from animal glands. The artificial production of the hormone, in a purer state than the natural product, raised unrealistic hopes of unlimited virility and "love bought in a bottle," according to *The New York Times* of August 25, 1935. Upon his return, he started a hectic program in the field of steroids to catch up with his competitors. After 1940, however, he devoted much of his time to outside activities and left most of his research to his able team of coworkers.

What finally rekindled his interest were the "new chemistry," the new electronic theories which began to change his terpene chemistry, and advances in physical methods—molecular spectroscopy, X-ray analysis, and chromatography—which he now introduced with great efficiency into his institute. At an age when most people are getting ready to retire, he did not find the return to a new and changed chemistry easy. In the meantime, his team had demonstrated conclusively the structural relationship between the terpenes and the steroids, and it was known that in nature cholesterol was synthesized from acetate units. In fact, nature itself seemed to conform to the isoprene hypothesis, which Ružička now reformulated as the "biogenetic isoprene rule." It was the crowning glory of his life's work. He suggested that complex terpenes are built up in nature from simple terpene units such as geraniol, farnesol, and squalene. Ružička had shown interest in the biogenetic origin of compounds as early as 1926, when he proposed that musk compounds in the organism of the civet cat were the product of fatty acid metabolism. In his later years, he developed an intense interest in biochemistry and the origin of life itself, which he considered to be mainly a sequence of chemical reactions.

Ružička was a fascinating teacher, but his unconventional style could be frustrating at times. He designed his own lectures and never followed a textbook. Instead, he scribbled complex structures on the blackboard at a furious pace. Students were forced to copy every one of those formulas lest they be haunted by them in his demanding oral exams. His standards were severe, and he was unapproachable to all but his assistants and doctoral candidates. To these he presented a friendly, helpful personality which, however, was occasionally offset by cynical remarks. He would not tolerate mediocrity and could be blunt in his criticism. By his later years he had acquired celebrity status: He was talented, famous, rich, and tremendously self-assured.

During his retirement, he spent much time in his garden, where he cultivated hundreds of alpine plants and various species of roses. (Interestingly, the name Ružička means "little rose.") At the tercentenary of Harvard University in 1936, Dr. James B. Conant, then Harvard's president, referred to him as a "chemist daring in his attack, brilliant in his methods, successful in his interpretations of the architecture of nature's baffling compounds." Vladimir Prelog, himself a Nobel Prize winner, has called him one of the most important organic chemists of his time.

Bibliography

Primary
CHEMISTRY: "Bedeutung der theoretischen organischen Chemie für die Chemie der Terpenverbindungen," in A. Todd, ed., *Perspectives in Organic Chemistry*, 1956; "History of the Isoprene Rule," *Proceedings of the Chemical Society*, 1959; "Rolle der Riechstoffe in meinem chemischen Lebenswerk," *Helvetica Chimica Acta*, vol. 54, 1971; "Nobelpreise und Chemie des Lebens," *Naturwissen-*

schaftliche Rundschau, vol. 24, 1971; "In the Borderland Between Bioorganic Chemistry and Biochemistry," *Annual Review of Biochemistry*, vol. 42, 1973.

Secondary

Greene, Jay E., ed. *McGraw-Hill Modern Men of Science. Vol. 2.* New York: McGraw-Hill, 1968. Ružička's work is described chronologically, from its start in 1916 to his retirement in 1957, with emphasis on his approach. It is concise and not difficult to read; it presupposes, however, some knowledge of organic chemistry. His main assistants are mentioned, and a short curriculum vitae is included. It also refers the reader to additional background information on hormones, terpenes, and stereochemistry.

Kenner, G. W. "Leopold Ružička." *Nature* 266 (1977): 392-394. In this obituary, Ružička's life and work are blended together to convey a comprehensive picture of the scientist and his ideas. His relationship with coworkers, colleagues, and industry is emphasized. His political views are explained, and his great interest in his arts collection receives special attention.

"New Male Hormone Found by Scientist." *The New York Times*, August 20, 1935, sec. 8: 1. Mainly of historical value, this article conveys some of the excitement in the United States over Ružička's report to the American Chemical Society about the synthetic production of the new "rejuvenation hormone," androsterone. It reveals that Ružička managed to create in the laboratory a hormone which corresponds very closely to the substance isolated from the glands of animals.

Ohloff, G. "Leopold Ružička: Scientist as Inventor." *Chimia* 41 (1987): 181-187. On the occasion of Ružička's one hundredth birthday, a group of eminent chemists gathered to honor the deceased scientist. This collection of papers contains contributions and reminiscences from people who knew him well and worked with him, some during the earliest part of his career. About half of the papers are in German, the rest are in English.

Prelog, Vladimir, and Oskar Jeger. "Leopold Ružička." *Biographical Memoirs of Fellows of the Royal Society* 26 (1980): 411-501. This represents the most comprehensive survey of Ružička's career and work, compiled from first hand experience by two of Ružička's closest collaborators. The first part contains six pages of personal biography, and the second part, a well-organized overview of his work, is geared mainly toward the chemist.

Tonja A. Koeppel

1943

Chemistry
Georg von Hevesy, Hungary and Sweden

Physics
Otto Stern, United States

Physiology or Medicine
no award

Literature
no award

Peace
no award

GEORG VON HEVESY
1943

Born: Budapest, Hungary; August 1, 1885
Died: Freiburg im Breisgau, West Germany; July 5, 1966
Nationality: Hungarian; after 1945, Swedish
Area of concentration: Isotopic tracer techniques

Hevesy was the first to study chemical and physical processes by using radioactive isotopes as tracers. His techniques advanced the field of chemistry and contributed to the other natural sciences, notably biology, medicine, mineralogy, and others. He was also a codiscoverer of the element hafnium

The Award

Presentation

Professor Arne Frederik Westgren, a member of the Nobel Committee for Chemistry of the Royal Swedish Academy of Sciences, gave the presentation lecture for Georg von Hevesy's 1943 Nobel Prize on Swedish radio on December 10, 1944.

Westgren's statement began with the period when young Hevesy was an assistant at the University of Manchester and was given, as it turned out, an impossible task. Ernest Rutherford asked Georg Hevesy one day to isolate radium D from radioactive lead; Hevesy could not do it. Radioactive radium D and inactive radium G, it was discovered at that time, are isotopes differing in atomic weight but more or less identical in chemical properties. Since active atoms can be traced by radiation, Hevesy used them as markers for the inactive atoms and was able to determine the solubility of lead compounds—the exact amount that was absorbed by various solvents.

Valuable new insights were gained by studying the absorption of lead salts with a mixture of active lead atoms by bean plants: The roots absorbed more lead than did the leaves and stem and absorbed more lead from dilute than from concentrated solutions. Hevesy also studied the way in which animal organisms absorbed and eliminated lead, bismuth, and thallium salts, research important to the field of medicine.

Originally this new method of using natural radioactive elements as markers was possible only with heavy metals and their compounds. Thus it had very limited applications. In the 1930's, however, Frédéric and Irène Joliot-Curie and Enrico Fermi produced radioactive isotopes from elements through bombardment with particles. After that, the study of chemical processes by means of radioactive markers became widespread, with Hevesy remaining the leader in the field. He observed the paths and the speed of formation of various organic compounds of phosphorus that had been injected into animals and humans. He also engaged in research with radioactive sodium and potassium. Besides several active isotopes, he used inactive isotopes, such as heavy hydrogen. In many tests, deuterium was used.

Nobel lecture

Hevesy delivered his Nobel lecture, entitled "Some Applications of Isotopic Indicators," on December 12, 1944. He acknowledged the roles of Ernest Rutherford and Fritz Paneth at the beginning of the research on isotopic indicators. Hevesy then discussed a number of examples of the application of his tracer method. Rutherford at the University of Manchester had received from the Austrian government a large amount of radium and radium D, one of the by-products of radium production. This radium D is found together with lead, and when Hevesy spent some time at the Institute of Physics at Manchester in 1911, Rutherford asked him to "try to separate radium D from all that lead." Hevesy accepted the challenge—and failed completely. He then decided to use radium D as an indicator of lead, because radium D was inseparable from lead. Late in 1912, he began to collaborate with Paneth at the Vienna Institute of Radium Research and developed with him the method of measuring lead through the radioactivity of radioactive isotopes. They used not only labeled lead but also labeled bismuth. Radium D and radioactive bismuth (radium E), among other isotopes, can easily be obtained from radium emanation.

Hevesy introduced special methods for measuring the rates of diffusion and self-diffusion of lead, bismuth, and other elements. The application of isotopic indicators also provided the most direct proof for the correctness of Svante Arrhenius' theory of electrolytic dissociation. Isotopic indicators have been used extensively in biochemical analyses and in analytical chemistry to determine, for example, the lead content of rock samples or of the earth's crust. With the help of artificial radioactive ions as indicators, the behavior of plant constituents has been studied.

Used as indicators in biological research were dilute heavy water to investigate water molecules in human and animal organisms and also radioactive phosphorus. Soon after administering the phosphorus, it can be located in all organs with a Geiger-Müller counter; with increasing time, more and more of it finds its way into the bones. Isotopic indicators also permit many kinds of permeability and elimination investigations. For quite some time, Hevesy was involved in studies of phosphorus compounds in chicken eggs, red corpuscles, and goat's milk.

Through isotopic indicators it was discovered that molecules in an animal or plant organism are constantly renewed. Food intake is one source of this renewal process. Atoms (and molecules) circulating through an organism may move from one organ to another, from one molecule to another, through a long chain of processes. This was called by Hevesy "the dynamic state of the body constituents."

At the end of his lecture, Hevesy expressed his opinion that the future use of isotopic indicators "may be much extended."

Critical reception

When the announcement was made in November, 1944, that Georg von Hevesy of Stockholm was to receive the 1943 Nobel Prize in Chemistry, most of the world was still in the throes of the final months of World War II. The giant battles in Europe and Asia understandably overshadowed the awarding of the Nobel Prizes, and there were few comments in the press. *The New York Times*, on November 10, 1944, noted that Hevesy had received the 1943 chemistry award, which had been reserved a year before, "for his work in the use of isotopes as indicators in studying chemical processes." The brief article went on to mention Hevesy's 1935 report "that bone formation is an ever-changing process in the body." This short note was followed by a more detailed discussion of the discovery of the new element called hafnium by Hevesy and Dirk Coster by an X-ray spectrum analysis of zirconium ore. Hevesy received the Nobel award for his work on isotopes as indicators, however, and not for the discovery of hafnium.

Time magazine's "Science" section in its November 20, 1944, issue devoted more than one column to the Nobel winners in physics and chemistry, including twenty-seven lines on Georg von Hevesy, most of it under the subheading "Isotopes and Hafnium." His method of using isotopes as indicators was described as "something like watching the movement of a dyed member of a school of fish." Finally, there was mention of one of Hevesy's experimental results, which concluded that water molecules usually remain in the human body for roughly thirteen days.

Fourteen years later, Hevesy received much more and quite favorable press coverage (in *The New York Times* and the *Christian Science Monitor*, among other publications), when he received the Atoms for Peace Award and accepted the award in person at the Rockefeller Institute in New York, on which occasion United Nations Secretary-General Dag Hammarskjöld spoke. Hevesy was interviewed and his achievements were highlighted. He was the second recipient—the first one was his friend Niels Bohr—of this $75,000 prize established in 1955 as a memorial to Henry and Edsel Ford for international efforts to develop nuclear energy for peaceful purposes. The prize was established following an appeal by President Dwight Eisenhower in Geneva.

Biography

Georg Hevesy was born György Bischitz in Budapest, Hungary, on August 1, 1885, the son of a prominent, well-to-do family. His father received a title of nobility in 1895. A few years later the family changed to the name Hevesy-Bischitz (Bisicz); eventually only Hevesy was used. His mother's family—her maiden name was Schosberger—was quite wealthy. Hevesy finished his elementary and secondary education in his native city, went on to the University of Budapest to study chemistry and physics, and continued his studies in Germany, where he earned his Ph.D. at the University of Freiburg im Breisgau in 1908. From there he moved to Zurich to work as an assistant at the famous Swiss Federal Polytechnic Institute; then, after a brief stay in Karlsruhe, Germany, he went to England to work under Ernest Rutherford. The work he started there in Manchester and continued in Austria at the Vienna Institute of Radium Research led to the development of his method of radioactive indicators. During World War I, Hevesy served as a lieutenant in the Austro-Hungarian army, but he was able to continue some of his research. After the war, he returned to Budapest and was appointed a university professor. These were turbulent years, however, and by 1920 Hevesy left for Copenhagen to work in Niels Bohr's new Institute for Theoretical Physics. Hevesy accepted the appointment as professor of physical chemistry at Freiburg, his alma mater, in 1926, but returned to Copenhagen in 1934. Nine years later, in 1943, he fled to Sweden, where he received the Nobel Prize the following year. A Swedish citizen since 1945, he spent many of his remaining years in Stockholm, constantly working on many research projects. He married Pia Riis in 1924; they had three daughters and one son. Hevesy died in Freiburg after a long illness on July 5, 1966.

Scientific Career

The subject of Hevesy's Ph.D. thesis was the interaction between metallic sodium and molten sodium hydroxide. His interest in high-temperature chemistry made him accept an assistantship at the Swiss Federal Polytechnic Institute. He attended in 1909—together with roughly twenty other people—Albert Einstein's inaugural lecture as associate professor at the University of Zurich on the determination of the ratio of charge and mass of the electron. On the occasion of a visit, Hevesy showed Einstein his laboratory. Many years later, the two met again in California and had a discussion on the problem of causality.

Although Hevesy's monthly salary was raised from the equivalent of $36 to $60—sums that he considered entirely adequate—he did not stay in Zurich, but, being interested in the field of catalytic synthesis, he moved on to Karlsruhe, where Fritz Haber was a prominent chemist at the Institute of Technology. From there Hevesy traveled to England, in 1911, to work under Rutherford at the University of Manchester. There he became a witness to some of the greatest discoveries in atomic physics, including the discovery of the atomic nucleus. He also met Niels Bohr in Manchester.

In the basement of the laboratory were stored large amounts of lead chloride extracted from pitchblende that came from the Joachimsthal (today Jáchymov) mines in northern Bohemia. Upon Rutherford's suggestion, Hevesy set himself the task of separating radium D from the lead. After many months of effort, he had to admit total failure. Satisfied, however, that radium D is indeed inseparable from lead, he hit upon the idea of "labeling" small amounts of lead by adding radium D. Because the Vienna Institute of Radium Research had the largest amounts of radium and of radium emanation, Hevesy went to Vienna and met there the assistant of the institute, Fritz Paneth, with whom he engaged in a most productive collaboration concerning radioactive indicators (the term "isotope" was introduced later). Paneth was most enthusiastic about this project, and he and Hevesy had the full support of the institute's director and of his assistant, Viktor Hess (winner of the Nobel Prize in Physics for 1936). Hevesy, Paneth, and Hess took balloon rides together. Hess had an electrometer with him on one of his balloon ascents to measure the change in ionization of the air. His findings marked the beginning of the discovery of cosmic radiation, and Hevesy was impressed by the simple means of that important discovery.

The collaboration of Hevesy and Paneth represents the basis for the development of the method "on the use of isotopes as tracers in the study of chemical processes." They used labeled lead in determining the solubility in water of salts such as lead sulfide and lead chromate and studied, with the help of radioactive indicators, the electrochemistry of bismuth and lead. They managed to prepare visible amounts of radium D from radium emanation.

Between 1913 and 1916, twelve coauthored publications appeared in the *Proceedings of the Vienna Academy of Sciences* and other periodicals about various phases of their projects, such as "Radio Elements as Indicators in Analytical Chemistry" (1913), "The Exchange of Atoms Between Solid and Liquid Phases" (1915), or "Galvanic Chains from Lead Isotopes" (1915). Hevesy was quite happy at the Vienna Institute and, reflecting back many years later, spoke of those "wonderful, unforgettable times."

In the Austro-Hungarian army, he served as an officer and technical supervisor of electrolytic copper works, but in his spare time he was able to work in a very modest laboratory studying "the difference in the chemical behavior of the active deposit of thorium when present in ionic and colloidal state." After the war, in 1918, he was appointed full professor of physical chemistry at the University of Budapest and continued his work with radium as indicator, this time studying the rate of self-diffusion in lead. During subsequent years in Copenhagen and Freiburg, he improved on his earlier methods. In Budapest he also experimented with labeled lead nitrate and nonlabeled lead chloride. His exchange studies by applying radioactive indicators proved the correctness of the theory of electrolytic dissociation by Svante Arrhenius, who expressed his satisfaction to Hevesy in 1922.

In 1920, Hevesy went to Copenhagen and accepted Niels Bohr's invitation to work in his Institute of Theoretical Physics. Together with Johannes Nicolaus Brønsted, he succeeded in the partial separation of the isotopes of chlorine and of mercury. In 1922, Hevesy and Coster discovered the element 72—unknown until then—by means of the X-ray spectroscopic technique and were able to prepare it in a pure state. They called the new element hafnium, because the Latin name for Copenhagen is Hafnia, but it took a while (one French and one British chemist claimed to have discovered element 72 before) until the scientific community was unanimous in its acceptance. After that, Hevesy's name became more widely known.

At approximately the same time, he studied the absorption of lead by bean seedlings and the removal of labeled lead by nonlabeled lead. This first application of radioactive tracers was pioneering work in biochemical studies, which soon were extended to the distribution of lead and bismuth in animal organisms. In 1926, Hevesy resigned from the institute in Copenhagen to accept a professorship of physical chemistry in Freiburg, Germany, from where he returned to Copenhagen in 1934, after the establishment of the Third Reich. In Freiburg he successfully continued the application and refinement of his tracer method in the field of biochemistry. He introduced the method of isotope dilution and, among others, determined the lead content of rocks, the mean lifetime of water molecules in the human body, and its water content. His keen interest in the chemistry of the meteorites and the chemical analysis of the interior of the earth also deserves mention.

In Copenhagen, Hevesy and coworkers again concentrated on biological research, in particular, phosphorus. They investigated the extent of renewal of the phosphatide molecules of the brain and their accumulation in various organs of rabbits, in dentine, in enamel, and penetration into yeast cells. They were deeply involved in the first application of radioactive tracers in radiobiology and in deoxyribonucleic acid (DNA) studies, and they also investigated the permeability of the red corpuscles for phosphates.

It is remarkable that Hevesy did not allow himself to be distracted by the tragic events of World War II. In his autobiographical sketch, he states that his "work was interrupted for only one day during the enemy occupation of Denmark." On that day, he was busy dissolving the gold Nobel medals of two friends, Max von Laue and James Franck, to prevent the gold from falling into the hands of the occupation forces. After the war, the gold was recovered and von Laue and Franck received new Nobel medals.

In 1943, however, it was time for Hevesy to leave Copenhagen and move to neutral Sweden, where the Institute for Organic Chemistry of the University of Stockholm became his home base. Radiobiological studies in conjunction with application of his radioactive indicators occupied much of his time. During the last period of his life, his research interests focused increasingly on physiological and medical projects. Some of his studies—"Hematological Effects of Ionizing Radiation in Cancerous Mice" (1964), "Studies on Cancer Anaemia . . ." (1963)—were contributions to cancer research. Detlev W. Bronk, president of the Rockefeller Institute, pointed out in 1959 that Hevesy's contributions were "among the most important advances in the peaceful use of atomic energy in our time."

Hevesy knew many of the great scientists of his era. In Paris he visited Marie Curie several times and also knew her son-in-law, Frédéric Joliot, and her daughter, Irène Curie. In Vienna he met Otto Hahn; Rutherford, Einstein, Henry Moseley, Robert Millikan, Francis Aston, Carl Auer von Welsbach, August Krogh, Ernest Lawrence, Hans von Euler, and Viktor Hess all had contacts with him. Hevesy made note that at a luncheon he attended in Liverpool, England, there were four Nobel laureates present.

Although he spent most of his life in laboratories, he was a prolific writer. Between 1908 and 1965, more than four hundred publications appeared, many with coauthors. Almost all publications are either in German or in English; few are in other languages, such as French or Swedish; some were published in translation. His book *Radioactive Indicators: Their Application in Biochemistry, Animal Physiology, and Pathology* (1948) had a Russian edition in 1951 and a second Russian edition in 1954. Hevesy and Paneth's *Lehrbuch der Radioaktivität* (1922) appeared in Russian in 1923, three years before the English translation (*A Manual of Radioactivity*, 1926).

Through the years, Georg von Hevesy received recognition and many honors. He was frequently invited to be a guest speaker. In 1930 he came to the United States as Baker Lecturer at Cornell University; in 1949-1950 he lectured at the University of Ghent; and in 1953 he delivered the Aschoff Memorial Lecture at the University of Freiburg.

The University of Cape Town was the first institution to give him an honorary degree (D.Sc. 1929). Twelve other universities bestowed honorary degrees upon him (the University of Freiburg even did so twice—Dr.rer.nat. 1949, M.D. 1959): Ph.D. (Uppsala and Copenhagen), Dr.h.c. (Ghent and Liège), M.D. (São Paulo, Rio de Janeiro, Turin), LL.D. (University of Vermont), doctor of engineering (Budapest), and D.Sc. (London and Cambridge).

Hevesy received—besides the Nobel Prize—the Premio Cannizzaro (Accademia Nazionale, Italy), the Copley Medal (Royal Society, London), the Faraday Medal (Chemical Society, London), the Bailey Medal (Royal College of Physicians, London), the Silvanus Thompson Medal (British Institute of Radiology, London), the order Pour le mérite für Wissenschaft und Künste (West Germany), the Cothenius Medal in Gold (German Academy of Natural Scientists "Leopoldina"), the Atoms for Peace Award (Ford Foundation), the Niels Bohr Medal (Danish Engineers Society), and the Rosenberger Medal (University of Chicago). Among other honors, he was elected an honorary member of the Academy of Sciences in Brussels, Copenhagen, Göteborg, Heidelberg, Rome, Stockholm, and Vienna.

Hevesy's achievements cut across the lines of chemistry, physics, and biology. His work with isotopes put him into the forefront of modern science and nuclear medicine.

Bibliography

Primary

CHEMISTRY, PHYSICS, BIOLOGY: *Über die Unterscheidung zwischen elektrolytischer und metallischer Stromleitung in festen und geschmolzenen Verbindungen,* 1921; *Lehrbuch der Radioaktivität,* 1922 with Fritz Paneth; (*A Manual of Radioactivity,* 1926); *Das Element Hafnium,* 1927; *Die seltenen Erden vom Standpunkte des Atombaues,* 1927; *Chemical Analysis by X-Rays and Its Applications,* 1932; *The Action of Neutrons on the Rare Earth Elements,* 1936 (with Hilde Levi); *Origin of Phosphorus Compounds in Hens' Eggs,* 1938 (with Ladislaus Hahn); *Interaction of Plasma Phosphate with the Phosphorus Compounds Present in the Corpuscles,* 1939 (with Adriaan H. W. Aten, Jr.); *Turnover of Lecithin, Cephalin, and Sphingomyelin,* 1940 (with Ladislaus Hahn); *Radioactive Indicators: Their Application in Biochemistry, Animal Physiology, and Pathology,* 1948; *Isotope als Indikatoren in der physiologischen Forschung,* 1955 (in French as *Les Isotopes comme indicateurs dans le recherche physiologique,* 1955); "Radioactive Tracers in Radiobiological Studies," Thirty-sixth Silvanus Thompson Memorial Lecture, *British Journal of Radiology,* vol. 465, 1956; *Adventures in Radioisotope Research,* 2 vols., 1962; *Selected Papers of George Hevesy,* 1967.

AUTOBIOGRAPHY: "A Scientific Career," *Perspectives in Biology and Medicine*, vol. 1, 1958.

Secondary

Cockcroft, John D. "George de Hevesy, 1885-1966." *Biographical Memoirs of Fellows of the Royal Society* 13 (1967): 124-166. Cockcroft received extensive, detailed notes from Hevesy himself and letters from his family and from Ernest Rutherford and Niels Bohr. This memoir was written because Hevesy was elected a Foreign Member of the Royal Society of London in 1939, and it contains a wealth of biographical and scientific information, plus fourteen pages of bibliography.

Farber, Eduard. *Nobel Prize Winners in Chemistry, 1901-1961*. Rev. ed. New York: Abelard-Schuman, 1963. A biographical sketch and excerpts from the Nobel lecture describing the prizewinning work constitute the bulk of this article. Added are comments on the consequences in theory and practice, including the significance of radioactive isotopes in modern science and medicine.

"George (Charles) de Hevesy." *Current Biography Yearbook, 1959*. New York: H. W. Wilson, 1959. This reference work brings biographical details not readily available elsewhere: that Hevesy had seven brothers and sisters, for example. There is a concise description of the scientific significance of his work. Added are a short bibliography and lists of the honorary degrees, memberships, prizes, and medals awarded.

Levi, Hilde. "George de Hevesy: 1 August 1885-5 July 1966." *Nuclear Physics* A98 (1967): 1-24. This is one of the best publications on the life and work of Hevesy, providing many details not found elsewhere. Hilde Levi was one of Hevesy's coworkers and coauthors. She points out that he switched the emphasis of his research from the physical to the life sciences after the discovery of artificial radioactivity. The bibliography contains 397 titles.

Robinson, Robert. "Award of Medals, 1949: Copley Medal." *Nature* 164 (1949): 1023. Also published in *Proceedings of the Royal Society of London*, series A 201 (1950): 1-2. This is part of the address of the president of the Royal Society of London on the award of the Copley Medal to Hevesy, a rare honor to a non-British scientist. Robinson mentioned hafnium, which Hevesy was able to separate from zirconium, and how he turned his failure to separate radium D from lead to good advantage.

Szabadváry, Ferenc. "György Hevesy." In *Dictionary of Scientific Biography*, vol. 6, edited by Charles Coulston Gillispie. New York: Charles Scribner's Sons, 1972. Szabadváry uses Hevesy's Hungarian first name "György" instead of "George" or "Georg." This is a most helpful article for quick reference, with a biography and a fairly detailed description of Hevesy's scientific achievements, including background information, with emphasis on the radioactive tracer method. Short bibliography.

Julius M. Herz

1944

Chemistry
Otto Hahn, Germany

Physics
Isidor Isaac Rabi, United States

Physiology or Medicine
Joseph Erlanger, United States
Herbert S. Gasser, United States

Literature
Johannes V. Jensen, Denmark

Peace
International Red Cross Committee

OTTO HAHN
1944

Born: Frankfurt am Main, Germany; March 8, 1879
Died: Göttingen, West Germany; July 28, 1968
Nationality: German
Areas of concentration: Radiochemistry and nuclear chemistry

Hahn began his career as an organic chemist but made his greatest contributions as a pioneer in understanding the nature and behavior of atomic nuclei. Hahn was a gifted experimentalist; his research (which included the identification of new elements) laid the foundation for the new field of radiochemistry and culminated in the discovery of nuclear fission

The Award

Presentation

Arne Frederik Westgren, himself a professor of general and inorganic chemistry and Chairman of the Nobel Committee for Chemistry of the Royal Swedish Academy of Sciences, gave the presentation speech for Otto Hahn's 1944 Nobel Prize in Chemistry on December 10, 1945. The awarding of the prize had been postponed for one year because of World War II. Because Hahn was unable to attend the ceremony, the actual presentation of the award was made another year later, on December 13, 1946, by Professor Arne W. K. Tiselius, Chairman of the Swedish National Science Research Council. Professor Tiselius made few comments except to express great pleasure at the fact that Hahn was able to attend at that time to receive his prize in person. Tiselius, instead, referred to Westgren's earlier detailed account of the results of Hahn's far-reaching research on atomic nuclei. Tiselius also added his hope that the application of Hahn's work would ultimately serve as a blessing to mankind. He then asked Hahn "to receive from the hands of His Majesty the King the Nobel Prize for Chemistry for the year 1944."

Westgren's initial presentation address of 1945 began with a review of the origins of the then new discipline of nuclear chemistry, which increasingly focused on the center parts of atoms, the nuclei, rather than the peripheral parts, or electron shells, where interaction occurs when chemical compounds form or decompose. The names of the pioneers in nuclear research along with their contributions were discussed, beginning with Ernest Rutherford and ending with Hahn. By using energy-charged particles of radioactive elements (which served as projectiles), Rutherford succeeded in breaking off very small fragments from certain nuclei, and hence set out on a path of progressively important discoveries that would culminate at a destination known as fission discovered by Hahn.

After Rutherford came Frédéric and Irène Joliot-Curie and then Enrico Fermi, who used the neutron discovered by Sir James Chadwick to produce, according to Westgren, new kinds of radioactive atoms. It happened then that Otto Hahn,

working with Lise Meitner and Fritz Strassmann and seeking to confirm Fermi's results, discovered something entirely new—"the splitting of heavy atomic nuclei
into two parts of more or less equal size." The "gift of this discovery" not only
evoked great surprise and interest in the scientific world but also paved the way for
further research on fission as well as for the identification of new elements along
the periodic table. Westgren paid a final compliment to Hahn when he said that
Hahn's work throughout was inspired by an invincible desire to solve the problems
he encountered.

Nobel lecture

On December 13, 1946, a little more than a year after having first learned that he
was to be awarded the Nobel Prize, Otto Hahn delivered his Nobel lecture, entitled
"From the Natural Transmutations of Uranium to Its Artificial Fission." Like its
author himself, the title was practical, conveying a sense of the general course of the
speech, which outlined how the investigations of the natural radioactivity of uranium led to the artificial splitting of atoms of that element in his own laboratory.

Hahn began his lecture by presenting a brief history of the origins of modern
scientific knowledge about uranium. Discovered in 1789 by Martin Heinrich Klaproth, uranium became the object of more intensive study only after Henri Becque-
rel uncovered its remarkable radiation phenomena, in spring, 1896, which were
grouped together under the name of radioactivity. It was only another few years
before Pierre and Marie Curie and others explained that radioactive substances
decompose according to definite rules into other elements with different chemical
and physical properties and in the process emit corpuscular particles, or alpha and
beta rays.

Investigation into the nature of the atom continued; in 1911, Rutherford proposed
his model of atomic nuclei, including the concept of electrically charged particles
(proton and electron) and particle mass concentrated in the nucleus. This model
provided the basis for more significant discoveries in 1932: the positron and the
neutron.

Hahn devoted appropriate space in his lecture to discussing the value and significance of the discovery of the neutron (something that had a bearing on his own
monumental discovery). Knowledge of the neutron helped readily to explain the
phenomenon of isotopy—a point presented with great clarity by Hahn. Also,
neutrons came to be seen as suitable projectiles for use in the transmutation of
atoms, because they have no charge and thus are not repelled by the positively
charged nuclei of elements. According to Hahn, the Italian scientist Enrico Fermi
was the first to realize the importance of the use of neutrons as projectiles for the
production of nuclear reactions and so began a series of tests, irradiating the various
elements of the periodic table to produce numerous artificial radioactive elements.
It was at this point that Hahn and his colleagues, Meitner and Strassmann, set out to
repeat Fermi's experiments in order to confirm his results, but once they had embarked on that course, it eventually led to something very different and unexpected.

Hahn spent the last half of his lecture presenting a detailed account of his work of the mid- and late 1930's, in which results contradictory to Fermi's were obtained—results that pointed toward fission as the only possible explanation. This was, in fact, in opposition to all the phenomena and laws observed up to that time in nuclear physics. Soon the process of fission was confirmed in a whole series of tests conducted in quick succession at European and American nuclear physics institutes.

Hahn's Nobel lecture constitutes a valuable and concise historical summary of the work done on the nature of radioactivity and especially uranium, which work laid the foundation for the discovery of fission. It was with uranium that Hahn was experimenting when he realized that the nuclei of that heavy element would split into two other distinct elements when bombarded with low-energy or slow neutrons. He concluded his remarks by describing some of the investigations into uranium and uranium isotopes conducted between 1939 (the year of his discovery) and 1946. He left his audience with a provocative and haunting question as he told them that the energy of nuclear reactions had been placed in men's hands: "Shall it be used for the assistance of free scientific thought, for social improvement and the betterment of the living conditions of mankind? Or will it be misused to destroy what mankind has built up in thousands of years?"

Critical reception

Otto Hahn learned of and received his Nobel Prize under unusual circumstances. During the spring of 1945, as World War II was ending in Europe, Hahn was detained by a British-American intelligence combat team at Tailfingen in Württemberg, to where the Kaiser Wilhelm Institute for Chemistry had been removed in 1944. He was then taken secretly, along with other German scientists, to a farm forty miles from London to be questioned about German scientific developments. The news that he had been awarded the Nobel Prize for 1944 reached Hahn during the months of internment in England. It must be remembered that the awarding of the 1944 prize had already been postponed one year because of the war.

The diary of a Professor Bagge, a fellow internee of Hahn, reported that on Friday morning, November 16, 1945, most of the scientists were sitting in a lounge before breakfast when Professor Heisenberg asked Hahn to read a page of the *Daily Telegraph*. Hahn, who was busy perusing another paper, said that it would have to wait. Heisenberg replied, "But it is very important for you; it says you're going to get the Nobel Prize. . . ."

Word of the honor that had come to Hahn was received with admiration and respect by his immediate colleagues interned with him in England. As a senior member of the scientific community, his "genius and industry" were praised and, on a less serious note, his achievement was touted with good-natured fun. An amusing collection of fictitious press notices was circulated, along with a very imaginative one from a so-called Frankfurt newspaper which bore the remarkable headline: "From Goethe to Hahn—two great Frankfurters." From all this there can be no mistaking the fact that Hahn's prize was very much applauded by those who knew him and his work most closely.

In the world outside his internment facility, the announcement of Hahn's award was accompanied by speculation concerning his whereabouts. At that time not even Hahn's wife knew with any certainty where he was. *Time* magazine of November 26, 1945, wrongly believed him to be in the United States as part of "human reparations" from Germany and said that if that were so, it would be the first time a Nobel Prize "was awarded to a virtual prisoner of war." The latter part of this statement was certainly true; Hahn was being detained against his will.

Hahn's predicament can be blamed completely on the war: He was forced to reply to the Nobel Committee that he could not set a date to receive the prize. He had no idea when he might be released. No doubt the Allies believed Hahn's internment to be well founded. No one doubted his competence as a scientist. *Time* magazine (January 21, 1945) reported, after the announcement of Hahn's great accomplishment, that while the war was on, no man in Germany worried the Allies more.

In fact, it was thought that the Kaiser Wilhelm Institute, under Hahn's direction, was working on the construction of an atom bomb. This story proved to be false, although, when the announcement came of Hahn's winning the Nobel Prize, people were naturally interested in any role the discoverer of fission might have played in Germany's drive toward procuring the bomb. As the New York *Herald Tribune* of February 3, 1946, reported, Hahn never thought that anything warlike would come of his discovery of uranium fission. He was a scientist, he said, and interested only in discovery and not application.

One year after the initial announcement of Hahn's award, *Newsweek* of December 2, 1946, reported, in a tone of respect for Professor Hahn's achievement, that British authorities had relinquished custody of the scientist, which would allow him to go to Stockholm and receive his Nobel Prize of $34,000. While in Stockholm at the ceremonies, Hahn eased the minds of some when he expressed his belief that the Russians were probably behind the United States in atomic research (*Newsweek*, December 16, 1946). It was unfortunate that one of the greatest moments in Hahn's professional life came at a time when the world was so filled with tension and conflict. It is apparent, however, that many did not fail to recognize his achievement or his commitment to humanity.

Biography

Otto Hahn was born in Frankfurt am Main, Germany, on March 8, 1879, to Heinrich and Charlotte (Giese) Hahn. The youngest of four boys in his prosperous middle-class family, Hahn had a happy childhood and lacked for nothing materially. Although he was a sickly child, he outgrew his childhood infirmities and became a healthy, active teenager.

Hahn was a good but not outstanding student in high school. Yet it was during this time that his lifelong interest in chemistry began to develop. In 1897 he was graduated from the equivalent of high school and entered the University of Marburg, where he decided to concentrate on chemistry, even though his father wanted him to become an architect. In 1898 Hahn went to the University of Munich for two terms but then returned to Marburg, where he completed his Ph.D. magna cum laude in 1901 at age twenty-two. His dissertation, "On Bromine Derivatives of Isoeugenol," was published shortly after graduation and was recognized as an important contribution to the field of organic chemistry for many years after its appearance.

As financial security came, resulting from scientific positions of increasing responsibility and prestige, Hahn could think of marriage. He wed Edith Junghans (a teacher of drawing) on March 22, 1913. Nine years later, on April 22, 1922, their only child, a son named Hanno, was born to the Hahns.

During World War I, Hahn served Germany in the gas-warfare corps. He was involved in the research, development, testing, manufacture, and use of new weapons. His assignments varied but were never without excitement or danger. Occasionally he had to go to Berlin or Döberitz to test the efficiency of gas masks by observing how long it took poison gas to penetrate them. After the war, he returned to his research at the Kaiser Wilhelm Institute for Chemistry.

As a result of his brilliant scientific work in the 1920's and 1930's, and its bearing on atomic weapons research, Hahn was arrested and interned in England by Allied troops in the spring of 1945. It was there that he learned that his discovery had led to the production of fission bombs detonated over Hiroshima and Nagasaki. Normally a man of dry, underplayed wit, Hahn conceived his personal responsibility to be so great that his colleagues feared that he might commit suicide. He became a firm opponent of and spokesman against nuclear weapons and in 1957 refused to cooperate in a planned West German manufacture of such weapons.

Grief came again to Hahn in 1960, when his son and daughter-in-law were killed in an automobile accident. His wife never recovered from this shock, and when he died in 1968 at age eighty-nine, she survived him by only two weeks.

Scientific Career

Hahn's fame and greatest achievement did not come as a result of continued research in organic chemistry, which was the focus of his doctoral work. Rather, Hahn became interested in the newly evolving field of radiochemistry and distinguished himself as a pioneer in it by investigating and unraveling the complexities of the phenomenon of natural radioactivity, culminating in experiments on artificially induced fission.

Following one year of military service after the completion of his degree, Hahn returned to Marburg for two more years as assistant to his mentor, Professor Theodor Zincke. This not only was a coveted post (the professor's recommendation would secure a position with almost any of the large chemical companies in Germany) but also was particularly fortuitous for young Hahn at that time, since Zincke was able to obtain for him a place in Sir William Ramsay's laboratory at University College, London, while Hahn was in England to learn the English language in preparation for promised employment with an international chemical company.

Hahn's association with Ramsay was of tremendous importance at this stage in his professional life. The latter guided the former into the realm of research of radioactivity. While with Ramsay, Hahn—ever the experimentalist—discovered a previously unknown radioactive element, radiothorium, when he extracted radium from barium using the Curie method. (Actually, radiothorium was an isotope of thorium, but the existence of isotopes was not yet known.)

Ramsay's kindness and professional connections enabled Hahn to establish ties that helped him to advance his knowledge of and research on radioactivity. Ramsay believed that such research ability as Hahn possessed would be wasted in industry and so encouraged him to accept a position with the Chemical Institute of the University of Berlin, which Ramsay acquired for him. Hahn's interest in organic chemistry was quickly fading in the face of the excitement of radioactivity.

Before going to Berlin, Hahn traveled in September, 1905, from England to McGill University in Montreal, Canada, to work with Professor Ernest Rutherford, at that time the best source of information on radioactivity in the world. Hahn spent a year at McGill, during which time he discovered another new radioactive element, radioactinium, and helped to determine the process or chains of radioactive decay.

Rutherford's laboratory was one of great excitement and intense activity. His enthusiasm and restless energy rubbed off on all present. Unfortunately, as Hahn himself indicated with a touch of humor, nobody at the time was overly concerned about the harmful effects of radiation. Rutherford once helped Hahn with a measuring device that was not behaving properly. While he corrected whatever was wrong, in the process he made the instrument radioactive.

In October, 1906, Hahn arrived in Berlin. At the Chemical Institute he felt quite alone, since he was the only person at the celebrated organic chemists' institute who knew anything of significance about radioactivity and one of only three there who took at all seriously research on the subject. Hahn's diligent work ultimately brought the respect of his colleagues, however, as well as the discovery of another isotope, which he called mesothorium. He was also acquiring in the course of his studies something that would prove to be of the greatest help later in discovering the fission process—a thorough familiarity with methods of separating radioactive substances.

Hahn was not long at the institute before the most important physicist to have entered his life came to Berlin from Vienna to do some postgraduate work in theoretical physics under Max Planck at the Institute of Physics. This was Dr. Lise Meitner, who arrived in the fall of 1907, already possessing some experience in the field of radioactivity. The association of Hahn and Meitner blossomed into a thirty-year fruitful collaboration which terminated only in the summer of 1938 because of the Nazi regime. Hahn brought to the team a splendid knowledge of organic chemistry and experimental methods; Meitner brought an expertise in theoretical physics and mathematics.

In October, 1912, the New Kaiser Wilhelm Institute of Chemistry opened its doors, and Hahn was afforded the opportunity to become the head of a small but independent radiochemistry department. He invited Meitner to join him to continue their work together: examining beta radiation, the decay products of radioactive isotopes, and the measurements of extremely weak radioactive substances (rubidium and potassium), since their new laboratory was as yet uncontaminated from previous radioactive experiments. Over the years this small department developed into two large departments, one for radiochemistry, under Hahn's direction, and one for nuclear physics, under Meitner.

Though Hahn's work with Meitner was interrupted by World War I, since he was usually stationed away from Berlin, on rare occasions he stopped by the laboratory when circumstances permitted. On one of those trips to Berlin, in 1917, he arranged his time to do some research with Meitner on one of the projects on which they had been working. This collaboration resulted in their discovery of a new radioactive substance—element 91, which they named protactinium.

After the war, Hahn returned to the institute with Meitner to work on various problems, including the decay processes of protactinium, uranium, and uranium isotopes. Because all the natural radioactive nuclides were known by that time, he increasingly turned his attention (over the next ten years) to applied radiochemistry. He started a new kind of experiment, which resulted in the development of the emanation method to study changes in the surface and formation of surfaces in certain precipitates. In 1928, Hahn became director of the Kaiser Wilhelm Institute for Chemistry.

In 1932, a breakthrough in radiochemistry was achieved when English physicist James Chadwick discovered the neutron. Immediately the Italian physicist Enrico Fermi recognized the value of this electrically neutral particle for conducting experiments. Fermi discovered that bombarding the elements of the periodic table up to uranium with low-energy neutrons caused almost all of them to be transformed into radioactive isotopes of the element with the next highest atomic number. When he bombarded the heavy nuclei of uranium, atomic number 92, with neutrons, Fermi concluded that he had produced a transuranium element with an atomic number of 93.

In 1934 Hahn and Meitner decided to repeat Fermi's experiments. They were joined by Fritz Strassmann, who had been at the institute since 1929. The three at first believed that they had verified Fermi's results, although the evidence looked very complicated and confusing. For the next four years, Hahn and his associates examined transuranium elements, their chemical and physical properties, and their decay patterns.

In July, 1938, Lise Meitner was forced to flee Germany in order to escape Nazi persecution of Jews, but Hahn and Strassmann continued their research. The neutron bombardment of uranium seemed to produce several radioactive substances whose chemical properties indicated either radium isotopes or barium. Since the prevailing views of physics at the time made barium production from uranium out of the question, radium was the only reasonable conclusion. When it proved impossible to separate out the radium, however, Hahn and Strassmann realized that, under the action of the neutrons, the uranium had split into two parts of unequal weight, the most accessible of which was barium. The two scientists confirmed their findings using differing procedures, though they could scarcely believe in the transmutation of uranium to barium.

Hahn sent news of his findings to Lise Meitner in Sweden. With her nephew, Otto Frisch, she correctly interpreted the phenomenon as splitting of the uranium nucleus and named it "fission." Shortly after the publication of this revolutionary information, Hahn and Strassmann announced the discovery of the second product of uranium fission, the rare gas krypton. Thus, the true picture was complete. When bombarded with slow neutrons, uranium (nuclear charge 92) split into two fractions, yielding barium (nuclear charge 56) and krypton (nuclear charge 36), with a release of energy.

Hahn did not have an interest in exploring the practical use or development of his discovery. As war broke out again, he was allowed to continue with his own research, which included investigation of the products of uranium fission. When the chemical institute was destroyed in an air raid, he moved his usable equipment to southern Germany and resumed work there until his internment in England.

Upon his release and return to Germany in 1946, Hahn accepted leadership of the Kaiser Wilhelm Society, which was renamed the Max Planck Society for the Advancement of Science after the death of Planck in 1947. Hahn reportedly refused an offer from the Soviet Union to do atomic research in Russia. In February, 1947, he was one of ten top German atomic scientists barred by the War Department from work on United States atomic projects for security reasons. Yet, in the spring of 1947, he was among the nine hundred selected German scientists who had volunteered to prepare reports summing up Germany's wartime scientific advances. From 1948 to 1960, Otto Hahn directed the policy of the Max Planck Society as its president. Accordingly, he played a major role in the revival of science and scientific institutions in Germany after World War II. In the 1950's, the quick and successful rebuilding of a series of important research institutes was largely his work.

Otto Hahn has justly been called the father of atomic fission, as well as the father of radiochemistry and its more recent offspring, nuclear chemistry. His was a life of tremendous scientific achievement and his work of historic significance. His careful experimentation and discovery of phenomena previously thought to have been impossible led to the practical conversion of matter into energy and helped usher in the atomic age. In short, Hahn's work turned theory into practice.

On a different level, Hahn's personal impact was great, as he held the unlimited trust and confidence of all who knew him. This was of no small help in restoring German science in the postwar years to some semblance of its former greatness.

Of his original publications, only one was a full-size scientific text, consisting of his 1933 Baker Lectures at Cornell University and entitled *Applied Radiochemistry* (1936). Hahn was prolific in the recording of his reminiscences about various developments in the evolution of radiochemistry (especially the discovery of nuclear fission), however, perhaps feeling that the personal touch was just as valuable and needful in the communication of scientific information as chemical equations and raw data.

The winning of a Nobel Prize is a tremendous accomplishment and says something profound about the significance of one's lifework. The magnitude of Hahn's accomplishment is, nevertheless, all the more emphasized by the awards that continued to come to him in later life. In 1966, he shared with Lise Meitner and Fritz Strassmann the prestigious Enrico Fermi Award issued by the United States Atomic Energy Commission. It was the first time the award went to foreign citizens and, thus, seems to lend credence to the idea that Hahn's great discovery marked the beginning of a new epoch in history.

Bibliography

Primary
CHEMISTRY: *Applied Radiochemistry*, 1936; *New Atoms, Progress, and Some Memories*, 1950.
AUTOBIOGRAPHY: *Vom Radiothor zur Uranspaltung*, 1962 (*Otto Hahn: A Scientific Autobiography*, 1966); *Mein Leben*, 1968 (*Otto Hahn: My Life*, 1970).

Secondary
Asimov, Isaac. "Otto Hahn." In *Asimov's Biographical Encyclopedia of Science and Technology*. Rev. ed. Garden City, N.Y.: Doubleday, 1972. This short article presents the essential and important events of Hahn's life, especially those associated with the discovery of fission. Its strength lies in its references to most of the important colleagues with whom Hahn had contact.
Badash, Lawrence. "Otto Hahn." In *Dictionary of Scientific Biography*, vol. 6, edited by Charles Coulston Gillispie. New York: Charles Scribner's Sons, 1972. This article presents in concise fashion an overall biography of Hahn, beginning with his childhood and ending with his involvement in the 1950's warning against nuclear weapons. Though it omits some important details of Hahn's later life, the article's strength consists of its extensive bibliography, including some foreign-language entries.
Graetzer, Hans G., and David L. Anderson. *The Discovery of Nuclear Fission: A Documentary History*. New York: Van Nostrand Reinhold, 1971. This short volume is an invaluable source on the context of Hahn's greatest discovery. The first part of the book provides reprints of the original papers and reports by the scientists who first uncovered the problem and meaning of nuclear fission. Prominent among these are the ones authored by Hahn and his colleagues. The last part of the book includes several of the original papers that provided a basis for the application of nuclear fission to military or peaceful purposes. The original papers are connected by explanatory narrative written by Graetzer and Anderson.
Heisenberg, Werner. "Otto Hahn, Discoverer of Nuclear Fission, Dies." *Physics Today* 21 (October, 1968): 101-102. Written by the then director of the Max Planck

Institute and younger associate of Hahn, this expanded obituary emphasizes the scientific accomplishments of the great scientist and pays tribute to his kind and winning personality. The author's personal admiration for Hahn is obvious.

Sparberg, Esther B. "A Study of the Discovery of Fission." *American Journal of Physics* 32 (1964): 2-8. This brief article reviews the history of the discovery of fission and succinctly discusses Hahn's place in that history. It contains some interesting statements made by Hahn. It is suitable for professionals and laypersons alike.

Andrew C. Skinner

1945

Chemistry
Artturi Ilmari Virtanen, Finland

Physics
Wolfgang Pauli, Austria and United States

Physiology or Medicine
Sir A. Fleming, Great Britain
Ernst Boris Chain, Great Britain
Lord Florey, Australia

Literature
Gabriela Mistral, Chile

Peace
Cordell Hull, United States

ARTTURI ILMARI VIRTANEN
1945

Born: Helsinki, Finland; January 15, 1895
Died: Helsinki, Finland; November 11, 1973
Nationality: Finnish
Areas of concentration: Agricultural and nutritive chemistry

Virtanen discovered a means of preserving green fodder by maintaining a pH level of slightly under 4. He did additional research on the natural synthesis of vitamins by plants and the chemical composition of higher plants

The Award

Presentation

Professor Arne Frederik Westgren, Chairman of the Nobel Committee for Chemistry of the Royal Swedish Academy of Sciences, presented the 1945 Nobel Prize in Chemistry to Artturi Ilmari Virtanen. Professor Westgren began his address by describing the traditional method of feeding cattle. For years, cattle in the northern latitudes were fed concentrated fodder in the form of oil cakes imported from warmer countries. Virtanen used his considerable talents to improve the supply of feeding stuffs in his country.

Virtanen attempted to preserve green fodder by developing a method that would avoid the loss of protein and vitamins. Applying a combination of hydrochloric acid and sulfuric acid, Virtanen discovered the varying degrees within which the acidity must be maintained. His development of the so-called AIV method (a name consisting of Virtanen's initials) of preserving fodder has many benefits to the farmer. The breathing of the plant cells, which consume carbohydrates, is reduced, as is the fermentation of butyric acid, which lowers the quality of milk. In addition, the decomposition of protein ceases, and vitamins A, B, and C are preserved. AIV fodder even improves the fertility of the animals and their resistance to disease. The AIV method also enables a second crop of grass gathered in the autumn to be placed in a silo.

Westgren ended his presentation by assessing the impact that Virtanen's work has had on his homeland. The system had become so well established in Finland that by 1944, the production of green fodder rose to 295,000 tons. The AIV method has also been adopted by Denmark, Great Britain, Norway, and Holland, and variants of the method have been implemented in America and Germany.

Nobel lecture

Virtanen delivered his Nobel lecture, entitled "The Biological Fixation of Nitrogen and the Preservation of Fodder in Agriculture, and Their Importance to Human Nutrition," on December 12, 1945. Nitrogen, he began, is one of the primary building blocks of life and is produced in nature by certain microorganisms. Of these, the bacteria of leguminous plants are the most effective nitrogen suppliers in nature. Today, he said, man knows how to fix atmospheric nitrogen industrially in fertilizers.

Most milk producers in Europe have to rely on imports of protein. Agricultural protein requirements, however, depend not on the production of protein-rich fodder but on the preservation of it. Thus, Virtanen said, research on the preservation of protein is as important as research on the production of it.

Virtanen began his research on the bacteria of leguminous plants in the spring of 1925. As research progressed, it became clear that his experimental methods had to be improved. In the summer of 1929, Virtanen began experiments with the sterile cultivation system. By eliminating all microorganisms from the soil, Virtanen attempted to determine whether legumen could subsist on atmospheric nitrogen without the help of microorganisms.

By 1930, Virtanen was able to study the secretion of nitrogen compounds more closely. Working on the assumption that the nitrogen compounds he collected were intermediate products of protein synthesis, Virtanen found that more than 90 percent of the diffused oxygen was amino nitrogen. He went on to say that leghemoglobin is produced by the symbiosis between the bacteria and the host plant. Bacteria is unable to fix atmospheric nitrogen because the root nodules do not contain leghemoglobin. Therefore, his experiments with sterile cultivation proved that the efficacy of bacterial strains is constant.

The same year that Virtanen conducted his research with bacterial activity in legumes, he also devised a plan for preserving fresh fodder. In 1925, there was no reliable theoretical basis for the preservation of fodder. Virtanen opted to use the chemical method of controlling fodder acidity in his search for a reliable method of preservation. His experiments showed that the quantities of acids required for acidification depended on the type of fodder that was used. The richer the plants are in protein, the greater their need for acid. The quantities of acid required are also determined by the acidity and lime content of the soil.

After performing his basic experiments, Virtanen discovered that if the acidity of the fodder is raised to pH 3-4 from the very beginning, the harmful fermentations and the splitting of ammonia from amino acids are virtually inhibited, the formation of butyric acid is entirely prevented, and the evolution of carbon dioxide is reduced to a minimum. He concluded that since the formation of ammonia in fodder acidified to pH 3-4 is minimal, the preservation of amino acids in the fodder must be excellent. Virtanen's laboratory tests also showed that the lactic acid fermentation in fodder acidified to pH 3-4 has no appreciable significance as far as preservation is concerned. Virtanen determined that this method of preservation was completely reliable by analyzing the gases formed in airtight containers.

This method, Virtanen said, known as the AIV method, has been used in Finland since 1929. Prior to that time, milk that was produced during the winter and spring months in Finland was low in vitamin A because vitamin A depends on the carotene content of the fodder, which is lower in these months. This meant that 52 percent of all families received insufficient amounts of vitamin A. Virtanen himself employed his method on the test farm that he purchased in 1933, without having to buy nitrogen in the form of fertilizers and protein-rich contaminants. Atmospheric nitrogen provided the entire nitrogen requirements for the farm.

In the early 1930's, Virtanen began studying the formation and importance of vitamins in plants and the preservation of vitamins in silage. This research demonstrated that the vitamin A effect of milk dropped considerably during the stable feeding period because the cows received only a fraction of carotene during pasturage. When the AIV method was applied, however, the carotene was retained completely because the grass was cut at an early stage of growth; thus, the AIV fodder corresponded to the summer fodder.

Virtanen concluded his lecture by discussing his research on butter. Butter, which is made from sour milk, cannot be stored long because it acquires an oily or fishy taste in cold storage after one to three months. He prevented these defects by raising the pH of butter to above 6; he accomplished this by using a salt in the preparation of butter.

Critical reception

Ilmari Artturi Virtanen was virtually unknown at the time that he received the Nobel Prize in Chemistry, which probably explains the dearth of reactions to his prize. Taking note of the fact that Virtanen was unknown outside Scandinavia, *Time* magazine of November 26, 1945, speculated that he and the other scientists who won the Nobel Prize, Otto Hahn for chemistry in 1944 (the award was presented in 1945) and Wolfgang Pauli for physics in 1945, were chosen because they had made their mark before a cloak of secrecy enshrouded the research of those scientists who were doing their work during World War II. Like *Time* magazine, *The New York Times* of November 16, 1945, devoted much less space to Virtanen's achievements than it did to the work of Pauli, who was better known. It simply mentioned the fact that Virtanen had won the 1945 award for chemistry for his discoveries of a method of conservation of fodder. In a follow-up article on December 11, 1945, *The New York Times* observed that Virtanen had won the Nobel Prize in Chemistry for his work with artificial fodder; the writer pointed out, however, that the atom researchers—Hahn and Pauli—dominated the awards in science that year.

The *Science News Letter* of December 1, 1945, gave the most attention to Virtanen's award. The article praised his "basic investigations into how plants turn air into food." It also listed some of the important discoveries that resulted from Virtanen's research, such as the fact that higher plants can capture nitrogen directly, without the aid of root bacteria.

Ironically, Virtanen gained public recognition not so much for his accomplishments, but because of political remarks he made while he was in Stockholm. *The New York Times* of December 10, 1945, reported that Virtanen caused a political scandal in Finland by making an anti-Russian statement at a press conference in Stockholm. When asked by a Swedish Communist reporter whether he was familiar with the latest Russian discoveries in the field of agricultural research and whether the Soviet Union would use the AIV method, Virtanen replied that he could not even consider collaborating with the Soviet Union "as long as [they] think it is right to conquer a neighbor's territory." The Swedish press seemed to take the side of the reporter, pointing out that it was Virtanen who started talking politics, not the press. *The New York Times* also quoted from an editorial in an afternoon paper that said, "It is regrettable that a man with Professor Virtanen's prominence makes such a careless statement at an open press conference."

Biography

Artturi Ilmari Virtanen was born January 15, 1895, in Helsinki, Finland. His family moved in that same year to Vilpuri, where Virtanen received his elementary education at the classical lyceum. He transferred his interest in natural science from high school to college when he entered Helsinki University. Although Virtanen majored in biology, he also immersed himself in botany and physics. After receiving his master of science degree in 1916, he served as first assistant in the Central Industrial Laboratory in Helsinki before returning to the university for his doctorate. A year after he received his doctorate degree in 1919, Virtanen married Lilja Matilda Isotalo.

In 1920, he ended his two-year association with laboratories that assisted in the manufacture of butter and cheese and began his work in physical chemistry in Zurich. The next year, Virtanen became director of the Finnish Cooperative Dairies Association, a position that he held for the next seven years. He found time, however, to study enzymology with Hans von Euler-Chelpin at Stockholm in 1923 and 1924. He was appointed *Dozent* at the University of Helsinki in 1924 and later became professor of biochemistry at the technical university in Helsinki. In 1933, Virtanen bought a farm in Sipoo, where he could conduct research into the preservation of green fodder; in that same year, his interest in agriculture resulted in his appointment to the Swedish Academy. Three years later, Virtanen became a member of the Finnish state committees that studied nutrition and agricultural planning. In 1939, Virtanen resigned his position at the technical university and became professor of biochemistry at the University of Helsinki, a position that he held until 1948.

The research that he conducted at his farm not only allowed his countrymen to maintain a constant supply of fodder in their silos but also brought him numerous awards. In 1936, he received an honorary doctorate of medicine from the University of Lund, Sweden; he was awarded the Adelskold Medal of the Swedish Academy of Sciences in 1943. In 1945, he was awarded the Nobel Prize in Chemistry for the discovery of his method of fodder preservation. He received the Great Medal of the University of Ghent in 1946. Virtanen died in Helsinki on November 11, 1973.

Scientific Career

Virtanen began his biochemical studies at Stockholm with von Euler-Chelpin in 1923. In 1924, Virtanen's study of bacterial fermentation revealed the indispensable role played by cozymase in lactic and propionic fermentations. Because he believed that most of the proteins in plant cells were enzymes, he began a comparison of protein content and enzyme activity of the cells.

Virtanen's investigations of enzyme activity led him to the nitrogen fixation of plants. In 1925, he began to study the production of nitrogenous substances in the root nodules of leguminous plants. Recognizing that much of the nitrogen was lost during storage, Virtanen tried to make fuller use of nitrogen fixation and to devise effective legume cultivation while solving the problem of fodder preservation.

He found that he was able to study the nitrogen compounds more closely after he had perfected the technique of sterile cultivation. He attempted to prove the hypothesis that nodule bacteria in a mutually beneficial relationship with the leguminous plants fix nitrogen. Having determined that aspartic acid is the primary amino acid in nitrogen fixation, he found that aspartic acid is produced from the symbiotic relationship between the host plant and bacteria. The host plant supplies the carbon component, oxalacetic acid, with which the hydroxylamine formed from the molecular nitrogen reacts to produce oxime, which in turn produces aspartic acid. Further research showed that the oxalacetic acid content of pea plants depends on the amount of sunshine to which they are exposed.

Virtanen's study of peas also revealed the importance of the red pigment leghemoglobin in active root nodules for the fixation of nitrogen. Because the formation of leghemoglobins in the root nodules results from the symbiosis between the nodule bacteria and the host plant, the bacterial strains cannot fix atmospheric nitrogen, because the root nodules formed do not contain leghemoglobin. He also found that when green plants ripen, the nitrogen fixation ceases, and the root nodules assume a green color. By combining Lemberg's research with his own, Virtanen concluded that if a section of a cut nodule is red, it shows that vigorous nitrogen fixation has occurred. A brown color indicates a temporary reduction of the nitrogen fixation, while green sections show that nitrogen fixations have ceased entirely.

Virtanen's experiments with nitrogen fixation began in 1925; at that time, there was no reliable theoretical basis for preparing silage. He decided to adopt the chemical method of controlling fodder acidity in his search for a reliable method of preservation. Using quantities of fodder of a few hundred grams, he proved that the acidity of the fodder remained constant if the pH of the fodder was adjusted to below 4. Thus, a pH of 4 proved to be the lowest acidity at which fodder can be preserved.

Quantitative experiments showed that a rapid acidification of the fodder is essential. His experiments also showed that the richer the plants are in protein, the greater the quantities of acid required. The lime content and acidity of the soil also affect the quantities of acid. Because the formation of ammonia in fodder acidified to pH 3-4 is minimal, Virtanen assumed that the preservation of the amino acids in the fodder must be excellent.

Virtanen tested the efficiency of this method of preservation by means of two experiments. To determine the losses of nutrients in fodder that had been preserved by maintaining a low pH level, Virtanen conducted tests in airtight containers. Analysis of the gases formed revealed that the substance losses in fodder acidified to pH 3-4 proved to be only a few percent if the dry substance content was so high that no pressed juice ran out of the fodder. He examined the possible harmful effects of the method by slaughtering a cow after one month's feeding of the fodder acidified to a pH 3.5-3.7. Chemical analyses carried out on the teeth, various tissues, and parts of the skeleton revealed no abnormalities. For the discovery of this method of preservation, known as the AIV method, Virtanen was awarded the Nobel Prize in 1945.

Virtanen turned his attention to the formation and importance of vitamins in plants and to the preservation of vitamins in silage at the beginning of the 1930's. He found that the vitamin A effect of milk, which depends on the amount of carotene in the hay that the cows have eaten, is reduced if the grass crops that the cows have eaten are not cut until the beginning of flowering. If the crops are cut earlier and the AIV method is used, the carotene is retained completely. In later years, he studied the chemical composition of higher plants and isolated a number of new compounds, some of which were of considerable nutritional importance.

While working for Valio, a diary cooperative concern, Virtanen attempted to improve the quality and preservation of butter and cheese. He found that if the pH of butter is adjusted to above 6, many of the defects common in stored butter never occur. This discovery resulted in the ready controllability of butter quality.

Virtanen's influence extends to nutritive chemistry and agriculture alike. His research into the formation of amino acids and plants and into the chemical composition of higher plants greatly advanced man's knowledge of organic metabolism. His investigation of methods of preserving fresh fodder, however, is his greatest legacy. The discovery of a method by which the deterioration of stored green fodder can be halted provided the farmers of Finland with a yearlong supply of feed for their cattle. His influence was most deeply felt, however, by the millions of people whose daily requirements of protein could be met as a result of the improvement that Virtanen made in the protein content of beef and milk.

Bibliography

Primary
CHEMISTRY: *Investigations into the Formation of Vitamins in Plants*, 1933 (with von Hausen and Saastomoinen); *Cattle Fodder and Human Nutrition, with Special Reference to Biological Nitrogen Fixation*, 1938; *Fermentation of Wood-dust by Cellulose Bacteria and Formation of Acetic Acid in the Process*, 1947; *Organic Nitrogen Compounds and Higher Plants*, 1947; *On Nitrogen Metabolism in Milking Cows*, 1968; *Fundamental Studies of Organic Compounds in Plants, Especially Vegetables and Fodder Plants, and Their Enzymatic and Chemical Splitting Products*, 1969.

Secondary

"Chemistry Nobelist." *Science News Letter* 48 (December 1, 1945): 341. This announcement of Virtanen's receipt of the Nobel Prize contains a detailed explanation of his most important work. It is written for the general audience.

Farber, Eduard. *Nobel Prize Winners in Chemistry, 1901-1961*. Rev. ed. New York: Abelard-Schuman, 1963. This book gives a brief biographical sketch and description of Virtanen's work, with quotes from his Nobel address and mention of consequences of the work.

Leicester, Henry M. "Artturi Ilmari Virtanen." In *Dictionary of Scientific Biography*, vol. 14, edited by Charles Coulston Gillispie. New York: Charles Scribner's Sons, 1976. This is the most comprehensive biography of Virtanen in English, although the emphasis is on his research. The article includes a short bibliography.

Loomis, Robert S. "Agricultural Systems." In *Food and Agriculture*, edited by Dennis Flanagan. San Francisco: W. H. Freeman, 1976. This article is concerned with a subject that was the focus of Virtanen's work: the nitrogen systems of legumes. Intended for an audience with a scientific background.

Revelle, Roger. "The Resources Available for Agriculture." In *Food and Agriculture*, edited by Dennis Flanagan. San Francisco: W. H. Freeman, 1976. Does not specifically mention Virtanen's work, but deals with modern efforts to maintain biological resources such as the nitrogen content of the soil. Intended for an audience with a scientific background.

Schlessinger, Bernard S., and June Schlessinger, eds. *Who's Who of Nobel Prize Winners*. Phoenix, Ariz.: Oryx Press, 1968. This reference book contains a very brief description of Virtanen's life and publications. This entry is valuable because of the bibliography. The "Commentary" section explains the nature of Virtanen's research and shows why he won the Nobel Prize.

Alan Brown

1946

Chemistry
James Batcheller Sumner, United States
John Howard Northrop, United States
Wendell Meredith Stanley, United States

Physics
Percy Williams Bridgman, United States

Physiology or Medicine
Hermann J. Muller, United States

Literature
Hermann Hesse, Switzerland

Peace
Emily Greene Balch, United States
John R. Mott, United States

JAMES BATCHELLER SUMNER
1946

Born: Canton, Massachusetts; November 19, 1887
Died: Buffalo, New York; August 12, 1955
Nationality: American
Areas of concentration: Enzyme and protein chemistry

Sumner was the first to isolate an enzyme in a pure state and demonstrate its protein nature. He succeeded in isolating several enzymes and in improving methods of protein isolation

The Award

Presentation

Arne W. K. Tiselius, a distinguished physical chemist and member of the Nobel Committee for Chemistry of the Royal Swedish Academy of Sciences, delivered the presentation speech for James Batcheller Sumner's 1946 chemistry award. He began by invoking the work of Eduard Buchner on cell-free fermentation in 1897. Buchner's discovery was rather trivial and incidental to the real purpose of his research, but to his contemporaries it was of great significance. It enabled research on the chemical nature of processes in organisms, hitherto blocked by the belief that life itself was essential to these processes, to make great headway.

Buchner's cell-free fermentation revealed the presence of an active enzyme, zymase, in yeast. The nature of this enzyme, and of enzymes in general, remained a major problem during the following three decades. In the 1920's some scientists doubted that they could be isolated in pure form. Thus, James Sumner's 1926 isolation of the enzyme urease in crystalline form marked a major breakthrough. Sumner showed the crystals to be both enzymatically active and of protein nature.

Richard Willstätter, the leading figure in the 1920's in the attempt to purify enzymes, questioned Sumner's research, causing the recognition of Sumner's achievement to be long delayed. In the early 1930's, Tiselius related, John Northrop (a corecipient of the prize) verified Sumner's results, and later Sumner's work became widely accepted.

Tiselius concluded his presentation by declaring that Sumner's discovery of the crystallizability of enzymes provided the first convincing proof that enzymes were proteins. This feat gave a firm foundation to some of the most important biochemical researches of the past ten years.

Nobel lecture

Sumner delivered his Nobel lecture, "The Chemical Nature of Enzymes," on December 12, 1946. His lecture differed from many others in that it did not provide a general, broad assessment of the field or trace its historical development. It was largely a straightforward exposition of his own research.

In 1917 he had begun to try to isolate an enzyme simply because it was something daring and important and had never been accomplished. His colleagues regarded the project as foolishness. He chose urease, the urea-splitting enzyme, because he was familiar with it, having used it for the estimation of urea in his doctoral work. His approach was to extract the enzyme from its richest source, the jack bean, by solvent extraction and precipitation. He encountered many difficulties—lack of time, funds, and apparatus. He determined to push on, to characterize as many chemical components in the bean as possible, and to separate urease from all other materials.

After several years of work, he became discouraged and temporarily abandoned the project. After four years of research, he finally found a solvent that dissolved most of the urease but not too much of the proteins present in the bean. Yet the extracts and precipitates continued to be extremely difficult to work with, and only in 1926 did he succeed in finding a suitable solvent. That year, using dilute acetone on ground jack beans, he obtained a filtrate that on chilling gave tiny, microscopic crystals. These he separated, purified, and tested. The crystals had high urease activity, and they proved to be protein. His experiments indicated that the crystals were truly urease, and in 1926 he published a paper on the isolation and crystallization of an enzyme, the culmination of nine years of research.

Sumner then gave a brief account of some of his subsequent studies on urease and of the rejection of his work by Willstätter and other chemists in Germany. Their argument was that the crystalline protein was merely the carrier of an adsorbed enzyme which itself remained of unknown nature. In the 1930's, however, Sumner, aided by the isolation of several enzymes by John Northrop, began to gain support for his work. By 1937, scientists had accepted the notion that enzymes could be isolated and were proteins.

In the closing portions of his lecture, Sumner indicated that, despite the still unsatisfactory methods in use for studying enzymes, so much had been done that there was now hope that every enzyme would be discovered and described for every chemical reaction that takes place in living matter. The great expansion of the field of enzyme chemistry had only just begun.

Critical reception

The award to James Sumner in 1946 received considerable notice in the American press, although general scientific and chemical journals devoted little space to it. Several articles emphasized the fact that the 1946 Nobel awards in the sciences were a clean sweep for Americans. Thus, *Science News Letter* entitled its November 23 article "All Nobelists American." *The New York Times*, in its announcement of the awards on November 15, presented a lengthy story on Sumner and how outstanding and important his research on enzymes was. The article mentioned that his accomplishment of an enzyme isolation was something that had been attempted for almost a century without success and that, until his achievement, the chemical nature of enzymes had remained a mystery. The newspaper also noted that he had to overcome several handicaps: He had lost an arm in his youth, and his teachers had tried to discourage him from pursuing a scientific career.

Time magazine repeated the theme of a clean American sweep and commented on Sumner's work and the importance of enzymes in determining the activity of living cells. Similar commentary appeared in *Newsweek* and *The Times* of London.

Biography

Born in Canton, Massachusetts, on November 19, 1887, James Batcheller Sumner was the son of Charles Sumner, a wealthy cotton manufacturer, and Elizabeth (Rand) Sumner. Both parents were descendants of English settlers in colonial New England. His father owned a large country estate, and his grandfather operated a cotton factory. He attended the Eliot Grammar school for a few years and then Roxbury Latin school from 1900 to 1906, where he found physics and chemistry to be his favorite subjects. In 1904, Sumner, an avid hunter, was accidentally shot in the left arm by his hunting companion. The arm had to be amputated near the elbow. Sumner was left handed, forcing him to become dexterous with his right hand. The accident stimulated him to excel in sports, and he became proficient in tennis (he would become the champion of the Cornell Faculty Tennis Club), skiing, mountain climbing, and other outdoor activities.

He attended Harvard College from 1906 to 1910. Following his graduation, he worked in the family textile business, putting in ten hours daily at the Sumner Knitted Padding Company. He then accepted the opportunity to teach chemistry and physiology at Mt. Allison College in New Brunswick, Canada. From 1911 to 1912, he had an assistantship in chemistry at Worcester Polytechnic Institute. He then decided to return to Harvard as a graduate student in biochemistry. His research director, Otto Folin, renowned for the development of accurate biochemical tests for blood sugar and urine, tried to discourage him, believing that a one-armed person could not succeed in laboratory work. Sumner's ability and determination won Folin over, and he received the Ph.D. in 1914.

During a European vacation, Sumner found himself temporarily stranded following the outbreak of World War I. A cable sent to him in Switzerland bore the news of an invitation to be assistant professor of biochemistry at Cornell Medical College in Ithaca, New York. Following his return to the United States, he served at Cornell from 1915 to his retirement in 1955, becoming professor of biochemistry in 1929. With the discontinuance of the medical college division in 1938, he became a member of the zoology department and then of the new department of biochemistry in the College of Agriculture in 1945. From 1947 he was director of Cornell's new Laboratory of Enzyme Research. In 1948 he was elected to the National Academy of Sciences.

Sumner was married three times: to Bertha Louise Ricketts (1915-1930), by whom he had five children; to Agnes Paulina Lundkvist (1931-1943); and to Mary Morrison Beyer (1943-1955), by whom he had two children. With his retirement in 1955, Sumner planned to move to Brazil for one or two years to organize an enzyme research program at the University of Minas Gerais. In apparent good health and actively planning the move, he was suddenly overtaken by an illness later diagnosed as cancer, to which he succumbed in a Buffalo hospital on August 12, 1955.

Scientific Career

Sumner belonged to the first generation of American biochemists, a new field that found its home in the medical schools or agricultural colleges of many universities. At Cornell Medical School, he gained a reputation as an excellent but demanding teacher. His heavy teaching load, consisting of biochemistry courses for both medical and home economics students, two advanced courses, and a seminar, continued unabated for more than thirty years. Not until after winning the Nobel Prize in 1946 did he gain some relief. His teaching so limited his time for research that he decided early in his career that whatever research he did would have to be something important. His graduate research and first publications were in his mentor Folin's area of biochemical analyses of body fluids, but he wanted to do something more exciting and recalled a 1912 Harvard lecture by Lawrence Henderson, who asserted that an enzyme would never be isolated unless someone discovered a new method. That, to Sumner, was something important. From 1917 the isolation of enzymes was his lifelong research concern.

Biochemists were aware of the importance of enzymes in the early twentieth century. Enzymes were active catalysts in organisms, possessing precise specificity. They mediated all physiological functions. They were, it was believed, impossible to obtain in a pure state, being present in very low concentration and highly susceptible to destruction by reagents.

Sumner chose urease as the enzyme to isolate, as it was present in unusually high concentration in jack beans. When he began, he firmly believed that enzymes were proteins, a notion held by several scientists for decades. Color tests and precipitation reactions with specific reagents on extracts containing enzymes often gave positive tests for proteins. These were inconclusive, however, as long as the enzyme was not present in a pure state.

The task of isolation proved immensely difficult. Sumner lacked not only time but also apparatus. At first he had neither ice chest nor centrifuge. He used a coffee mill for grinding. The commercial jack beans he purchased proved too variable in their urease content. He eventually persuaded individuals to grow beans with a high urease content. The low concentration and sensitivity of the enzyme to reagents made the work tedious and unpromising. For four years he tried different solvents and methods of extraction from the ground jack beans; he did obtain three globular proteins but not the enzyme.

In 1921, he got his first sabbatical leave and went to Belgium to work with Jean Effront, the author of several books on enzymes. The year in Belgium was a disappointment. Effront had no laboratory and a request for laboratory space at the University of Brussels was denied. Effront himself advised Sumner to give up his quest, since enzymes were present in concentrations too low to be isolated. With

Effront unsympathetic, Sumner instead spent the year working with a Brussels pharmacologist on blood coagulation.

Sumner's return to Cornell did not result in any further progress. Then Folin suggested that he try dilute alcohol as a solvent. Sumner found it to be a better solvent than anything he had tried previously. It dissolved most of the urease from jack bean meal and left behind most of the proteins. His extracts were roughly one hundred times more active than anything yet obtained.

Sumner decided to isolate all the substances in the jack bean and by 1925 had separated several proteins, carbohydrates, lipids, and pigments. He worked his way to a residue from which he could not extract anything. The isolation of the enzyme itself came in 1926, when he tried a dilute acetone solvent on this residue. After filtering and chilling the filtrate in an ice chest overnight, he centrifuged the filtrate to remove any insoluble matter and with a microscope observed tiny octahedral crystals in the filtrate. He tested these on urea; the crystals had urease activity. They also gave various protein test results. He concluded that the crystals were urease and that urease was a protein. His paper announcing the isolation appeared in the *Journal of Biological Chemistry* in 1926.

The nine years of frustration and discouragement proved worth the effort. He had isolated for the first time an enzyme in a pure state. Sumner, however, could not enjoy his triumph for long. The reception of his findings was not positive, being met with skepticism or hostility. The leading expert on enzyme chemistry was the Nobel laureate Richard Willstätter in Germany. He had been trying to produce pure enzymes from yeast for twenty years. He had developed methods of adsorption for this purpose and had enriched enzyme extracts to one thousand times the concentration yet achieved, all the while never coming close to isolating an enzyme completely from other substances. Furthermore, he had compelling evidence that enzymes were not proteins; his highly purified active preparations from yeast gave no positive tests for proteins. Willstätter theorized that enzymes were low-molecular-weight-specific catalysts adsorbed and stabilized on a colloidal carrier and therefore potentially separable from the noncatalytic part of the system. They were not proteins, he asserted, nor did they belong to any known category of organic chemical substance.

Willstätter's studies were important. He introduced better methods of concentrating enzymes by selective adsorption with gels. He studied the specificity of enzymes and how they were inhibited by various reagents. He could not be taken lightly. Hence, when he declared that Sumner's urease was an adsorption complex of the true enzyme with a protein carrier, scientists listened.

Sumner responded by producing ten more papers over the next five years, becoming in the process a skillful protein chemist. The attacks on him by Willstätter and his German disciples left him embittered, believing that they were attributable to personal animosity. Sumner wrote an absorbing personal account of the reaction to his work, "The Story of Urease," in the *Journal of Chemical Education* in 1937, revealing the extent of bitterness between him and his opponents.

Willstätter gave two lectures at Cornell in 1927. He spoke with Sumner and advised him to digest his crystals with trypsin, a protein-splitting enzyme. It should digest the protein away, leaving the enzyme behind. Sumner told him that he had tried that; the crystals were resistant to trypsin. Willstätter asked if he had obtained the trypsin using his methods. Sumner had used a different one, and Willstätter claimed that the trypsin extract must have been inactive. Mutual annoyance followed, and the two men parted in disagreement. In 1928 another German chemist came to Cornell, Hans Pringsheim of the University of Berlin. He lectured on Sumner's errors and told Sumner to go to Germany and learn some chemistry from the masters there. Sumner was convinced that the attacks on him were unjustified and attributable to the fact that so many Europeans had tried and failed to isolate an enzyme and scoffed at the possibility that an unknown American had done so.

Reports in German journals appeared, claiming that chemists could not get urease by Sumner's method or that the crystals could be separated into protein and enzyme components. In 1929, Sumner had another opportunity to go to Europe on a sabbatical. This time he was determined to reproduce his work there and convince chemists by showing them how to get the urease crystals. He decided to go to Stockholm and work with the Nobel laureate Hans von Euler-Chelpin. He took roughly forty pounds of jack beans with him and repeated his isolation there. By 1931, some Europeans had been able to confirm his work, but others tried with the beans he left behind and said that they could not. The dispute continued. Some said that they obtained the crystals but had digested the protein away, and therefore Willstätter was correct. Nothing had been decided.

During the 1930's, publications defending Willstätter's arguments appeared in German journals. Sumner himself exchanged experiments and ideas with German chemists, but Willstätter's carrier theory held firm. Sumner, by 1936, had published twenty more papers on urease in this context of debate and dispute.

As the literature grew larger, no one seemed able to resolve the debate. Sumner by himself was never able to do so. The turning point came with the research of John Northrop and his colleagues at the Rockefeller Institute between 1930 and 1935, when they crystallized pepsin, trypsin, and several other enzymes, showing them to be crystalline proteins. Northrop's work was more extensive than Sumner's and convinced scientists by its thoroughness that the carrier theory of Willstätter lacked validity. Sumner's work needed strong confirmation, especially his claim that he could not separate enzyme activity from the crystals and that the crystals were nothing but protein. Northrop provided confirmation on just those issues, although he, too, was challenged by Willstätter and his disciples.

Northrop's work was followed by that of others in Europe, as major chemists entered the field. Otto Warburg's studies showed relationships between enzyme activity and the presence of individual proteins. Belief in Willstätter's ideas declined sharply, and by 1937 the debate was over: Enzymes were proteins.

In that year, Sumner announced the isolation of the enzyme catalase from beef liver, showing it to be a conjugated protein with a protein and iron-porphyrin group both necessary for full activity, the first of several enzymes that consisted of proteins with a prosthetic group. Sumner continued his researches. In the years prior to World War II, he traveled to Europe again to work in Sweden with Theodor Svedberg in Uppsala, where he established the molecular weights and physical properties of several enzymes, using Svedberg's ultracentrifuge for this purpose. During the 1940's, he made important contributions to the methods of protein isolation and, by his retirement in 1955, had crystallized several of them. Sumner published more than one hundred papers and personally did most of the experiments reported in them.

Sumner's isolation of urease subsequently came to be considered the single most important achievement by an American in natural product chemistry between the world wars. Although the impact was long delayed, his research placed enzyme chemistry on a new level of significance, much as had Eduard Buchner's 1897 separation of an enzyme from yeast cells. Enzymes were now proteins, each doing a specific job by combining with a substrate to produce a product. The task of biochemistry was to understand the details of how this happened in terms of kinetics, reaction mechanisms, and the structures of enzymes and substrates.

Since all work with enzymes before Sumner had been done on mixtures of substances in extracts, the 1926 isolation was important. Acceptance of his work led to chemical and structural studies and to extensions into related fields, such as the establishment that viruses were proteins (in the 1930's) by using the methods of protein isolation of Sumner and Northrop. Indeed, much of modern biochemistry is an outgrowth of Sumner's work.

Bibliography

Primary
CHEMISTRY: "The Isolation and Crystallization of the Enzyme Urease," *Journal of Biological Chemistry*, vol. 69, 1926; "The Story of Urease," *Journal of Chemical Education*, vol. 14, 1937; "Crystalline Catalase," *Journal of Biological Chemistry*, vol. 121, 1937 (with Alexander L. Dounce); *Chemistry and Methods of Enzymes*, 1943 (with G. Fred Somers); *The Enzymes: Chemistry and Mechanism of Action*, 2 vols., 1950-1952 (edited with Karl Myrbäck).

Secondary
Allen, Garland E. *Life Science in the Twentieth Century*. New York: John Wiley & Sons, 1975. This fine study of the recent history of biology is especially strong on enzyme research and the growth of biochemistry, including the work of Sumner.
Cori, Carl F. "James B. Sumner and the Chemical Nature of Enzymes." *Trends in Biochemical Science* 6 (July, 1981): 194-196. This is an appreciation of Sumner by the Nobel laureate (1947 in Physiology or Medicine), focusing on the nature of urease and the controversy surrounding it.
Dixon, Malcolm. "History of Enzymes and Biological Oxidation." In *The Chemistry of Life: Eight Lectures on the History of Biochemistry*, edited by Joseph

Needham. Cambridge, England: Cambridge University Press, 1970. This is the first chapter in a collection of essays on the history of biochemistry. It is a good overview of the history of enzyme research, although not very penetrating.

Fruton, Joseph S. *Molecules and Life: Historical Essays on the Interplay of Chemistry and Biology.* New York: John Wiley & Sons, 1972. This is the best secondary source on the history of biochemistry. The second chapter, "The Nature of Proteins," is a superb account of investigations and ideas about proteins and enzymes. The studies of Sumner, Willstätter, and those who helped establish the protein view of enzymes receive detailed treatment.

Maynard, Leonard A. "James Batcheller Sumner." *Biographical Memoirs of the National Academy of Sciences* 31 (1958): 376-396. This is one of the most detailed studies of Sumner's life and career, written by a Cornell University colleague and fellow biochemist. In addition to the biography, Maynard provides a complete bibliography of Sumner's books and articles.

Albert B. Costa

1946

Chemistry
James Batcheller Sumner, United States
John Howard Northrop, United States
Wendell Meredith Stanley, United States

Physics
Percy Williams Bridgman, United States

Physiology or Medicine
Hermann J. Muller, United States

Literature
Hermann Hesse, Switzerland

Peace
Emily Greene Balch, United States
John R. Mott, United States

JOHN HOWARD NORTHROP
1946

Born: Yonkers, New York; July 5, 1891
Died: Wickenberg, Arizona; May 27, 1987
Nationality: American
Areas of concentration: Enzyme and virus research

Northrop proved that enzymes obey chemical laws by preparing several pure enzymes in crystalline form. He also crystallized a virus that destroys bacteria

The Award

Presentation

Professor Arne W. K. Tiselius, a member of the Nobel Committee for Chemistry of the Royal Swedish Academy of Sciences, delivered the presentation address for the awarding of the 1946 Nobel Prize in Chemistry to John Howard Northrop and corecipient Wendell Meredith Stanley. Tiselius began his speech by explaining the importance of Eduard Buchner's discovery that sugar will ferment with the aid of yeast that does not contain cells of the *Saccharomyces*. Buchner proved that many processes that characterize living cells can be imitated in the test tube. He also showed that the fermentation processes are subject to chemical laws when extracts of such cells are added to the solution in the test tube. Tiselius went on to say that the investigation of these once-unknown substances, called enzymes, had occupied scientists for the past century.

Many of the important questions of the nature of enzymes remained unsolved until James Batcheller Sumner of Cornell University (a third 1946 winner) discovered that it is possible to dissolve an enzyme and recrystallize it several times. About three years after Sumner's pioneering discovery, Dr. John Northrop began to work on the purification of the protein-splitting enzymes. Northrop and his collaborators also researched the homogeneity and purity of purified enzymes, thereby proving their nature as protein substances. Northrop undertook more detailed chemical studies on his material than did Sumner.

Tiselius ended his presentation speech by praising Dr. Northrop and his collaborators for perfecting the "art" of crystallizing enzymes and other proteins. He predicted that Northrop's work would eventually provide clues to greater understanding of the mode of action of enzymes.

Nobel lecture

John Howard Northrop delivered his Nobel lecture, entitled "The Preparation of Pure Enzymes and Virus Proteins," on December 12, 1946. Through the course of the presentation, he graciously gave his collaborators credit for the invaluable contributions that they had made to his research. In fact, he gave Dr. Stanley the honor of talking about their work on a bacterial virus that they isolated because this was

Dr. Stanley's field. Even though there were many scientists in the audience, Northrop delivered a speech that could be easily understood by the nonscientist.

He began by recounting the history of the study of enzymes, beginning with the eighteenth century scientists who referred to the enzymes' work as "vital processes." Despite the rapid progress made more recently in the study of enzymes, all attempts to determine their chemical nature by isolating them had failed until Sumner, Northrop, and Stanley began their research.

Inspired by James Sumner's successful isolation of a crystalline bean protein in 1926, Northrop began work on crystallizing proteins in 1930. As a result of these experiments, Northrop concluded that all enzymes and at least some viruses are proteins. He admitted that at the time, however, there was not sufficient proof of his conclusion, because of the difficulty of establishing the purity of proteins. He attributed the fact that homogeneous proteins are difficult to prepare to the large number of closely related groups of proteins that are synthesized by an organism. He was able to determine that the enzymes pepsin, trypsin, chymotrypsin, hexokinase, and ribonuclease are as homogeneous as any known proteins.

Northrop went on to describe the various tests that were used to analyze the relation of the enzymatic activity to the protein: diffusion measurements, denaturation of the protein, hydrolysis of the protein, and formation of definite chemical derivatives of pepsin. He concluded that enzymatic activity is attributable to the protein molecule and not to an impurity.

Critical reception

Although the media took note of Northrop's Nobel Prize, most of the immediate attention seems to have been based primarily on the fact that he was an American. *The New York Times* of November 16, 1946, argued that Northrop's lack of notoriety should not detract from the significance of his achievement. The writer attributed the absence of public acclaim to the fact that scientific research is a stern and lonely discipline. *The National Cyclopædia of American Biography: 1943-46* tried to correct this situation by demonstrating that the award represented a lifelong commitment to increasing man's understanding of proteins and viruses.

The real value of Northrop's work was not known until several years after he received the Nobel Prize, possibly because of the advances that had been made in the study of enzymes and viruses as a result of Northrop's work. In 1953, Eduard Farber praised Northrop for providing the first real proof that enzymes are chemicals by demonstrating that they could be purified to pure substances. He went on to say that even though enzyme research was still in its infancy, the problems could be formulated with more confidence than ever before.

In 1964, Isaac Asimov credited Northrop with "breaking the back" of the enzyme controversy as to the properties of viruses. He went on to say that awarding the Nobel Prize to Northrop might have settled the issue in the minds of the Nobel Committee, but not in the minds of the investigators, who were not yet convinced that viruses were composed of nonliving material. If anything, Northrop's work divided the scientific community even more sharply; the matter was not finally settled until subsequent research upheld Northrop's findings.

Biography

John Howard Northrop was born in Yonkers, New York, on July 5, 1891, not far from Milford, Connecticut, to which his ancestor, Joseph Northrop, had come in 1632. His other illustrious ancestors include Jonathan Edwards, president of Princeton University in 1798, and Frederick C. Havemeyer, whose family presented a chemical laboratory to Columbia University. His father, John I. Northrop, was a member of Columbia University's department of zoology; his mother, Alice Belle (née Rich) Northrop, taught botany at Hunter College and introduced nature study into the curriculum of New York public schools. Because his father was fatally injured in a laboratory accident, Northrop was reared by his mother.

After his public school education, Northrop entered Columbia University in 1908, where he majored in chemistry and minored in biology. In 1912, Northrop received his B.S. degree; in 1913, he received his M.A. For three years, he was a member of the university's championship fencing team. He tried his hand at farm work in 1913 and at prospecting in Arizona in 1914.

Northrop's scientific career began after he obtained his doctorate from Columbia in 1915. He was appointed W. B. Cutting Travelling Fellow and spent the next year in Jacques Loeb's laboratory at the Rockefeller Institute. He was then appointed to an assistantship at the institute and became an associate in 1917. After marrying Louise Walker in 1917, he served as a captain in the Chemical War Service of the United States Army. In 1920, he became an associate member of the Rockefeller Institute; he became a member in 1924, a position that he held until his death. He was appointed professor of bacteriology at the University of California in 1949, and later, professor of biophysics. Retiring in 1962, Northrop spent his time riding, sailing, playing golf and tennis, and field shooting. He died on May 27, 1987.

Scientific Career

Because Northrop's mother worked in the field of natural sciences, Northrop became accustomed to scientific language at an early age. After obtaining his doctorate from Columbia in 1915, Northrop delved into the subject of duration of life at the Rockefeller Institute for Medical Research. Northrop's earliest research was concerned with the effects of environmental factors on the hereditary properties of fruit flies. His work is significant because he cultivated the flies free of microorganisms—the first time that this had ever been done. He then destroyed the accepted hypothesis that the duration of life was regulated by an energy limit. He demonstrated that, although carbon dioxide output (a measure of energy expended) was greater at 15 degrees Celsius than at 22 degrees Celsius, the flies lived longer at 15 degrees Celsius than at 22 degrees Celsius.

By 1920, he was focusing his research on enzymes. At that time, these substances, vital to digestion, respiration, and other life processes, were still a mystery that divided the scientific community. Some scientists believed that enzymes conformed to the laws of chemistry; others did not. Northrop's research over the next two decades was devoted to bringing about a better understanding of the chemical nature of enzymes.

After James Sumner's discovery of crystalline urease in 1926, Northrop began the work that eventually settled the enzyme controversy. Since many scientists were still skeptical about Sumner's conclusions, Northrop decided to try to crystallize pepsin, a feat that had eluded scientists ever since Pekelharing first attempted it in 1896. Pepsin is the protein-splitting digestive enzyme in gastric secretions. Over the next four years, Northrop employed a wide variety of methods. Although he did not discover one general method that led to the isolation and crystallization of an enzyme, he did follow certain general principles. He began with large quantities of material, such as gastric juice, so that actual solid material was handled instead of the dilute solutions that many of Northrop's predecessors had used. He then employed filtration by suction whenever possible, because this method produced better separation of the precipitate from the original material than the centrifuge did. Northrop was convinced that Pekelharing would have crystallized the enzyme fifty years before if he had filtered his pepsin preparation and then dissolved it in a small amount of water instead of centrifuging the preparation. Finally, he used neutral salts to bring about fractionation because proteins are much more stable in the presence of these salts than in dilute salt solutions.

In collaboration with Moses Kunitz, Northrop crystallized the enzymes trypsin in 1932 and chymotrypsin in 1935. Like pepsin, trypsin and chymotrypsin were derived from inactive precursors or parent substances that had been crystallized. The formation of trypsin from trypsinogen is an autocatalytic reaction, as is the formation of pepsin from pepsinogen. Therefore, these enzymes may be propagated, just as bacteria are. Northrop also discovered that the formation of trypsin from trypsinogen may be catalyzed by an enzyme of the digestive tract called enterokinase and by an enzyme produced by a mold. As far as Northrop could tell, only trypsin could be used to catalyze the formation of chymotrypsin from chymotrypsinogen. In all these reactions, he found that an increase in enzymatic activity was accompanied by the appearance of the new enzyme protein. Northrop considered these results to be the best evidence that enzymatic activity is a property of the protein molecule.

Even as this work was in progress, Northrop turned his attention to a new controversy concerning the chemical nature of viruses, although he never really considered this to be his field. Actually, he had entered this field in the 1920's, when he examined the ways in which the tobacco mosaic virus and bacterial viruses reproduce. He was particularly interested in bacteriophages, viruses which are abundant in the intestinal tracts of man and animals. These substances possess the remarkable ability to dissolve bacteria. In 1936, he isolated a bacteriophage from the intestines of mammals that exhibited the properties of a nucleoprotein that acts upon staphylococcus. He showed that highly purified staphylococcus bacteriophage contained nucleic acid as well as protein; in fact, he was one of the first scientists to point out the presence of nucleic acid in a virus. In the late 1930's, he proposed that the nucleic acid in bacterial viruses might correspond to the free deoxyribonucleic acid (DNA) of the transforming principle, which in the virus is encased in a protein unit that serves to protect the DNA and to introduce it into the susceptible cell. Northrop's work on bacteriophages also helped break down the distinction between living matter and "dead" crystals with respect to the ability to reproduce.

Northrop's work with proteins resulted in a hypothesis regarding their precursors: He hypothesized that all proteins, whether they occur in meat, enzymes, viruses, or antibodies, are derived from a single precursor, which he called proteinogen. This theory became the central thesis of his major work, *Crystalline Enzymes* (1939).

In 1941, Northrop announced the production, for the first time, of purified diphtheria antitoxin. He maintained that this crystalline form was forty to fifty times as effective as the crude form of the antitoxin. Moreover, it left no unpleasant secondary serum reactions.

Throughout the remainder of his career, Northrop expanded his research. He studied phosphoric acid in starch, the effect of temperature on insects, and the agglutination, or joining together by adhesion, of bacteria. After the closing of the Rockefeller Laboratories, Northrop moved to Berkeley, California, where he continued to work on the mechanisms by which viruses arise in apparently healthy cells. He also worked with Jacques Loeb on the effect of temperature in prolonging life and demonstrated that extending the growing period can increase longevity. Yet, he never ceased his search for the ultimate structure of enzymes. He also wrote numerous papers on the physical chemistry of proteins, the kinetics of enzyme reactions, and the isolation and chemical nature of enzymes.

Northrop's research helped to dispel much of the mystery that had surrounded the study of enzymes for centuries. He not only established that enzymes are proteins that obey the laws of chemical reactions, but he also demonstrated that they are actually nucleoproteins that are able to reproduce themselves. Northrop's pioneering research paved the way for a number of scientists who have also crystallized proteins and have substantiated Northrop's claim that enzymes are proteins. His lifelong study of self-duplicating systems expanded man's knowledge of viruses and led to the development of several antitoxins. Northrop's researchers can be said to have greatly increased man's knowledge of protein constitution and of the chemistry of digestion.

Bibliography

Primary
CHEMISTRY: *The Organic Phosphoric Acid of Starch*, 1915; "The Dynamics of Pepsin and Trypsin," *Harvey Lecture*, 1927; "Pepsin, Trypsin, Chymo-trypsin," *Angewandte chemische und physikalische methoden*, 1936; *Crystalline Enzymes: The Chemistry of Pepsin, Trypsin, and Bacteriophage*, 1939.

Secondary

Asimov, Isaac. *Asimov's Biographical Encyclopedia of Scientists*. Garden City, N.Y.: Doubleday, 1964. This short entry explains why Northrop's work is important primarily by explaining the effects that his research has had on other scientists.

Farber, Eduard. *Nobel Prize Winners in Chemistry, 1901-1961*. Rev. ed. New York: Abelard-Schuman, 1963. This article, composed primarily of excerpts taken from Northrop's Nobel lecture, is important because in the end of the article, Farber explains the far-reaching effects that Northrop's research has had on enzyme research.

Herriott, Roger M. "John Howard Northrop." In *McGraw-Hill Encyclopedia of World Biography*. New York: McGraw-Hill, 1973. This two-page biography is especially useful for the information it provides on Northrop's early work with fruit flies and his later work with DNA.

"John Howard Northrop." In *A Biographical Encyclopedia of Scientists*. New York: Facts on File, 1981. Concise biography serves as a good introduction to Northrop's career but would not be very helpful to a reader with a scientific background.

"John Howard Northrop." In *Current Biography, 1947*, edited by Anna Rothe. New York: H. W. Wilson, 1947. Contains excellent biographical detail on Northrop's life. It also explains his major scientific achievements and includes a short list of references in the end. Highly recommended.

"John Howard Northrop." In *The National Cyclopædia of American Biography*. Vol. G, *1943-46*. New York: J. T. White, 1946. Although this short entry covers the highlights of Northrop's life and scientific career, its bibliography of Northrop's publications and listing of the awards he received is especially helpful.

Alan Brown

1946

Chemistry
James Batcheller Sumner, United States
John Howard Northrop, United States
Wendell Meredith Stanley, United States

Physics
Percy Williams Bridgman, United States

Physiology or Medicine
Hermann J. Muller, United States

Literature
Hermann Hesse, Switzerland

Peace
Emily Greene Balch, United States
John R. Mott, United States

WENDELL MEREDITH STANLEY
1946

Born: Ridgeville, Indiana; August 16, 1904
Died: Salamanca, Spain; June 15, 1971
Nationality: American
Area of concentration: Biochemistry and virus research

Stanley's isolation of the tobacco mosaic virus destroyed the widely held assumption that viruses were submicroscopic living organisms by proving that viruses are protein molecules

The Award

Presentation

The 1946 Nobel Prize in Chemistry was presented to Wendell Meredith Stanley and John Howard Northrop by Professor Arne W. K. Tiselius, member of the Nobel Committee for Chemistry of the Royal Swedish Academy of Sciences. He prefaced his speech with a brief history of enzyme research. Tiselius stated that Stanley was working in the same tradition as Eduard Buchner, who destroyed the widely held belief that fermentation was inextricably associated with the vital processes in living cells. Despite the fact that Buchner proved that fermentation could not occur without the assistance of active substances called enzymes, their essential nature remained unknown until Stanley and his collaborators began their research.

Using methods that had been pioneered by James Sumner (who also won the Nobel in 1946) and John Howard Northrop, Dr. Stanley explored the chemical nature of viruses. When Stanley began his work, viruses could be identified only by the symptoms of the disease that they occasioned, because the effects of viruses could not be measured as easily as the effects of enzymes. In 1945, Stanley succeeded in producing small amounts of extremely active crystals from large quantities of tobacco leaves. Stanley demonstrated that the crystals were protein substances that were the bearers of the virus' activity.

In his closing statement, Tiselius credited Stanley with advancing the field of enzyme research by proving that "dead" substances such as the virus molecule also possess the ability to reproduce. It was Stanley's discovery that viruses are actually proteins, however, that Tiselius believed would create an area of research with unlimited possibilities.

Nobel lecture

Stanley delivered his Nobel lecture on December 12, 1946; he began his address, entitled "The Isolation and Properties of Crystalline Tobacco Mosaic Virus," by pointing out landmark discoveries that had been made in virus research. Stanley focused his attention on the inability of investigators to explain the fact that no metabolic activity could be detected in viruses, even though they seemed to possess the ability to reproduce. The most significant work was that of Vinson and Petre, who showed in 1930 that tobacco mosaic virus could be subjected to several kinds of chemical manipulations without loss of virus activity.

In 1932, when Stanley began his experiments with tobacco mosaic virus, the true nature of the virus was a complete mystery. Over a period of two and one-half years, Stanley succeeded in isolating the crystalline mosaic virus. The majority of the lecture was devoted to describing these experiments.

Tobacco mosaic virus was selected for these experiments because it is unusually stable. In addition, this virus can easily be measured in preparation. In 1934, Stanley concluded that the tobacco mosaic virus was a protein, because it could be hydro-lyzed by pepsin. After crystallizing the virus, Stanley had to determine whether the virus activity was a specific property of the crystalline material. He found that most of the virus activity present in infectious juice could be isolated in the form of crystalline material. The results indicated that the crystalline material was, in fact, tobacco mosaic virus. Because of the old idea that viruses were living organisms, finding the crystalline material to be tobacco mosaic was a breakthrough discovery.

Stanley's second task was to examine the characteristics of the crystalline material. When it appeared that nucleic acid could not be removed without causing loss of virus activity, Stanley decided that the virus was a nucleoprotein. He also found that the rodlike particles within the crystal were very large and were able to attach themselves to one another end-to-end. Further, if a concentrated solution of purified tobacco mosaic virus is allowed to stand, it will separate into two distinct layers.

Stanley concluded by mentioning the most important work that has followed this discovery: the analysis of mutant strains of the virus. Stanley found that the muta-tion of a virus can be accompanied by the elimination of one or more amino acids in the virus structure, by the introduction of one or more amino acids to the virus structure, or by a change in one or more of the amino acids in the virus structure. He admitted in the end, however, that much remains to be accomplished in this relatively new field.

Critical reception

Wendell Meredith Stanley was not an unknown figure in the scientific community when he received the Nobel Prize in 1946. In fact, he had already received several awards in the previous ten years, which had been reported in *Science*, *Science Monthly*, and even *Literary Digest*. As *The New York Times* of November 16, 1946, pointed out, however, Dr. Stanley and his collaborators were virtually unknown to the general public at the time they received the award. The writer hoped that Stanley's lack of public recognition would not detract from the importance of his achievement. He concluded by stating that Stanley and the other recipients of the Nobel Prize were important in that they represented the millions of others who had taken up the stern and lonely discipline of science as their profession.

Although Stanley's achievement did not have much of an effect on the general public, it galvanized the scientific community. Instead of settling the controversy concerning the properties of viruses, Stanley's receipt of the Nobel Prize polarized scientific opinion even more. Isaac Asimov, in 1964, stated that Stanley's contention that viruses were protein and not living organisms was difficult for many to accept because the virus seemed poised on the boundary between life and nonlife. Many investigators believed that conferring the Nobel Prize on Stanley was, in effect, endorsing Stanley's solution to a problem that, in their minds, would not be solved until more proof could be offered.

Some publications, on the other hand, had no trouble accepting Stanley's hypothesis. *Current Biography: 1947* credited Stanley not only with displacing the long-held notion that viruses were submicroscopic organisms but also with causing many scientists to consider the possibility that viruses could be links between living and nonliving matter. *The National Cyclopædia of American Biography: 1943-46* applauded the awarding of the Nobel Prize to Stanley because his research opened up an entirely new field of scientific investigation.

Biography

Wendell Meredith Stanley was born on August 16, 1904, in Ridgeville, Indiana; in 1920, his family moved from Ridgeville to Richmond. Becoming a scientist was the furthest thing from his mind when he was a boy. After school, he would help his parents, who published a small newspaper, by gathering news and doing odd jobs. After he was graduated from Richmond High School, Stanley entered Earlham College, where he majored in chemistry and mathematics and played football. He fully intended to become a football coach until he visited the University of Illinois in connection with his contemplated football career and spoke with Professor Roger Adams only a few months before he was to receive his B.S. degree in the spring of 1926. Stanley was so impressed with Dr. Adams' explanation of that university's chemistry program that he enrolled at the university's summer school immediately after his graduation from Earlham.

Working primarily under Professor Adams, Stanley majored in organic chemistry and minored in physical chemistry and bacteriology. While at graduate school, Stanley published thirteen papers and worked at the DuPont Experimental Station. Following his receipt of his M.A. in 1927 and his Ph.D. in 1929, Stanley married Marian Staples. He remained for a year at the University of Illinois to continue working as a research associate with Roger Adams, who exerted the greatest single influence on Stanley's future career.

Stanley's scientific career actually began in 1930, when he became an International Research Council fellow, studying in Munich, Germany, in the laboratory of Professor Heinrich Wieland. Upon his return to the United States in 1931, Stanley worked as a staff member of the Rockefeller Institute with Dr. W. J. Osterhout. In 1932, he transferred to the institute's department of animal and plant pathology at Princeton, where he studied viruses with Simon Flexner and Louis Kunkel. Advanced to an associate of the institute in 1935, he then became an associate member in 1937 and a member in 1940. He was a Hickock Professor at the University of

California in 1940 and a visiting professor of chemistry at Earlham College in 1941.

Stanley's academic career was interrupted temporarily during World War II, when he became the director of a project sponsored by the Committee on Medical Research to develop an influenza vaccine. He was also appointed a consultant to the secretary of war and a member of the Army Commission on Influenza.

After returning to the Rockefeller Institute in 1946, Stanley resumed his scientific investigations of viruses. Following a series of four Silliman Lectures at Yale University in 1947, Stanley was appointed to establish and direct a new laboratory for virus research at the University of California in 1948. In the course of the next five years, Stanley successfully staffed both the chemistry department and the virus laboratory. He was also chairman of the department of biochemistry during this time. In 1958, Stanley became professor of virology and chairman of the department. Stanley retired as director of the virus laboratory in 1969, and he died in Salamanca, Spain, on June 15, 1971. In his memory, the molecular biology and virus laboratory at the University of California at Berkeley was named Stanley Hall in 1971, and the new science building at Earlham College was named Stanley Hall in 1972.

Scientific Career

Stanley's important research actually began while he was still in graduate school. Working with Professor Roger Adams, he examined the stereochemistry of biphenyls. He also attempted to synthesize the properties of a new group of organic acids related to those found in chaulmoogra oil, which was considered at that time to be the best remedy for leprosy. While he was at the University of Munich on a research fellowship in 1930, Stanley carried out experiments on the isolation of compounds from yeast and prepared a resolvable disubstituted biphenyl derivative.

When Stanley returned to the United States in 1931, he found a position at the New York Rockefeller Institute for Medical Research, where he worked with Dr. Winthrop J. Osterhout, who was analyzing the permeability of the cell walls of a large one-celled plant called a valonia. Stanley developed a model of a living cell that could selectively transport sodium and potassium ions across a membrane. Stanley's methods illustrated his characteristic approach: direct thinking and experimentation.

In 1932, Stanley went to Princeton, where Dr. Louis Kunkel encouraged him to apply chemistry to medical problems. Stanley then spent the next two years trying to purify the active material in the juice of infected tobacco plants. This amounted to a monumental undertaking, since no one had been able to obtain the tobacco mosaic virus in pure form. Since the pioneering work performed by Vinson and Petre had indicated that the virus could be a protein, Stanley directed his researches along this line of approach. He mashed the infected leaves and put the mash through the usual procedures used by chemists to crystallize proteins. The work led to the isolation from mosaic-diseased plants of a crystalline protein that possessed the properties of the virus. It proved to be a protein of surprisingly high molecular weight: seventeen thousand times that of the hydrogen atom. No other known protein approached this magnitude. Most scientists thought viruses to be primitive living organisms, and Stanley tried to overcome the opposition to his findings by embarking on a series of lectures in the United States and England in 1935. His research also led within three years to an epoch-making paper in *Science*: "Chemical Studies on the Virus of Tobacco Mosaic."

Between 1935 and 1941, Stanley and his coworkers investigated the nature of virus reproduction and mutation. Although Stanley had increased man's knowledge of viruses, he had missed an important point that was discovered by two British scientists, Frederick C. Bawden and Norman W. Pirie: The material was not a simple protein but a nucleoprotein containing about 5 percent by weight of ribonucleic acid. In other words, the virus was on the boundary between the organic and the inorganic world. Although Stanley himself did not care whether the virus were called a molecule or an organism, he still proved that the viruses of numerous plant and animal diseases were also nucleoproteins of high molecular weight. Further, a series of experiments that changed the chemical structure of tobacco mosaic virus in the test tube advanced man's knowledge concerning mutation in higher organisms.

During World War II, Stanley turned his attention from plant viruses to research that would benefit the war effort. Working for the Office of Scientific Research and Development, he developed a centrifuge-purified influenza vaccine from preparations of particles from a strain of the virus. This vaccine was reportedly ten times more successful in combating influenza virus than any other known remedy. He also investigated methods for the production of vaccines against Japanese encephalitis.

After the war, Stanley delivered a series of four Silliman Lectures at Yale University in the fall of 1947. In these lectures, he promoted the theory that the hereditary pattern of living organisms may someday be altered by chemical products in the laboratory. He based this opinion on experiments that he had conducted with tobacco mosaic virus that resulted in the altering of the virus' chemical composition.

Near the end of 1947, he discontinued his personal participation in laboratory work in order to turn the virus laboratory at the University of California into one of the world's major centers for work in biochemistry. Under his direction, H. Fraenkel-Conrat separated the protein and the nucleic acid components of tobacco mosaic virus to show that the mosaic virus was the true infectious agent. In 1955, Frederick L. Schaffer and Carlton E. Schwerdt succeeded in crystallizing the poliomyelitis virus.

In the mid-1950's, Stanley's interest turned toward tumor-causing viruses. Since this was a time when few investigators believed that viruses could cause cancer, his work was challenged by many of his fellow scientists. He eventually came to believe that viruses not only held the key to the cure of cancer but also could provide clues to understanding biological evolution and to controlling heredity. As an adviser to the National Institutes of Health, Stanley persuaded congressmen in Washington, D.C., to support a large-scale study of cancer-causing viruses. Eventually, the study of viruses became one of the primary concerns of cancer researchers.

Wendell Meredith Stanley's career was unusual in that it embraced both the theoretical and the pragmatic. His crystallization of the tobacco mosaic virus gave investigators the first definite indication of what constitutes viruses, thereby answering the question of whether the virus is a living or a nonliving entity. Thanks to Stanley's research, it is now possible to list protein molecules alongside living organisms as infectious disease-producing agents. This discovery also indicated that bacteriologists were on the right path to the isolation of lethal viruses that attack human beings. Stanley himself proved the practical importance of his findings by isolating the influenza virus and preparing a vaccine against it. Toward the end of his career, his theory that viruses could be the cause of malignant tumors garnered a considerable amount of support among his fellow scientists, who were inspired to continue his fight against virulent disease.

Bibliography

Primary

CHEMISTRY: *The Synthesis of Certain Octadecanoic and Related Acids and Their Bactericidal Action Toward Mycobacterium Lepras*, 1929; "The Isolation from Diseased Turkish Tobacco Plants of a Crystalline Protein Possessing the Properties of Tobacco-Mosaic Virus," *Phytopathology*, 1936; "The Reproduction of Virus Proteins," *The American Naturalist*, vol. 72, 1938; *Problems and Trends in Virus Research*, 1947 (with Thomas Rivers and Wilbur A. Sawyer); "Chemical Properties of Viruses," *Scientific Monthly*, vol. 58, 1941; *Viruses and the Nature of Life*, 1961.

Secondary

Asimov, Isaac. *Asimov's Biographical Encyclopedia of Science and Technology.* Garden City, N.Y.: Doubleday, 1964. Although this entry includes adequate biographical detail, Asimov's primary purpose is to discuss the controversy that Stanley's discovery caused, to emphasize the importance of his findings to virus research.

Courant, Heinz Fraenkel. "W. M. Stanley." In *McGraw-Hill Encyclopedia of World Biography.* New York: McGraw-Hill, 1973. Instead of providing extensive biographical details of Stanley's life, Courant concentrates on the effect that Stanley's findings had on the scientific community. The list of primary and secondary sources is very helpful.

Du Vigneaud, Vincent. "The Prize Paper and Its Author." *Science* 85 (February 5, 1937): 132-133. This announcement of the prize awarded to Stanley for his paper "Chemical Studies on the Virus of Tobacco Mosaic" provides detailed descriptions of the experiment that resulted in the crystallization of the tobacco mosaic virus. Also includes a capsulized biography.

Farber, Eduard. *Nobel Prize Winners in Chemistry, 1901-1961.* Rev. ed. New York: Abelard-Schuman, 1963. This entry is composed primarily of excerpts taken from

Stanley's Nobel Prize address. The closing section, "Consequences in Theory and Practice," speculates on how enzyme research will benefit from Stanley's discovery.

Trelease, Sam F. "Award of the American Association Prize to Dr. Stanley." *Scientific Monthly* 44 (February, 1937): 193-195. Contains a very detailed (although somewhat technical) explanation of Stanley's experiments with tobacco mosaic virus. Also contains a short biography of Stanley. Recommended for readers with a scientific background.

"Virus Apparently Made Visible at Last." *Literary Digest* 120 (July 13, 1935): 18. This article highlights the threefold importance of Stanley's crystallization of the tobacco mosaic virus. By briefly tracing the history of virus research, the author places Stanley's work in perspective.

"Wendell Meredith Stanley." In *Current Biography, 1947*, edited by Anna Rothe. New York: H. W. Wilson, 1947. This three-page entry presents an excellent biography of Stanley as well as a complete description of his scientific achievements. Also contains a short listing of references. Highly recommended.

"Wendell Meredith Stanley." In *The National Cyclopædia of American Biography*. Vol. G, *1943-46*. New York: J. T. White, 1946. A complete biography of Stanley's life that goes into his scientific achievements in more detail than do any of the other sources. Marred only by the absence of a bibliography.

Alan Brown

1947

Chemistry
Sir Robert Robinson, Great Britain

Physics
Sir Edward Victor Appleton, Great Britain

Physiology or Medicine
Carl F. Cori, United States
Gerty T. Cori, United States
Bernardo Houssay, Argentina

Literature
André Gide, France

Peace
American Friends Service Committee, United States
Friends Service Council, Great Britain

SIR ROBERT ROBINSON
1947

Born: Rufford, Derbyshire, England; September 13, 1886
Died: Grimm's Hill Lodge, Great Missenden, Buckinghamshire, England;
  February 8, 1975
Nationality: British
Area of concentration: Organic synthesis

Robinson pioneered in the development of both the electronic theory of organic chemistry and the methodology of organic synthesis. He determined the structures of a wide variety of compounds occurring in plants, particularly the anthocyanins and the alkaloids. He developed methods by which numerous important alkaloids were synthesized in the laboratory

The Award

Presentation

Arne Fredga, professor of chemistry and a member of the Nobel Committee for Chemistry, presented Robert Robinson as recipient of the Nobel Prize in Chemistry for 1947. In his presentation, Fredga emphasized that Robinson was an outstanding chemist whose extraordinary creativity and experimental skill were evident in his scientific work; he deduced the correct structure of morphine and helped clarify the essential features of the strychnine structure. Both morphine and strychnine are complex alkaloids possessing one or more basic nitrogen atoms and occurring in the vegetable kingdom. Their structures had eluded chemists for many years. Other well-known alkaloids, Fredga noted, include quinine, cocaine, and atropine. Many alkaloids have medicinal properties; quinine, for example, has been used for centuries to treat malaria. Morphine and cocaine are used to produce euphoria, although they are exceedingly addicting. Atropine is used to dilate the pupil of the eye and to reduce muscle spasms.

Although the work on alkaloids was the primary reason for the committee's recognition of Robinson, Fredga praised the variety and wide benefit to mankind of Robinson's pioneering efforts. Fredga mentioned specifically that Robinson and his associates made significant contributions to the successful development of synthetic antimalarials. He also noted Robinson's important work on the sex hormones and his famous synthesis of tropinone. Fredga observed that by devoting his life to organic chemistry, Robinson greatly influenced the fields of biological and medicinal research.

Nobel lecture

Robinson delivered his Nobel lecture, entitled "Some Polycyclic Natural Products," on December 12, 1947. It covered three polycyclic classes of compounds: anthocyanins, alkaloids, and steroids. These substances are referred to as polycyclic because they have two or more rings in their structures. The naturally occurring anthocyanins are plant pigments that give flowers and fruits their characteristic vivid red, blue, and violet colors.

Robinson reported that his interest in this class of compounds stemmed from the early years he spent in the laboratory of Professor William H. Perkin, Jr., at Manchester University. William Perkin and his brother, Arthur, were leading dye chemists in the late nineteenth and early twentieth centuries. They helped to develop England's infant dye industry.

Although Robinson's initial synthetic work in Perkin's laboratory had no immediate practical application, it led to the development of methodology that subsequently has been widely employed in the synthesis of important polycyclic compounds by chemists in both academia and industry. From this experience, Robinson concluded that investigation of a difficult problem without consideration of eventual application is not without virtue, for frequently fundamental knowledge can be acquired unexpectedly. A compound that Robinson prepared in his study on brazilin, a naturally occurring dye, was later applied to the synthesis of papaverine, an alkaloid used for dilating blood vessels and treating glaucoma. Other alkaloids were synthesized as his interest in this class of compounds developed.

In the course of his work, Robinson observed that some of the reactions proceeded very smoothly, which led him to speculate that comparable reactions must occur in nature. He postulated that the alkaloid pseudopelletierine was prepared in nature by a series of reactions involving the amino acid lysine, a building block of the proteins, and citric acid, a product found in abundance in citrus fruits.

The opportunity for Robinson to test his hypothesis experimentally came during World War I, when a shortage of atropine appeared imminent. He was able to demonstrate that tropinone, an intermediate in the synthesis of atropine, could be readily prepared in an aqueous medium at room temperature according to the biogenetic scheme he had proposed. The concept of biogenesis proved fruitful not only for synthetic purposes but also for the elucidation of structures. As a result, Robinson revised the hitherto accepted structures of a number of alkaloids, including that of morphine, so that they conformed to his biogenetic scheme.

Robinson's interest in the synthesis of natural products was exceedingly broad. Not long after the structures of the sex hormones were determined, he and his collaborators undertook the synthesis of the class of products known as the steroids, to which the sex hormones belong. He devised elegant reaction sequences for the construction of the tetracyclic system of the steroids. Some of these sequences were described in his lecture. Although he did not succeed in being the first to synthesize the sex hormones, he paved the way for chemists in the United States and Switzerland to accomplish this remarkable feat.

Critical reception

The award of the Nobel Prize in Chemistry to Robert Robinson in 1947 was widely acclaimed. He was recognized as a great master of organic chemistry and, in his time, as the doyen of synthetic organic chemists. England, in particular, was pleased, for Robinson was the first organic chemist to be awarded the Nobel Prize whose entire training was acquired on the British Isles and whose productive years were spent in the British Empire and Commonwealth. Thus, the award of the Nobel Prize produced considerable pride in a nation that was in the process of recovering from the devastation of World War II.

The award also drew attention to the excellent training in chemistry offered in England. As a result, British chemists were lured to the Western Hemisphere with attractive offers during the postwar era. In turn, young chemists from the United States, as well as from Canada, India, Japan, Australia, Israel, and continental Europe, increasingly went to England for postdoctoral training.

The Nobel Prize was one of the many awards Robinson received. In addition to being honored by the Chemical Society and the Royal Society of his own country, he was honored by the chemical societies of France, Germany, Switzerland, and the United States. Moreover, the United States government awarded him the Medal of Freedom in recognition of his contributions to science and the war effort. More than twenty universities at home and abroad conferred upon him honorary doctorate degrees, and more than fifty scholarly organizations welcomed him into their membership. In reporting the award of the Nobel Prize in Chemistry to Sir Robert Robinson and that in physics to Sir Edward Appleton, *The Times* of London commented on November 14, 1947, "Men like these not only bring honour to their country; they can also give the right compass bearings to the course of scientific thought."

Biography

Robert Robinson was the son of William Bradbury Robinson and his second wife, Jane Davenport. Together they had two sons and three daughters. William's first wife, Elizabeth Lowe, had died, leaving him with seven children at the time of his remarriage. Robert was born on September 13, 1886, in Rufford Farm, near Chesterfield, Derbyshire, England. He grew up in a large, intellectually stimulating family. His father was a pioneer manufacturer and tireless inventor. As a boy, Robert was captivated by his father's fascination with machines. He later remembered not only making scientific observations at an early age but also being challenged by his father to invent machines that could be used in manufacturing processes.

Robert attended Chesterfield Grammar School. At the age of twelve, he enrolled at Fullneck School in Pudsy Greenside. After graduating from Fullneck School, Robert expected to enter his father's firm, but several clergymen in the community persuaded his father to send him to a university. The senior Robinson acquiesced, but on the condition that Robert enroll in the school of chemistry, so that he could be of later use in the family's business.

The chemistry department of Manchester University was headed by Professor William H. Perkin, Jr., an illustrious organic chemist who was the son of the founder of England's coal tar dye industry. Robinson enrolled at Manchester and quickly distinguished himself in chemistry. Even before he formally completed his undergraduate studies, he was appointed to Perkin's private laboratory in 1905. As a graduate student, he developed the habit of working until three in the morning in the laboratory. He received the doctor of science degree in 1910 and stayed on at Manchester in a teaching position for an additional two years. During this period, he married one of his students, Gertrude M. Walsh. Following the wedding, he took his bride to Australia, where he became a professor of organic chemistry at the University of Sydney. After spending three years in Australia, they returned to England. A succession of teaching positions at the University of Liverpool, University of St. Andrews, and Manchester University followed.

From 1929 to 1955, Robinson was associated with Magdalene College of the University of Oxford. He became Waynflete Professor of Chemistry at Oxford in 1930 and subsequently chairman of the chemistry department until his retirement in 1955. His industrial experience included service as Director of Research at the British Dyestuffs Corporation and as a director of Shell Chemical Company. He served on numerous academic, scientific, and government committees. In recognition of his accomplishments and service, he was knighted in 1939 and awarded the Order of Merit in 1949.

Since youth he had had a fondness for chess, cricket, alpine mountaineering, and the theater and music hall. Gertrude, his wife and collaborator in chemistry since their early years at Manchester, died in 1954. She was the mother of his son and daughter. In 1957, he remarried. The second Lady Robinson was the former Stern Sylvia Hillstrom of New York. Sir Robert Robinson died on February 8, 1975, in Grimm's Hill Lodge, Buckinghamshire, England.

Scientific Career

From his earliest childhood, Robinson had an interest in science and machines. Although chemistry was not his first choice as a career, the enthusiasm with which he subsequently carried out his studies in organic chemistry belied this fact. He was fortunate to have at Manchester University Professor William H. Perkin, Jr., as his mentor and several outstanding chemists as colleagues, one of whom was Chaim Weizmann, who was to become the first President of the State of Israel almost forty years later. Another was Arthur Lapworth, who was to have a profound influence on Robinson's development in theoretical organic chemistry. Perkin was the heir to a fortune made by his father in the dye industry and served as a consultant to the British Dyestuff Corporation. Besides chemistry, he had a great interest in music and gardening. He did postdoctoral work in chemistry under Adolf von Baeyer, who had received the Nobel Prize in Chemistry in 1905. Perkin acquired renown when he succeeded in synthesizing cyclobutanecarboxylic acid. This acid contains a ring composed of four carbon atoms. Hitherto, chemists had believed that a ring consisting of fewer than six atoms was too unstable to exist. The Perkin Condensation, named for him, is a reaction that he developed.

When Robinson began his doctoral studies, Perkin offered him the opportunity to work on the synthesis of either the monoterpenes or the analogues of natural coloring matters. Suspecting that the former would be lengthy and tedious, he chose the latter. This work led him to investigate the anthocyanins and alkaloids. The first alkaloid he synthesized was papaverine, but this work was never published, because publication was preempted by the disclosure of other investigators that they had also synthesized this compound. Thirty years later, Robinson discovered that a claim made in their publication was erroneous. This only added indignation to his earlier disappointment in having to withhold publication of his own work.

Priority in claims is an issue that often besets scientists, prompting acrimonious exchange at scientific meetings and in the literature. In the development of the electronic theory of organic chemistry, Robinson and Christopher K. Ingold engaged in numerous heated debates, not only on the interpretation of the data but also on the priority of discovery. Both chemists made major contributions to the understanding of how organic reactions occur; Robinson, however, applied the concepts developed to the synthesis of complex molecules, thereby adding validity and value to these concepts.

Robinson's synthetic approaches were characteristically novel and clever. Often by modifying a reactant or the conditions of a reaction, he would be able to accomplish several transformations in a single step. In studying the literature, he would occasionally encounter an obscure reaction, which he would adapt to the synthesis of a desired product. Not surprisingly, several reactions have been named in his honor, including the Robinson-Mannich reaction and the Robinson-Schöpf reaction. The former refers to a transformation that is frequently used to convert a monocyclic ketone into one that is bicyclic. This reaction is also referred to as the Robinson annellation reaction. The Robinson-Schöpf reaction applies to a transformation in which reactants having the requisite functional groups can be converted into an alkaloid or its precursor under conditions that mimic those found in a living system.

In the synthesis of a complex molecule, it is essential that a substitution reaction, such as the introduction of a methyl group, occur not only at the desired site but also from the correct side of the molecule so that the substituent—for example, the methyl group—will have the correct orientation in space. To prevent the possibility of substitution occurring at an alternate site, Robinson introduced the concept of blocking groups. After the alternate site is protected by a blocking group, substitution occurs only at the desired site, following which the blocking group can be removed. By this means Robinson was able to achieve "site selectivity" in his attempted synthesis of the equine female sex hormone equilenin. Unfortunately, because the introduction of the methyl group at the desired site proceeded from the wrong side of the molecule, the required "stereoselectivity" was not achieved. Thus, the final product had all the atoms joined together in the correct order, but a portion of the molecule had the wrong spatial orientation. Instead of equilenin, Robinson and his associates had synthesized isoequilenin, a product lacking the physiological properties of the natural hormone.

The difficulties encountered by Robinson in the synthesis of the female sex hormones were overcome during the next fifteen years by Werner E. Bachmann, William S. Johnson, Karl Miescher, and their associates. Both Bachmann and Miescher utilized tricyclic intermediate compounds similar to the one employed by Robinson for their successful syntheses, while Johnson employed the blocking technique of Robinson to accomplish the synthesis of estrone, a human female sex hormone.

Robinson became a pacesetter for chemists to follow. To surpass him was considered the high point in the career of many an aspiring chemist. Although Robinson did not always view kindly what may be regarded as encroachment on his domain, he was not one to withhold commendation of an outstanding piece of work. In the British education system, external examiners are engaged to examine the dissertations of doctoral candidates. A young chemist whose dissertation was lauded by Robinson could not hope for a more auspicious start for his career.

Robinson attracted many promising young chemists to his laboratory; Alexander R. Todd and John W. Cornforth received the Nobel Prize in Chemistry later in life. Outstanding studies in organic chemistry were carried out by students of Robinson at the Dyson Perrins Laboratory at Oxford. Arthur J. Birch made significant contributions to the development of the sodium-ammonia-alcohol reduction of aromatic compounds containing an oxygenated benzene ring. A benzene ring contains six carbon atoms in which single and double bonds are alternately present in the ring. The Birch reduction, as this reaction has become known, was a key step in the syntheses of the first oral contraceptives. Although Robinson's wife, Gertrude, was not his first collaborator, she was his most consistent. Working alongside him at the laboratory bench, she helped him considerably, especially in the investigation of the coloring matters from plants.

Robinson had more than six hundred scientific publications. He was on the editorial boards of numerous scientific journals. Together with the American Nobel laureate Robert B. Woodward, he cochaired the honorary editorial advisory board of *Tetrahedron*, the international journal of organic chemistry which he founded in 1957. In 1947, he was a member of the United Kingdom's delegation to the first conference of the United Nations Educational, Scientific, and Cultural Organization (UNESCO). Over a period of twenty years, from 1939 to 1958, he was president of four of England's most distinguished scientific societies: the Chemical Society, the Royal Society, the British Association for the Advancement of Science, and the Society for the Chemical Industry.

Among other awards that he received in his brilliant career are the Flintoff, Faraday, and Longstaff medals of the Chemical Society; the Copley, Davy, and Royal medals of the Royal Society; the Albert Gold Medal of the Royal Society of Arts; and the Franklin Medal of the Franklin Institute of Philadelphia. The government of France conferred upon him the title Commandeur de la Légion d'Honneur, and the government of the United States awarded him the Medal of Freedom.

On the occasion of his seventieth birthday, a group of his friends, colleagues, and pupils honored Robinson with a volume of essays entitled *Perspectives in Organic Chemistry*, which was edited by Sir Alexander Todd. The essays covered a wide range of subjects, which reflected Robinson's immense interest. The royalties realized from the sale of this volume of essays helped establish the biennial Robert Robinson Lectureship of the Chemical Society.

Bibliography

Primary

CHEMISTRY: "Brazilin and Haematoxylin. Part VII. Synthesis of Derivatives of Hydrindene Closely Allied to Brazilin and Haematoxylin," *Journal of the Chemical Society*, 1907 (with William H. Perkin, Jr.); "Strychnine, Berberine, and Allied Alkaloids," *Journal of the Chemical Society*, 1910 (with William H. Perkin, Jr.); "An Extension of the Theory of Addition of Conjugated Unsaturated Systems. Part 1. Note on the Constitution of the Salts of 1-Benzylidene-2-methyl-1:2:3:4-tetrahydroisoquinoline," *Journal of the Chemical Society*, 1916 (with E. E. P. Hamilton); "A Theory of the Mechanism of the Phytochemical Synthesis of Certain Alkaloids," *Journal of the Chemical Society*, 1917; "A Synthesis of Tropinonc," *Journal of the Chemical Society*, 1917; "An Explanation of the Property of Induced Polarity of Atoms and an Interpretation of Partial Valences on an Electronic Basis," *Journal of the Chemical Society*, 1922 (with W. O. Kermak); "The Morphine Group. Part I. A Discussion of the Constitutional Problem," *Journal of the Chemical Society*, 1923 (with J. M. Gulland); "Experiments on the Synthesis of Anthocyanins," *Journal of the Chemical Society*, 1926 (with A. Robertson); "Attempts to Find New Antimalarials. Introduction by George Barger and Robert Robinson. Part I. Some Pyrroloquinoline Derivatives," *Journal of the Chemical Society*, 1929 (with Gertrude Maud Robinson); "Distribution of Electrons in the Aromatic Nucleus and the Early Stages of Aromatic Substitution," *Nature*, 1932 (with A. Lapworth); "Experiments on the Synthesis of Substances Related to the Sterols. Part IX," *Journal of the Chemical Society*, 1936 (with J. Walker); "Development of Electrochemical Theories of the Course of Reactions of Carbon Compounds: The Eighteenth Faraday Lecture," *Journal of the Chemical Society*, 1947; "Synthesis of Cholesterol," *Nature*, 1947 (with J. W. Cornforth); "Willstätter Memorial Lecture," *Journal of the Chemical Society*, 1953; *The Structural Relations of Natural Products* (Weizmann Memorial Lectures), 1955; "The Polymerization of Propylene Using an Optically Active Catalyst," *Tetrahedron*, 1962 (with G. I. Fray); "The Synthesis of Brazilin and Haematoxylin," *Tetrahedron*, 1970 (with F. Morsingh).

MISCELLANEOUS: *The Art and Science of Playing Chess*, 1974 (with R. Edwards); *Memoirs of a Minor Prophet*, vol. 1, 1976.

Secondary

Anand, A., J. S. Bindra, and S. Ranganathan. *Art in Organic Synthesis*. 2d ed. New

York: John Wiley & Sons, 1988. A hallmark of Robinson's syntheses of natural products is the elegance of conception and execution. Additional examples of the artistry of organic synthesis are given.

Birch, Arthur J. "Sir Robert Robinson: A Contemporary Historical Assessment and a Professional Memoir." *Proceedings of the Royal Society*, 1976. Robinson's brilliant accomplishments in organic chemistry were assessed a year after his death by a former student from Australia.

Ingold, C. K. "The Nature of the Alternating Effect in Carbon Chains. Part I. The Directive Influence of the Nitroso Group in Aromatic Substitution." *Journal of the Chemical Society*, 1925. In this publication, Ingold attacked the theoretical ideals of Lapworth and Robinson, thereby provoking a bitter and protracted polemic with Robinson.

Saltzmann, M. D. "Sir Robert Robinson: A Centennial Tribute." *Chemistry in Britain* 22 (1986): 543. On the one hundredth anniversary of his birth, Robinson's contributions to the understanding of the reactions of aromatic compounds and his dispute with C. K. Ingold were reviewed.

Todd, Sir Alexander R., ed. *Perspectives in Organic Chemistry*. New York: International Publishers, 1956. The essays in this volume were contributed by eighteen distinguished chemists, nine of whom were recipients of the Nobel Prize, and dedicated to Robinson on his seventieth birthday. They reflect Robinson's broad interest in chemistry and afforded the authors an opportunity to speculate on the subjects in which they were acknowledged authorities.

Todd, Sir Alexander R., and J. C. Cornforth. *Biographical Memoirs of the Fellows of the Royal Society* 22 (1976). Robinson's success in explaining the reactions of aromatic compounds was attributed to his being "first and foremost a very great organic chemist with an intuitive feeling [that came from] a combination of ability and experience."

Leland J. Chinn

1948

Chemistry
Arne Tiselius, Sweden

Physics
Patrick M. S. Blackett, Great Britain

Physiology or Medicine
Paul Müller, Switzerland

Literature
T. S. Eliot, Great Britain

Peace
no award

ARNE TISELIUS
1948

Born: Stockholm, Sweden; August 10, 1902
Died: Uppsala, Sweden; October 29, 1971
Nationality: Swedish
Areas of concentration: Physical chemistry and biochemistry

Tiselius advanced the elucidation of molecular structure by developing the analytical techniques of electrophoresis and adsorption chromatography. His studies made possible the precise separation and characterization of biological molecules, including proteins, nucleic acids, carbohydrates, and lipids

The Award
Presentation

Professor Arne Fredrik Westgren, Chairman of the Nobel Committee for Chemistry of the Royal Swedish Academy of Sciences, presented the 1948 Nobel Prize in Chemistry to Arne Tiselius. During his presentation speech, Westgren integrated Tiselius' work into the history of Swedish physical chemistry. He began with a reference to the great Swedish chemist Karl Wilhelm Scheele, whose primary focus was precision chemical analysis.

In order to achieve precision analysis at the molecular level, adequate separation and purification methods would be required. Research at the University of Uppsala's Institute of Physical Chemistry began to produce positive results in molecular separation techniques, beginning with the invention of the ultracentrifuge by 1926 Nobel chemistry laureate Theodor Svedberg.

As Svedberg's student, Tiselius continued to improve methods for molecular separation and analysis. He developed the techniques of electrophoresis and adsorption chromatography. Electrophoresis involved the separation of molecules in an electric field, from negative electrode to positive electrode, based upon molecular size and electrical charge. Adsorption chromatography involved the separation of substances in solution based upon each substance's adsorption (its ability to stick) to a particular solid surface. Tiselius applied these two techniques to the purification and analysis of several biochemically and medically important molecules, including sugars, amino acids, and blood plasma proteins such as globulins and antibodies.

Westgren praised Tiselius' work for being continued in biochemistry and medical laboratories throughout the world. Westgren also praised Tiselius for his comprehensive knowledge of many scientific disciplines, including physics. Tiselius' comprehensive view of scientific unity gave him a distinct advantage over specialists confined to single fields of study.

Nobel lecture

Arne Tiselius delivered his Nobel lecture, entitled "Electrophoresis and Adsorption Analysis as Aids in Investigations of Large Molecular Weight Substances and Their Breakdown Products," on Monday, December 13, 1948. He began the lecture with a discussion of important biological molecules such as enzymes, nucleic acids, and viruses, and the importance of their analysis and characterization. In order to understand these molecules properly, they first must be isolated from the tissues of a particular organism.

To address this problem, numerous experimental techniques had been devised. Tiselius selected two techniques for his research, electrophoresis and adsorption analysis chromatography. Electrophoresis, initially developed in various forms by Oliver Lodge, Leonor Michaelis, and Theodor Svedberg, among others, involved the migration of molecules in an electric field. Adsorption analysis chromatography, initially developed by Mikhail Tsvett, involves the affinity, or attractiveness, of molecules for a defined solid substance.

Tiselius' early experimental work with electrophoresis borrowed from Svedberg's ultracentrifuge research. He separated proteins in an electric field through a U-shaped glass tube, photographing the electrophoretic separation of the molecules using ultraviolet illumination. Several technical difficulties, however, prevented his electrophoresis apparatus from reaching its full potential. A major problem was differences in the thickness of various regions of the electrophoresis solution; the differences were caused by temperature variations, and they severely distorted molecular separations. He minimized these heating effects by performing the electrophoresis experiments at approximately 4 degrees Celsius, where water is most dense.

Tiselius' improvements upon the electrophoretic U-tube apparatus substantially enhanced its separation ability. It became useful for the isolation of a variety of proteins, including albumin and globulins from horse blood plasma and bird eggs. The method still was not without its faults. Electrophoresis of certain substances required electrophoretic solutions having high electrical conductivities—that is, solutions that could transfer electrons very efficiently. Another problem was electrophoresing large proteins that were composed of many inseparable smaller molecules.

Tiselius was aware that no single analytical technique was enough to separate molecules from one another completely. Instead, the task would require a series of complementary techniques. One alternative technique was adsorption chromatography, of which there were three principal types: frontal analysis, elution analysis, and displacement analysis. These techniques proved very useful for the separation of fatty acids, sugars, amino acids, proteins, polymethylmetacrylates, and viruses.

Critical reception

Arne Tiselius' 1948 Nobel Prize in Chemistry was well received worldwide. His extensive research in molecular separation had already established an outstanding reputation. Therefore, the Nobel Prize reaffirmed his preeminence in physical chemistry. The members of the Swedish Nobel Committee for Chemistry had been studying many excellent candidates, and they did not want to be perceived as being biased in favor of their own countryman, even more so one who was a member of the Nobel Foundation. Nevertheless, Tiselius' scientific contributions were of such importance that he was awarded the chemistry prize.

The award significantly bolstered Tiselius' research efforts at the University of Uppsala, along with the work of his fellow biochemists. For years, he and his colleagues had worked laboriously within cramped, insufficiently supplied facilities. The Institute of Biochemistry was nothing more than a small corner of Svedberg's Institute of Physical Chemistry. After Tiselius' Nobel Prize, the Swedish administration hastened to establish a new, independent Institute of Biochemistry with its own building in 1952. His increased worldwide reputation also stimulated a large influx of students, thereby giving a much-needed boost to the advancement of biochemistry as a serious field of study. More money was budgeted to support the works of Tiselius and his colleagues. The events following Tiselius' Nobel Prize were, in fact, remarkably similar to those following Svedberg's 1926 Nobel Prize. Each award followed a major European war, and each award initiated a major period of intensive research in its respective fields of chemistry.

Both the November 15, 1948, *Time* and *Newsweek* editions honored Tiselius' achievement. *Time* portrayed him as a popular scientist and teacher: He was handsome, well-dressed, and very active. They discussed his contributions to protein electrophoresis, stressing the importance of proteins to all life processes.

After winning the Nobel Prize, Tiselius not only was involved in accelerated research efforts but also became concerned with developing research strategies for chemistry and other fields internationally. He served as president of the Nobel Foundation, president of the International Union of Pure and Applied Chemistry, and chairman of the Royal Swedish Academy of Sciences. He also served on numerous other governmental and academic decision-making bodies. He was devoted to activities promoting scholarship, such as Nobel Symposia, where individuals in specialized fields worldwide could meet to exchange ideas and advance research.

Tiselius, much like many other Nobel laureates, was concerned about the effects of the scientific explosion upon human welfare. Having seen the military applications of science during World War II, he sought to steer science toward more peaceful purposes to help mankind. These efforts included the expansion of medical research, especially cancer research.

Tiselius' achievements were further recognized with eleven honorary doctorates and appointments to many scientific societies. He was much admired throughout the scientific community. After his sixtieth birthday, in 1962, the editors of *Archives of Biochemistry and Biophysics* dedicated a special supplementary volume to him. It included forty research articles on protein biochemistry by his friends and colleagues. The editors praised him for his contributions to science and for his inspiration of other scientists. His techniques of electrophoresis and adsorption chromatography had been adopted by protein chemists worldwide. Furthermore, his accomplishments paved the way for several later Nobel chemistry laureates, including Frederick Sanger (1958) and Stanford Moore and William H. Stein (1972).

Upon Tiselius' death in October, 1971, a December *Nature* obituary lamented the loss. He was praised for his brilliance, wisdom, caring, and incredible energy. He and his mentor, Theodor Svedberg, represented the two principal figures in Swedish physical chemistry during the twentieth century; Svedberg had died earlier the same year.

Biography

Arne Wilhelm Kaurin Tiselius was born in Stockholm, Sweden, on August 10, 1902, the son of Hans Abraham Tiselius and Rosa Kaurin Tiselius. After his father's death in 1906, the family lived with relatives in Göteborg, where his interest in science developed at the local grammar school. In 1921, he entered the University of Uppsala, where he earned the M.A. in chemistry, physics, and mathematics. In 1925, he became a research assistant for Svedberg at the Institute for Physical Chemistry in Uppsala. He received his doctorate and married Ingrid Margareta Dalen in 1930. They had two children, Eva in 1932 and Per in 1934.

Tiselius was assistant professor of chemistry at Uppsala from 1931 to 1938. He held a Rockefeller Foundation fellowship for study at Princeton University from 1934 to 1935. He became professor of biochemistry at Uppsala in 1938 through a donation from Major and Mrs. Herbert Jacobsson. He helped to establish the Institute of Biochemistry at Uppsala in 1946.

Tiselius was president of the Swedish Natural Science Research Council (1946-1950), vice president of the Nobel Foundation (1947-1960), president of the Nobel Foundation (1960-1964), chairman of the research committee of the Swedish Cancer Society (1951-1955), and president of the International Union of Pure and Applied Chemistry (1951-1955). He served on numerous government committees, including the Atomic Energy Research Committee, the Medical Research Council of Sweden, and the Committee for the Reformation of the Universities. He belonged to numerous scientific organizations, including the Royal Swedish Academy of Sciences, the National Academy of Sciences (United States), and the Royal Institute (Great Britain). He held eleven honorary doctorates. Arne Tiselius died of a heart attack on the morning of October 29, 1971.

Scientific Career

Arne Tiselius was one of the first major physical biochemists of the twentieth century. As a physical chemist, he continued the technical expertise and experimental innovation of Theodor (The) Svedberg. He shared with Svedberg a deep interest in the elucidation (chemical understanding) of biological molecules, especially proteins, and consequently steered his research in that direction. He used the techniques of physical chemistry to provide the analytical background for modern biochemistry, specifically with the development of electrophoresis and adsorption chromatography. Throughout his studies, he demonstrated an overt concern for the applications of his research to the welfare of humanity.

After a brilliant undergraduate career, Tiselius entered Svedberg's laboratory in 1925, at a time during which Svedberg was making monumental breakthroughs in ultracentrifugation. This was a very opportune moment for Tiselius, especially with the acceleration of Swedish physical chemistry following Svedberg's 1926 Nobel Prize. Svedberg was deeply impressed with Tiselius' intellectual promise. Because of his own preoccupation with the ultracentrifuge, Svedberg gave the electrophoresis project to his young student.

Tiselius advanced the methods of electrophoresis, developing them as both separatory and analytical tools. Electrophoresis involves the separation of molecules in an electric field based on the size and electric charge of the molecules. For size, the smaller molecules moved faster than larger molecules within the electrophoretic solution. For charge, the molecular electric charge determined the speed and direction of migration within the electric field. In early experiments, Tiselius and Svedberg electrophoresed egg albumin in a solution of acetic acid and sodium acetate, photographing the gradual movement of proteins from the negative to positive electrodes with ultraviolet light illumination. They varied the temperature and acidity of the electrophoretic solution, finding that the protein mobility changed considerably at different acidities.

Because of his interest in the electrophoretic separation of proteins, Tiselius independently studied biochemistry, a subject that received little attention in the physical chemistry curriculum of the period. He also assisted Svedberg's ultracentrifuge studies. He finally mastered the electrophoretic technique and focused its use upon the separation of blood plasma proteins, with which he was very successful. He received his doctorate in 1930 for this work and was immediately appointed assistant professor.

Despite his success with serum proteins, Tiselius was very disappointed with electrophoresis. Alone, it was inadequate for the separation of many substances. The ultracentrifuge shared the same dilemma. He realized that proper separation and analysis of molecules would require the development of many complementary techniques, among them being adsorption chromatography. While keeping these alternative techniques in mind, he focused on improving electrophoresis for several more years.

In 1934-1935, Tiselius received a Rockefeller Foundation Fellowship to study at Princeton University, where he worked with Professor Hugh S. Taylor of the Frick Chemical Laboratory. He began to study adsorption analysis chromatography, using a variety of substances (such as zeolite minerals) to adsorb molecules. He was inspired by contacts with many renowned chemists, including Henry Eyring, Wendell Stanley, and John Northrop. The experience fueled his ideas for improving electrophoresis and adsorption chromatography.

Upon returning to Uppsala, Tiselius improved his electrophoresis apparatus by performing experiments at 4 degrees Celsius and by using schlieren refractive optics, a special technique for magnifying samples with less optical distortion.

Lowering experimental temperatures reduced the effects of convection currents, which had seriously distorted the electrophoretic migration of molecules. Refractive optics provided better molecular resolution. Using this improved apparatus, he successfully separated horse serum (blood plasma) into five components, which appeared as five separate migratory "bands" in the electrophoretic medium. The five separate components were the proteins albumin, alpha-globulin, beta-globulin, gamma-globulin, and immunoglobulin (antibodies).

Tiselius applied electrophoresis to the separation, purification, and analysis of other biologically relevant molecules. With Florence B. Seibert and Kai O. Pedersen, he determined the molecular weights and other biochemical properties and carbohydrates from the tuberculosis bacillus *Mycobacterium tuberculosis*. With Harry Svensson and G. E. Henschen, he isolated the protein-catabolizing enzyme pepsin and also studied its properties. He performed similar experiments with H. L. Horsfall on the snail plasma protein hemocyanin. The research of Tiselius and his colleagues played an important role in the growth of protein chemistry.

Svensson and Tiselius discovered that proteins migrated freely from negative to positive electrodes in electrophoretic solutions having low salt content. Protein migration was reduced, however, at higher salt concentrations. Furthermore, each protein's isoelectric point varied with the salt concentration. The isoelectric point of a protein is the pH where electrophoretic migration ceases because the protein's electric charge is effectively zero, canceled by the opposite charges in the electric field.

Throughout these studies, Tiselius and his colleagues separated and purified more proteins. They characterized the isolated proteins and amino acid components based upon molecular weight, size, shape, formation of multiprotein aggregates, electrochemical properties, and other biochemical properties. Furthermore, electrophoresis proved to be useful in medicine for the identification of disease agents and for characterization of blood plasma. Tiselius continued Svedberg's focus on respiratory and cardiovascular proteins.

While continuing experimental modifications of electrophoresis, Tiselius turned more to adsorption analysis chromatography during World War II. With the help of Stig Clæsson, he developed a chromatography system by which solutions were separated in a column packed with zeolite crystals as adsorbent, with gold-plated metal filters. Instead of visually reading the component separation on the column using colored substances, they constructed a microrefractometer, which gauged the composition of solutions eluting from (coming off) the column. This device provided quantitative measurements of the separation process. They used this technique to study amino acids, short protein sequences, and sugars. Their work with the polysaccharide dextran had an important medical application: It was a suitable blood plasma replacement.

Tiselius was the first physical biochemist to differentiate among three methods of adsorption chromatography: frontal analysis, elution analysis, and displacement analysis. Frontal analysis involved running a solution through the adsorption column, with the solution components adhering to the adsorbing material to various degrees, based upon each component's affinity (chemical attractiveness) for the adsorbing material. Consequently, those components with lowest attraction for the adsorbent left the column first, whereas those components with higher affinities left the column later. Tiselius' microrefractometer measured volume compositions exiting the columns so that fractions could be collected to isolate the components.

Elution analysis was similar, although it involved the loading of the sample into the adsorbing column, followed by the flushing of the column with large quantities of elution solvent. Again, the weaker affinity components eluted (were given off) first, although in a more concentrated grouping, followed by the higher-affinity components. Elution analysis provided highly efficient separations of many, but not all, substances. Its primary drawback was "tailing," in which molecules from one component class contaminated the next-higher-affinity component class.

Displacement analysis involved loading the sample solution onto the adsorbing column, followed by the forced replacement of the solution components from the column by a competitor molecule with a very high affinity for the adsorbing column. The weaker-affinity solution components would be removed first, followed by the higher-affinity components. For example, separation of amino acid residues used phenol as the displacement solvent. This technique eliminated the elution tailing problem, although overall purification was poorer.

Tiselius applied these adsorption techniques to separate, purify, and characterize many proteins of medicinal importance. With Richard L. M. Synge, he studied the properties of the antibacterial proteins gramicidin, gramicidin S, tyrothricin, and tyrocidine. Furthermore, in 1947, Tiselius and eventual 1958 Nobel chemistry laureate Frederick Sanger separated insulin into four components by frontal analysis. The four components were correctly believed to be the four peptide subunits of the insulin precursor protein "proinsulin."

After the 1948 Nobel Prize, Tiselius continued chromatography and electrophoresis experiments. Synge and Tiselius used charcoal adsorption analysis effectively to separate different types of proteins. They also experimented with paper chromatography. David A. Hall and Tiselius used alcohol buffers to separate amino acids, achieving separation efficiencies as high as 96 percent.

With students R. S. Alm and R. J. P. Williams, Tiselius explored other novel approaches to adsorption analysis. One advance was gradient elution, in which several solvent buffers were mixed to produce a buffer concentration gradient which gradually increased as it washed sample components through the column. Another advance was ion-exchange chromatography, in which the chromatography adsorbent consisted of positively charged atoms (cations) or negatively charged atoms (anions). Sample components separated in such a column were isolated based upon their attractiveness to the oppositely charged ion-exchange adsorbent. Positively charged components would bind negative adsorbents, whereas negatively charged components would bind positive adsorbents. Ion-exchange chromatography using cellulose was perfected by Elbert A. Peterson and Herbert A. Sober in 1956.

Tiselius combined adsorption with electrophoresis to produce "zone electrophoresis," which involved the separation of molecules in an electric field based on charge, plus separation based on size using an adsorbing material (such as starch or agar gel) as the electrophoretic medium. Tiselius' earlier "boundary electrophoresis" had relied primarily upon charge separation. The addition of adsorbent in zone electrophoresis greatly improved separation. The technique attained widespread use in protein and nucleic acid separation experiments.

Much like Svedberg, Tiselius pushed experimental techniques to their limits. His excellent knowledge of physical chemistry contributed to insightful and elaborate experimental modifications; his knowledge of biochemistry directed his research toward molecules of biological and medical importance. His achievements greatly advanced the separation, purification, and quantitative analysis of molecular structure.

Bibliography

Primary
CHEMISTRY: "A New Method for Determination of the Mobility of Proteins," *Journal of the American Chemical Society*, vol. 48, 1926 (with The Svedberg); "A New Apparatus for Electrophoretic Analysis of Colloidal Mixtures," *Transactions of the Faraday Society*, vol. 33, 1937; "Molecular Weight, Electrochemical and Biological Properties of Tuberculin Protein and Polysaccharide Molecules," *The American Review of Tuberculosis*, vol. 38, 1938 (with Florence B. Seibert and Kai O. Pedersen); "The Influence of Electrolyte Concentration on the Electrophoretic Mobility of Egg Albumin," *Transactions of the Faraday Society*, vol. 36, 1940 (with Harry Svensson); "Adsorption Analysis of Amino Acid Mixtures," *Advances in Protein Chemistry*, vol. 3, 1947; "Adsorption Analysis of Oxidized Insulin," *Nature*, vol. 160, 1947 (with Frederick Sanger); "Adsorption Experiments with Gramicidin and Related Substances," *Acta Chemica Scandinavica*, vol. 1, 1947 (with R. L. M. Synge); "Some Adsorption Experiments with Amino Acids and Peptides, Especially Compounds of Tryptophan," *Acta Chemica Scandinavica*, vol. 3, 1949 (with R. L. M. Synge); "The Separation of Small Amounts of Aromatic Amino Acids," *Acta Chemica Scandinavica*, vol. 5, 1951 (with David A. Hall); "Zone Electrophoresis," *Advances in Protein Chemistry*, vol. 8, 1953 (with Per Flodin).
SCIENTIFIC AUTOBIOGRAPHY: "Reflections from Both Sides of the Counter," *Annual Review of Biochemistry*, vol. 37, 1968.

Secondary
Farber, Eduard. *Nobel Prize Winners in Chemistry, 1901-1961*. Rev. ed. New York: Abelard-Schuman, 1963. An informative reference, this book provides short synopses of the first sixty Nobel Prize winners in chemistry. Each laureate is discussed with a biographical sketch, description of the individual's scientific work, and importance of the work.

Heidelberger, Michael, et al., eds. "Perspectives in the Biochemistry of Large Molecules." *Archives of Biochemistry and Biophysics*, supp. 1 (1962). This special supplement to a major physical chemistry journal honored Arne Tiselius on his sixtieth birthday. It includes a complete listing of his research articles up to 1962. It also includes forty research articles in physical biochemistry by his friends and colleagues.

Morris, C. J. O. R., and P. Morris. *Separation Methods in Biochemistry*. New York: Interscience, 1963. This reference work, while dated, is an excellent, comprehensive summary of major experimental techniques in physical chemistry, most of which are still used. The various analytical techniques are discussed from theoretical and historical viewpoints. Several thousand references are listed.

Pedersen, Kai O. "Arne Wilhelm Kaurin Tiselius." In *Dictionary of Scientific Biography*, edited by Charles Coulston Gillispie. New York: Charles Scribner's Sons, 1970. This short biographical sketch, written by one of Tiselius' colleagues, provides a close look at his life and scientific career. It provides glimpses of Tiselius' childhood, personal interests, major research experiments, and honors.

Stryer, Lubert. *Biochemistry*. San Francisco: W. H. Freeman, 1975. Stryer's textbook is a classic biochemistry text for undergraduates. It is very clearly written, with excellent diagrams and illustrations. The chapter on protein structure includes concise explanations of electrophoresis and chromatography.

Tinoco, Ignacio, Kenneth Sauer, and James C. Wang. *Physical Chemistry: Principles and Applications in Biological Sciences*. Englewood Cliffs, N.J.: Prentice-Hall, 1978. A book of physical methods in molecular biology, this textbook is aimed primarily at advanced undergraduates and graduate students. The book presents a mathematical discussion of basic physical concepts, including electrophoresis, adsorption, and ultracentrifugation.

David Wason Hollar, Jr.

1949

Chemistry
William Francis Giauque, United States

Physics
Hideki Yukawa, Japan

Physiology or Medicine
Walter Rudolf Hess, Switzerland
António Egas Moniz, Portugal

Literature
William Faulkner, United States

Peace
Lord Boyd-Orr, Great Britain

WILLIAM FRANCIS GIAUQUE
1949

Born: Niagara Falls, Ontario, Canada; May 12, 1895
Died: Oakland, California; March 28, 1982
Nationality: American
Area of concentration: Chemical thermodynamics

Giauque, by developing methods for studying matter at extremely low temperatures, proved the third law of thermodynamics and opened the range of temperatures below 1 Kelvin for research. His studies of the low-temperature properties of matter provided data for the prediction of the behavior of chemical species at higher temperatures

The Award

Presentation

Arne W. K. Tiselius, a member of the Nobel Committee for Chemistry of the Royal Swedish Academy of Sciences, presented William Francis Giauque for the Nobel Prize in Chemistry on December 10, 1949. In his presentation speech, Tiselius noted that a few exact general laws enable chemists to predict the results of chemical reactions under varying conditions of temperature and pressure. The laws of particular importance are those that predict the affinity of substances for one another, namely, the second and third laws of thermodynamics.

In a brief historical overview of modern thermodynamics, Tiselius praised Willard Gibbs, who provided the equations necessary to predict affinity (chemical attractiveness). What is needed in addition to reaction heat is the entropy (the degree of disorder in matter) change during the process. Giauque, during his fruitful career, contributed greatly in terms of both methods and data to the knowledge of entropy. He proved the third law of thermodynamics first stated by Walther Nernst and made possible not only the calculation of entropy changes for chemical processes but also the entropy itself of many elements and compounds. In order to work on low-temperature entropy determinations, Giauque developed the method of magnetic cooling to reach temperatures near absolute zero and also produced important methods of measuring temperatures.

His careful comparisons of results obtained from spectroscopic and calorimetric methods have provided many insights into matter; for example, Tiselius noted the discovery of the additional isotopes of oxygen. Tiselius also commended the precision with which Giauque worked. He pointed to the recognition by Giauque that very small entropy differences in molecules with high symmetry, such as carbon monoxide, were caused by different ways that the molecules could orient.

Tiselius closed by noting that Giauque's careful investigations in the area of cryogenics (low-temperature physics) represent a major contribution to the field of physical chemistry.

Nobel lecture

Giauque delivered his Nobel lecture, entitled "Some Consequences of Low Temperature Research in Chemical Thermodynamics," on December 12, 1949, to an audience of roughly four hundred students and faculty. He began his lecture by noting that the focus of most of his low-temperature work was the study of entropy. Knowledge of entropy and entropy changes is extremely important since it allows the thermodynamic feasibility of chemical processes to be predicted. The chemical equation for any desired reaction may be written but the spontaneity of the reaction and the position of chemical equilibrium cannot be known from the equation itself. Ability to predict the occurrence of a specific process requires the calculation of free energies, which are functions of both the heat of reaction and the entropy of reaction.

Giauque then pointed to the Nernst heat theorem, from which the third law of thermodynamics developed. Nernst suggested that the entropy of all perfect crystalline substances approached zero as the absolute temperature approached zero. A knowledge of heat capacity behavior at low temperatures would then allow calculation of the entropy of a substance at all temperatures. This possibility gave direction to Giauque's lifelong research into low-temperature behavior.

Giauque noted that discoveries of unexpected physical properties of matter had resulted from his careful determinations of entropy. Among the most important of these was the discovery of the oxygen isotopes of atomic weights 17 and 18. Giauque pointed to the connections made in his research between determinations of entropy using low-temperature calorimetric data and the entropy calculated using quantum statistics and the energy levels of gas molecules obtained from spectroscopic data. Giauque illustrated this with the band spectrum of atmospheric oxygen photographed by Harold D. Babcock at Mount Wilson Observatory. The spectrum showed the usual doublets of oxygen, 16-16 molecules which gave entropy values in exact agreement with those from the low-temperature work. Giauque was, however, reluctant to use this spectroscopic entropy because of a number of unexplained lines in the oxygen spectrum. He described months of pondering the origin of these lines, contemplation which resulted in the realization that there must exist additional isotopes of oxygen.

Giauque described his adiabatic (without heat transfer) demagnetization method for producing temperatures below 1 Kelvin in clear, simple terms. The idea of using magnetic fields to lower temperatures came to him after he saw data on magnetic susceptibility measurements done by Woltjer and Heike Kamerlingh Onnes at the University of Leiden. He realized and later showed, through both thermodynamic and statistical mechanical calculations, that successive magnetization and demagnetization steps could be used to remove heat and hence lower temperatures in paramagnetic materials. This theory was proved in 1933 by experiments carried on at the University of California at Berkeley by Giauque and D. P. MacDougall.

Giauque then addressed the question of the measurement of low temperatures. He described his use of magnetic susceptibility changes, then entropy changes themselves as indicators of temperature, as well as thermometers that he devised for accurate measurement of temperatures below 1 Kelvin. He also described and illustrated various calorimeters, gas liquefiers, and heat exchangers used in his work, most of which were designed by Giauque himself. Giauque ended his lecture by recommending the subject of entropy as a rich field for further study.

Critical reception

The awarding of the Nobel Prize in Chemistry to William Giauque was received by both popular and scientific press without strong response, either positive or negative. Both *The New York Times* and *The Washington Post* published articles on November 4, 1949, the day following the official announcement. The articles outlined the major accomplishments of Giauque and gave short biographical sketches. The lack of controversy seemed to be attributable primarily to Giauque's habit of shunning publicity whenever possible; avoiding meetings, since he could get more done by staying at work; and not openly involving himself in politics of any type, either local or national.

Robert Brunn, a writer for *The Christian Science Monitor*, called Giauque a "natural scientist's scientist," who is happiest working in his laboratory: "All he wants to do is probe the unknown." Brunn claims that the research of William Giauque has made possible "better gasoline, stronger steel, long-wearing rubber, better glass, and cheaper fertilizer."

Milton Silverman, in an article in *The Saturday Evening Post*, called Giauque "one of the most brilliant theoretical chemists in the world." Silverman pictured Giauque as a person who lacked "competitive spirit." He illustrated this point with Giauque's lack of interest in pursuing the search for isotopes of other elements after he had discovered those of oxygen, as well as his unwillingness to use his own magnetic cooling technique to get to temperatures lower than anyone else could. This is truly a compliment in disguise, since Giauque was not interested in claiming records, only in continually searching for one thing—truth.

The cover article in the November 28, 1949, issue of the *Chemical and Engineering News* pointed to the importance of Giauque's demand for precision in all of his work. He was pictured as one who "energizes his research students by example," frequently working with them all night and on weekends. "Admiration by his students seems to be in direct proportion to the grueling pace he still expects of them."

Biography

William Francis Giauque was born on May 12, 1895, in Niagara Falls, Ontario, Canada. He was the first of three children of William Tecumseh Sherman Giauque and Isabella Jane (Duncan) Giauque. Both parents were United States citizens. Giauque spent his early years in the United States, receiving his elementary education in public schools, principally in Michigan. The family returned to Niagara Falls after the death of his father in 1908. Giauque received his secondary education at the Niagara Falls Collegiate Institute.

At this time Giauque was interested in a career in electrical engineering. Financial necessity and the desire to gain experience in the field made him seek employment at a power plant in the Niagara Falls area. Unable to secure employment there, he worked at the Hooker Electrochemical Company in Niagara Falls, New York. Curiosity about the technical problems he encountered caused him to choose a career in chemical engineering. He entered a program for chemistry and engineering at the University of California at Berkeley in 1916. He received the bachelor of science degree with highest honors in 1920 and the Ph.D. degree in 1922, with a major in chemistry and a minor in physics.

Giauque became an instructor in chemistry at Berkeley in 1922 and moved through the ranks to become a professor by 1934. He worked for the United States government during World War II, designing a mobile unit for producing liquid oxygen. He married Muriel Frances Ashley, a physicist, in 1932. They had two sons, William Francis Ashley G. and Robert David Ashley G. Giauque's hobby was his work; he spent the little free time he allowed himself swimming or attending sports events with his sons. Giauque retired in 1962 but returned to Berkeley to direct the low-temperature research laboratory until one year before his death in 1982.

Scientific Career

William Francis Giauque spent his entire academic career (with the exception of the few years in government research) at the University of California at Berkeley. Giauque chose Berkeley, in 1916, partly for its low tuition and partly for the reputation of the chemistry faculty at this young, but quickly growing, institution. Influenced by Gilbert N. Lewis, Giauque became interested in the field of chemical thermodynamics. As an undergraduate, he worked on the measurement of low-temperature entropies under G. E. Gibson and became interested in the third law of thermodynamics. After graduating in 1922, Giauque continued graduate studies under Gibson. His thesis work on the experimental measurement of heat capacities of crystalline and glassy glycerol allowed calculation of the entropy difference between the two forms and provided one of the earliest verifications of the third law of thermodynamics. His research experiences as a student as well as his innate attraction to accuracy and precision prompted Giauque to undertake a career in basic research. His entire research career has focused with single-minded dedication on the behavior and properties of matter at very low temperatures.

The attempt to reach the absolute zero of temperature appeared to have come to a standstill after the liquefaction of helium by Heike Kamerlingh Onnes in 1908. The techniques of cooling by reducing the vapor pressure and subsequent expansion of boiling gas had by 1922 allowed the attainment of temperatures to 1 Kelvin. Kamerlingh Onnes realized that the limit of low temperatures obtainable by the gas expansion method had been reached and that further investigation into the properties of matter at low temperature would show the way toward the absolute zero.

Two months after the February, 1926, death of Kamerlingh Onnes, Professor

Latimer of the University of California at Berkeley presented in a paper to the American Chemical Society the ideas of William Giauque on reaching temperatures below those of liquid helium. Giauque's ideas were submitted for publication in detail in December, 1926, to the *Journal of the American Chemical Society*. The paper was entitled "A Thermodynamic Treatment of Magnetic Effects: A Proposed Method of Producing Temperatures Considerably Below 1° Absolute." The cooling proposed by Giauque was based on Nernst's third law of thermodynamics, which states that, as absolute zero of temperature is approached, entropy (the degree of disorder in matter) will also approach zero. Giauque showed that magnetic fields can produce the desired degree of orderliness in the electronic spins of a salt system; hence, the name magnetic cooling.

All matter is composed of atoms with electrons orbiting the nucleus and each spinning on its own axis. This spin becomes very important at very low temperatures, at which most other types of motion are greatly reduced. Any acceleration of a charged particle creates magnetic effects, and the electron's spin makes it behave like a tiny bar magnet. The application of a strong external magnetic field can cause the tiny electron magnets to line up in the direction of the field. According to the third law, at absolute zero the spins would be all lined up in the same direction, that is, in complete absence of disorder.

Giauque proposed to impose order on the random spins by a two-step process: an isothermal (constant temperature) magnetization followed by an adiabatic (without heat transfer) demagnetization. In the first step, a salt, gadolinium sulfate, was cooled to liquid helium temperatures and then subjected to a strong magnetic field. The heat produced by this process was carried away from the salt system by evaporating helium gas. In the second step, the system was isolated from the helium gas by evacuating the sample chamber and the magnetic field was turned off. Cooling then takes place in the salt. The temperature change made possible by this method depended on the strength of the magnet. Experiments were carried out with D. P. MacDougall in the spring of 1933. The magnet available allowed the temperature to be lowered to 0.25 Kelvin. The method was proved and an entire new range of temperatures became available for research. Other cryogenic (low-temperature) laboratories adopted the new method, and magnetic cooling became the standard method for low-temperature research all over the world. For this accomplishment, Giauque received the Chandler Medal of Columbia University in 1936 and the following year the Elliott Cresson Medal of the Franklin Institute.

The implications of this ability to study matter at extremely low temperatures are enormous. If data on the entropies and heat capacities of substances at low temperatures are available, then the entropies can in theory be calculated at any temperature. Knowledge of these entropies, combined with information about the enthalpies (heat) of formation of substances, allows calculation of free energies. This, in turn, permits the prediction of the direction that any chemical process will take. The results of Giauque's research on entropies have been applied extensively to the designing of chemical processes and the determination, without expensive and time-consuming tests, of the possibility of many chemical processes.

In 1928, Giauque, working with R. Wiebe, developed procedures for the calculation of entropies and free energies from spectroscopic data. He used data from band spectra of gases and statistical thermodynamics to calculate entropy values and compared these to values obtained experimentally from low-temperature measurements of heat capacity. The validity of the calculation method and the third law of thermodynamics were verified by many tests during the 1920's and 1930's that showed close agreement between theoretical and experimental entropy values for various gases, such as hydrogen bromide, hydrogen chloride, and hydrogen iodide. Similar work on many other gases was conducted until almost 1940.

In 1927, Heisenberg had suggested that the alternating intensity pattern found in the band spectrum of hydrogen and other homonuclear diatomic molecules was attributable to the presence of two forms of different symmetry. In the case of the hydrogen molecule, the two protons could have spins that are parallel to each other (ortho hydrogen) or antiparallel (para hydrogen). The normal ratio of the two is approximately three ortho to one para. Hydrogen kept at 20 Kelvins for a period of time would eventually change to the pure para form. To support this theory, Giauque and H. L. Johnson kept a sample hydrogen gas at the temperature of liquid air for roughly six months. After this time, they measured the triple point pressure of this hydrogen, as well as that of ordinary hydrogen. The small difference in pressure was unexplainable in terms of experimental error and was seen as support for the suggestion that the two different forms did in fact exist.

In 1928, Giauque and Johnson were occupied with calculating the entropy of oxygen from the absorption bands of atmospheric oxygen. The presence of an additional weak band in the spectrum of atmospheric oxygen had up to this time no satisfactory explanation. Being unwilling to base entropy calculations on a spectrum that lacked clear interpretation, Giauque proceeded to investigate the problems in greater detail. The additional weak band was almost an exact duplication of the prominent band except that the lines showed slightly different spacings. The question that Giauque and Johnson addressed was whether the two bands could have originated from a common source. After trying many ways of combining the lines found, they could find no scheme that accounted for a single molecular form as the origin of the bands. The weak band could, however, be explained by the existence of an isotope of oxygen having an atomic mass of eighteen. In the same year, after examining data obtained from H. D. Babcock at Mount Wilson Observatory, Giauque and Johnson proposed a third isotope of oxygen of mass seventeen, which is present in the atmosphere in minute amounts. For discovering these two isotopes of oxygen, Giauque and Johnson shared the 1929 Pacific Division Prize of the American Association for the Advancement of Science.

Among the important consequences of the discovery of the oxygen isotopes were the use of the different isotopes as tracer atoms in the study of photosynthesis and respiration and the realization that two different atomic weight scales were in use by chemists and physicists. The scale used by chemists set 16.000 as the weighted average of the three isotopes, while physicists used a scale based on the assignment of 16.000 to the smallest isotope of oxygen. These two scales persisted until 1961, when the atomic weight standard was changed to the carbon 12 isotope. The discovery of the additional isotopes of oxygen prompted other researchers, using the same methods as Giauque and Johnson, to search for isotopes of other elements in the atmospheric gases; the isotopes of carbon, nitrogen, and hydrogen were found.

Giauque's passion for precision and accuracy and his concern with the problem of accurate temperature measurement are evidenced by the many papers and notes on that topic published during his career.

In 1927 he investigated copper-constantan thermocouples and compared them to the hydrogen gas thermometer from 15 to 284 Kelvins as well as to oxygen and hydrogen vapor pressure thermometers. Yet, various properties usually used for temperature measurements, such as volume changes in gases, become extremely unreliable at very low temperatures and make accurate determination of temperature difficult. Giauque used magnetic susceptibilities for temperature measurements below 1 Kelvin in early work but reported in 1938 the development of amorphous carbon resistance thermometers that proved very reliable for those temperatures.

Giauque also addressed the problem of the disagreement that surrounded the assigning of reference point values in different temperature systems. The use of the property of liquid expansion as a temperature indicator in the sixteenth and seventeenth centuries made a two-reference-point system necessary. The practice was to assign two temperatures to two "reproducible" systems, thereby fixing the size of the degree on a particular scale such as the Celsius or Fahrenheit system. The "reproducible" systems usually employed were the ice point and boiling point of water. Difficulties in making accurate measurements particularly at the boiling point of water caused these values to change frequently, depending on the observations being accepted as more reliable. Giauque, in a humorous paper published in *Nature* in 1939, argued very convincingly for a redefinition of the thermodynamic temperature scale using only one fixed point, namely, the ice point.

Giauque wrote approximately seventy-five papers up to the awarding of the Nobel Prize in 1949. All but one of these, an article on Gilbert N. Lewis in 1946, were in the area of low-temperature research. At the time of the awarding of the Nobel Prize, the University of California committed $500,000 for a new laboratory for Giauque's research in low-temperature chemistry, which he continued until the year before his death in 1982.

Bibliography

Primary

CHEMISTRY: "The Third Law of Thermodynamics: Evidence from the Specific Heats of Glycerol," *Journal of the American Chemical Society*, vol. 45, 1923 (with G. E. Gibson); "The Entropies of Hydrogen Chloride, Hydrogen Bromide, and Hydrogen Iodide," 1928 (with Richard Wiebe); "The Entropies of Methane and Ammonia," *Physical Review*, vol. 38, 1931 (with R. W. Blue and Roy Overstreet);

"Temperatures Below 1 Degree Absolute," *Industrial and Engineering Chemistry*, vol. 28, 1936.

MISCELLANEOUS: *The Scientific Papers of William F. Giauque*, 1969.

Secondary

Mendelssohn, K. *The Quest for Absolute Zero*. New York: Halsted Press, 1977. A history of low-temperature chemistry and physics. It contains a chapter on the work of Giauque, particularly his magnetic cooling experiments.

Rock, Peter A. *Chemical Thermodynamics*. Mill Valley, Calif.: University Science Books, 1983. This book contains a very clear chapter on the third law of thermodynamics. It describes magnetic cooling and the determination of absolute entropies.

Silverman, Milton. "He Works at 459 Below." *Saturday Evening Post* 222 (December 10, 1949): 38-39. This account in the popular press presents a lively, readable description both of Giauque the person and of his work at low temperatures.

White, G. K. *Experimental Techniques in Low-Temperature Physics*. New York: Oxford University Press, 1979. This is a technical manual on various aspects of low-temperature physics. There are many references throughout the text to the contributions of Giauque.

"William Francis Giauque." In *Current Biography, 1950*, edited by Anna Rothe. New York: H. W. Wilson, 1951. This article presents a good biographical sketch of Giauque and a clear, matter-of-fact description of his work.

Grace A. Banks

1950

Chemistry
Otto Paul Hermann Diels, West Germany
Kurt Alder, West Germany

Physics
Cecil Frank Powell, Great Britain

Physiology or Medicine
Philip S. Hench, United States
Edward C. Kendall, United States
Tadeusz Reichstein, Switzerland

Literature
Bertrand Russell, Great Britain

Peace
Ralph Bunche, United States

OTTO PAUL HERMANN DIELS
1950

Born: Hamburg, Germany; January 23, 1876
Died: Kiel, West Germany; March 7, 1954
Nationality: German
Area of concentration: Organic synthesis

Diels, together with Kurt Alder, developed a method for the synthesis of cyclic organic molecules using dienes. He also discovered the highly reactive substance carbon suboxide and devised dehydrogenation reactions using metallic selenium in identifying the carbon framework of cholesterol

The Award

Presentation

Professor Arne Fredga, member of the Nobel Committee for Chemistry of the Royal Swedish Academy of Sciences, presented the award to Otto Paul Hermann Diels and Kurt Alder, cowinners of the 1950 Nobel Prize in Chemistry, on December 10, 1950. After describing the chemistry of carbon compounds as "somewhat recondite and not easy to describe in words that everyone can understand," Fredga drew a comparison of the chemistry of carbon compounds to a Chinese puzzle whose pieces consist of atoms and which has fixed rules and a large number of possible combinations. He outlined the role of such a chemist as a scientist who tries to figure out the way in which nature has put together this puzzle, himself imitating, modifying, and supplementing it. He then proceeded to describe the so-called Diels-Alder reaction of a diene with another alkene (called a dienophile) to produce a cyclic compound. The reaction was hailed for its potential to yield an incredibly high number of compounds of unusual carbon framework, such as those of essential oils and synthetic motor fuels, from simple molecules that could not be prepared via the standard methods. The possibility of understanding the various paths of biosynthesis of natural products was also mentioned as a direct result of the Diels-Alder reaction. Fredga praised both chemists for their long, active scientific lives and continuous contributions to the field, despite Diels's ill health.

Nobel lecture

Otto Diels was prevented by illness from attending the award ceremonies, but his Nobel lecture, "Description and Importance of the Aromatic Basic Skeleton of the Steroids," was published the following year. In it he did not mention at all the Diels-Alder reaction, which was described in detail by Alder in his Nobel lecture on December 12, 1950, but instead he chose to elaborate on his contribution to the structure determination of cholesterol. After outlining the importance of this project, he gave the background knowledge of the subject at the time he undertook the task. Very little was known at that time apart from the molecular formula, the presence of an alcohol group and a double bond. Noting the findings of other scientists, such as Adolf Windaus, Heinrich Wieland, Schlichting, and Jacobi, he then described his successful and unsuccessful procedures in trying to convert cholesterol into a fully aromatized system, which he eventually identified. These processes included metal hydrogenations and dehydrations and the unexpected catalytic properties of selenium over the popularly used sulfur. The overall sequence of reactions, certainly a masterpiece in organic synthesis, was capped by his observation that the cholesterol ring skeleton is part of many steroids, bile acids, and sapogenins, as well as other compounds of both the vegetable and animal kingdoms. He mentioned the examples of corticosterone and desoxy-corticosterone (which had recently been isolated and identified) as well as ergosterol. In concluding, Diels identified the role of gamma-methylcyclopentenophenanthrene in the biosynthesis of many naturally occurring compounds as one of the important research problems of the future.

Critical reception

Kurt Alder, Diels's cowinner, noted in his Nobel lecture that the 1950 award was the first one given to scientists involved with pure organic synthesis since 1912, when Victor Grignard (for his organomagnesium reagent) and Paul Sabatier (for his hydrogenation methods) were honored. Diels was age seventy-four at the time, and the prize was considered overdue; the impact of the diene synthesis both academically and industrially was enormous. The industrial significance was realized by H. P. Kaufmann of Münster, who introduced the diene number as a way to measure analytically the presence of unsaturated conjugation in fatty oils used in paints and varnishes. Moreover, the reaction provided many answers about the biosynthesis of compounds such as phellandrene (a terpene found in water fennel or eucalyptus plants) and catharidin (an old, medically used venom produced by the Spanish fly). Robert Burns Woodward (the Nobel Prize winner in chemistry in 1965) used the diene synthesis in his successful synthesis of cortisone, a heart stimulant. As Fredga said in his presentation lecture, the reaction helped in the synthesis of "compounds which it would be quite impossible or very difficult to produce in any other way." *The New York Times* (November 11, 1950) announced the award with the comment that the Diels-Alder reaction provided "a drastic shortcut for the production of complicated chemical compounds that could previously be achieved only by natural means." A separate article in the same issue reported the cheering of Kurt Alder's students (he was then a professor at Cologne University) in a torchlight procession outside his home, to celebrate their mentor's Nobel Prize award. The 1951 *Britannica Book of the Year* (a record of the events of 1950) provided a short biography of Diels and claimed that the formation of organic chemical compounds by diene synthesis had been recorded by earlier workers, but that Diels and Alder had provided "the first experimental proof of the nature of the reaction and demonstrated its wide application to the synthesis of ring compounds of many types."

Although Diels was awarded the Nobel Prize for the discovery and development of the diene synthesis, the Nobel Prize Committee also took into consideration his significant contribution to steroid chemistry, with his identification of the carbon framework in cholesterol. The award restored the pride among Germans, who for a long time had considered that "chemistry was a predominantly German science" (*Le Temps*, November 28, 1912). Diels's withdrawal of his initial resignation in 1944, in an effort to rebuild the chemistry department, which was destroyed by air raids during World War II, contributed also to the boosting of the German advancement of chemistry. The award was given to both scientists only a few years before they died (Diels died four year later, Alder in 1958) and could be coincidental with the great interest in the synthesis of natural products in the 1940's and 1950's.

Biography

Otto Paul Hermann Diels, the second of three sons of famous philologist and Prussian Academy professor Hermann Diels and Bertha Ducbell Diels, was born in Hamburg, Germany, on January 23, 1876. He received his high school education in Berlin and proceeded to earn his Ph.D. in chemistry (1899) at the University of Berlin under Emil Fischer. He continued working at his former mentor's institute as an assistant, a lecturer, and, eventually, a professor until his appointment as a full professor at the University of Kiel in 1916. He remained there as a faculty member and an administrator until 1948, the year he permanently resigned at age seventy-two. His research dealt almost exclusively with organic synthesis, and his contribution to the field of natural products is unique. Apart from determining the structure of cholesterol, a project on which scientists spent more than forty years, he established the so-called Diels-Alder reaction as one of the premier methods in the field of natural products and the use of selenium metal as a catalyst in organic synthesis.

Diels was a person of excellent pedagogic talents and sincere dedication to chemistry and research. Kurt Alder, the cowinner of the 1950 Nobel Prize, was a former student of his. Diels was the author of many papers and books, the most important being the *Einführung in die organische Chemie* (1907), which went through fifteen editions and was used as the ultimate textbook in organic chemistry for universities and colleges.

Diels married Paula Geyer in 1909 and became the father of two daughters and three sons, two of whom were killed in the battlefields of the eastern front during World War II. He experienced great turmoil during World Wars I and II. He was a shy but humorous person and an avid reader, music listener, and traveler. He enjoyed mountaineering when he was young and painted during his spare time. He died on March 7, 1954, in Kiel.

Scientific Career

Otto Diels's interest in chemistry was keen since the time he performed experiments with his brother Ludwig while a student at the Joachimsthalsches Gymnasium in Berlin. He was fortunate to be reared in an educated environment: His father was a professor of classical philology at the University of Berlin and a member of the Prussian Academy of Science; his mother was the daughter of a district judge. His eldest brother became a ßotanist and his youngest brother a Slavonic philologist. Diels studied chemistry in Berlin and obtained his degree magna cum laude in 1900 with a dissertation entitled "Zur Kenntnis der Cyanverbindungen" (on the knowledge of cyanocompounds). The next five years he spent with his mentor, 1902 Nobel laureate Emil Fischer, who proved to be valuable to the young Diels, who was appointed lecturer at the same university in 1904. Many science biographers agree that Emil Fischer ended a period of chemistry that Richard Willstätter called "the age of simple methods and direct observation." Thus, the early 1900's were characterized by the importance of theoretical chemistry, physicochemical measurements, and the performance of tedious and complicated experiments that required the scientific collaboration of several chemists, who formed groups. As a result of the intensity of competition between groups in different countries, great discoveries and improvements in the fields of science were accomplished.

In 1906, Diels isolated and identified carbon suboxide, an unknown gas with a penetrating odor and an irritating action on the eyes, formed upon dehydration of (that is, removal of water from) malonic acid. The unusual property of this compound was the proportion of carbon to oxygen (3:2). In the other common carbon oxides, the ratio varies from 1:1 (carbon monoxide, formed by incomplete combustion of an organic compound) to 1:2 (carbon dioxide, formed by the complete combustion). The discovery was remarkable, not only for the properties of carbon suboxide but also because it concerned such common elements.

After this discovery Diels switched to pure organic chemistry, with which he occupied himself the rest of his life with no significant digressions in physical chemistry or biochemistry. Diels served as full professor and director of the Christian Albrecht University, Kiel, until his final retirement in October, 1948.

In 1906, Diels started, together with E. Abderhalden, his long research project of the structure verification of cholesterol originally postulated by Adolf Windaus. He isolated pure cholesterol from gallstones and proceeded to convert it to gamma-methylcyclopentenophenanthrene (currently known as "Diels hydrocarbon"). This dehydrogenation (hydrogen removal) process was achieved via the use of metallic selenium (1927) and was accomplished after numerous unsuccessful attempts using other common reagents, such as palladized charcoal and sulfur. This success not only corrected the problems associated with the errors in the previously postulated structure of cholesterol but also gave other scientists the tool with which to identify numerous natural products. These included cardiac glycosides (such as digitoxin), D vitamins, toad venom, bile pigments, and adrenal-cortex and sex hormones. The Diels hydrocarbon proved to be a very basic substance, and its discovery corresponded in importance to the discovery of the benzene ring for organic chemistry. The question that Diels addressed in his Nobel lecture, "What is the synthetic principle on which this obviously highly important product of [the Diels hydrocarbon] is built up in nature, . . . why is [it] indispensable to life, [and why does it play] such a vital role in the vegetable and animal kingdoms?" has not yet been fully understood. His belief about its significance, though, is correct, unlike Grignard's suggestion, which he presented in his own Nobel lecture, that "for living matter there [is probably] life due to synthesis by means of magnesium and life due to oxidation by means of iron." The success of the project also established selenium as one of the premier catalysts in mild dehydrogenation processes and is now extensively applied in the synthesis of polyunsaturated oils.

In 1928, Diels started his twenty-two-year collaboration with Kurt Alder in the so-called Diene synthesis, which came to be a cornerstone in the three-dimensional isomerism of organic compounds and eventually earned for both scientists the Nobel Prize in 1950. The reaction, which involves a conjugated diene (a compound in which two double bonds are separated by a single bond) and an alkene (known as a dienophile or philodiene—literally, a diene lover), always spontaneously forms a six-membered cyclic compound (called a Diels-Alder adduct). The reaction had been observed by other chemists in the past, but it was Diels and Alder who eventually explained the formation of the product by revision of the carbon bonds. The unusual observation in this reaction was the fact that the presence of a catalyst and heat were not needed. Until this time, many organic reactions were very difficult to study, because of the harsh conditions involved and the lack of available analytical methods. The reaction proved to be a cornerstone in organic synthesis because many unusually complicated structures could be prepared via the Diels-Alder reaction in very high yields under extremely mild, uncatalyzed conditions. Many reactions in the natural products field of chemistry are spontaneously formed at room temperature via this same reaction. Thirty-three papers were published by Diels and Alder on the applications of this reaction, and its use became so popular that many natural products (such as steroids, camphor, and other terpenes), plastics, and synthetic rubber were synthesized and their structure proven in the laboratory. The collaboration between the two scientists continued, despite the fact that Alder joined the staff of the Interessen-Gemeinschaft Farbenindustrie Aktiengesellschaft (I. G. Farben) plant in Leverkusen and later accepted the directorship of the chemical institute at the University of Cologne (1940).

World War II was disastrous for Diels. Two of his sons were killed at the eastern front; his Chemical Institute, its library, and Diels's own home were destroyed by the Allied bombing. It was only his dedication to the field of chemistry that made him withdraw his resignation, which he had originally submitted in 1944 at age sixty-eight. As an emeritus, he tried to rebuild the facilities and continued giving lectures, but he eventually retired permanently in 1948. *The New York Times* (November 11, 1950) reported that, once Diels found out about the Nobel Prize, he declared that he "would use the money [of the award] to acquire a large scientific library" to replace the one destroyed by the war.

Otto Diels was exceptionally successful in his pedagogic accomplishments. He published his *Einführung in die organische Chemie* (introduction to organic chemistry) in 1907, and this influential book, which was proof of his tremendous academic talent, had gone through nineteen editions by 1962. His book is considered the pioneer in the teaching of organic chemistry, because it correlated nicely the lectures with the experimental part of his course.

The appreciation for Diels's contribution to organic chemistry was expressed from the early years of his association with the field. His first major award was the gold medal he received for his exhibit at the Louisiana Purchase Exposition in St. Louis (1904). He also served as "rector magnificus" at the University of Kiel for the academic year 1925-1926. He was a member of the academies of Halle (Leopoldina), Göttingen, and Munich and was an honorary member of the Royal Spanish Society for Physics and Chemistry. He also received the Adolf v. Baeyer Medallion in 1930 and the Grand Cross of Verdienstordens of the Federal Republic of Germany in 1952. He held the honorary degree of Doctor of Medicine from the University of Kiel in 1946.

In its obituary, *The New York Times* (March 9, 1954) announced Diels's death by quoting scientists as saying that ". . . without the process [of the Diels-Alder reaction] cortisone could [not] have been produced artificially. . . ."

Bibliography

Primary
CHEMISTRY: "Über das Kohlensuboxyd I," *Berichte der deutschen chemischen Gesellschaft*, vol. 39, 1906 (with B. Wolf); *Einführung in die organische Chemie*, 1907; "Über die Bildung von Chrysen bei der Dehydrierung des Cholesterins," *Berichte der deutschen chemischen Gesellschaft*, vol. 60, 1927 (with W. Gadke); "Über Dehydrierungen mit Selen" *Berichte der deutschen chemischen Gesellschaft*, vol. 60, 1927 (with A. Karstens); "Synthesen in der hydroaromatischen Reihe, I. Mitteilung, Anlagerungen von 'Di-en'-kohlen-wasserstoffen" *Justus Liebigs Annalen der Chemie*, vol. 460, 1928 (with Kurt Alder); "Mein Beitrag zur Aufklarung des Sterinproblems" *Angewandte Chemie*, vol. 60, 1948.

Secondary
Farber, Eduard. *Nobel Prize Winners in Chemistry, 1901-1961*. Rev. ed. New York: Abelard-Schuman, 1963. This book gives a biographical sketch, a description of the prizewinning work, and a section on the consequences in theory and practice of the awarded chemical achievement of all Nobel Prize winners in chemistry from the beginning until 1961. The short biographies of both Diels and Alder are followed by the translation of the article published in *Zeitschrift für angewandte Chemie* (vol. 42, 1929), in which the reaction is outlined. A one-page description of the applications of the diene synthesis in the synthesis of important chemicals is also given.
Herman, Armin, et al. *German Nobel Prizewinners*. Munich: Heinz Moos Verlagsgesellschaft, 1968. This book gives a one-page biographical summary for each of the German Nobel Prize recipients, together with their individual photographs. This report uses very simple language to describe Diels's research accomplish-

ments. The book was originally written in German and later translated into English; the chemistry part was translated by John Fosberry.

Ihde, Aaron J. *The Development of Modern Chemistry*. New York: Harper & Row, 1964. This book gives an account of the development of modern organic chemistry using the discoveries and reactions of chemists, the majority of whom did not win a Nobel Prize. Diels and Alder's contribution of the diene synthesis and its significance in the fatty oils field is described in one paragraph.

Nobelstiftelsen. *Nobel Lectures: Chemistry, 1942-1962*. New York: Elsevier, 1966. This book is a compilation of all Nobel Prize award presentation speeches and the laureates' acknowledgment lectures. It also includes short biographies with dates and important highlights of the recipients' lives.

Olsen, Sigrud. *Chemische Berichte: Fortsetzung der Berichte der deutschen chemischen Gesellschaft* 95 (1962): 5-46. This article, written in memory of Otto Diels, is in German and describes his whole life and accomplishments. It is divided into several sections, such as an introduction, the childhood period, his studies, academic achievements, and family life, and it ends with an epilogue. It also provides a complete bibliography (chronologically arranged) of Diels's 184 scientific publications and books and includes several photographs.

Schmauderer, Eberhard. "Otto Paul Hermann Diels." In *Dictionary of Scientific Biography*, vol. 4, edited by Charles Coulston Gillispie. New York: Charles Scribner's Sons, 1972. This is a short biography on Otto Diels with a brief description of his scientific work. It also includes a good bibliography on original works and secondary literature.

Wasson, Tyler, ed. *Nobel Prize Winners*. New York: H. W. Wilson, 1987. This book gives a brief but detailed account of the lives of all Nobel Prize winners. Diels's work is not described in scientific terms, and the article gives only a few references and selected works of every individual recipient.

Paris Svoronos

1950

Chemistry
Otto Paul Hermann Diels, West Germany
Kurt Alder, West Germany

Physics
Cecil Frank Powell, Great Britain

Physiology or Medicine
Philip S. Hench, United States
Edward C. Kendall, United States
Tadeusz Reichstein, Switzerland

Literature
Bertrand Russell, Great Britain

Peace
Ralph Bunche, United States

KURT ALDER
1950

Born: Königshütte, Germany; July 10, 1902
Died: Cologne, West Germany; June 20, 1958
Nationality: German
Area of concentration: Organic synthesis

In collaboration with his teacher, Otto Diels, Alder developed the diene synthesis. In the two decades since its first announcement, this synthetic method proved to be a matchless tool for the preparation of organic molecules of practical and theoretical significance

The Award

Presentation

On December 10, Professor Arne Fredga of the Royal Swedish Academy of Sciences discussed the significance of the research that led to the awarding of the 1950 Nobel Prize in Chemistry to Kurt Alder and his teacher-colleague Otto Diels. Fredga remarked how difficult it is for the nonchemist to understand the complexity of Kurt Alder's field, the chemistry of carbon compounds. He made an apt analogy with a Chinese puzzle, in which the rules are few and simple but the number of possible combinations so large as to approach the infinite. Explaining the significant bonding features of the two reactants, the diene and the dienophile, he went to the heart of the matter, stating that addition takes place in such a manner as to provide rings of six atoms. He contrasted this specific cyclization with the more general and related case of polymerization or plastic formation. In appropriately nontechnical, precise language, Fredga described the original examples which had led Diels and Alder to their discovery and to the numerous additional examples that they and others had found.

In this presentation address, there are several references to the beauty, elegance, and simplicity of the Diels-Alder reaction. Although no one could have predicted the importance of the Diels-Alder reaction, Fredga stated that he had found "the prophetic leading ideas" in their first paper, "Synthesen in der hydroaromatischen Reihe" (1928; "Syntheses in the Hydroaromatic Series"). Reference was made to the difficulties that both scientists had to face as a result of World War II and to the fact that Alder had retained his position as research leader in the field with work on the steric and energetic conditions in the polycyclic systems.

Nobel lecture

Alder's address, entitled "Diene Synthesis and Related Reaction Types," and given on December 12, 1950, is almost certainly the best introduction to his difficult chemistry available in English.

Alder began by noting that it was only the third time a purely synthetic organic method had been recognized with the Nobel Prize. He selected cyclopentadiene and isoprene as the molecules most useful for discussing the earliest days of his and Diels's search to understand this complex and elegant chemistry.

In a fashion surprisingly free of technical jargon, Alder cited the earliest appropriate chemistry, discussed the shortcomings of its interpretation, and showed how he and Diels had set about clarifying the picture. He gave full credit to the numerous workers in other laboratories who had contributed to scientists' understanding. Alder then presented a most useful general formulation of the Diels-Alder reaction, along with two tables illustrating the enormous range of dienes and dienophiles. These tables were supplemented with good notes to aid understanding. In the case of both diene and dienophile, those structural types that appear appropriate and yet do not react, or react in some unexpected fashion, were also discussed, with special attention paid to the importance of certain isomeric acids in the development of a detailed picture of the Diels-Alder reaction.

The remainder of Alder's lecture was much more technical. He examined in detail the reactions of all dienes having a five-atom ring but which differ by replacing one carbon atom with an oxygen, sulfur, or nitrogen atom. While this change might appear insignificant, it led to the appreciation of an important related reaction.

Beginning with a discussion of the styrene molecule, Alder gave a view of the exact fashion in which the two reactants could possibly unite, at the same time introducing the subtle pathways by which this union might occur. In elaborate detail Alder pointed out all the product structures possible for the reaction in its most general form. He then showed how reasonable it is to find, ordinarily, only one of these cases as the product of the reaction.

Alder showed his youthful vigor in seriously applying the details of electronic theory to organic chemistry and presented persuasive evidence for the radical or unpaired electron pathway. While aware that only a start had been made in exploring this area, he was also clear in his statements that useful detailed discussions would come from this research. Finally, Alder noted that, while rings of six carbon atoms had been most explored, there were numerous examples in which other atoms are present in either the diene or dienophile.

Critical reception

The popular press of November, 1950, showed excitement over the selection of the Nobel laureates in literature for the previously reserved 1949 prize (William Faulkner) and the 1950 prize (Bertrand Russell) but had little to say regarding the chemistry award. *Newsweek* described Alder and Diels as "a German teacher-pupil team," and *The New York Times* offered a few words about the torchlight parades of German students, adding that some undefined "authorities" believed that "diensynthesis may in fact be one of nature's methods. . . ." The semitechnical *Science News Letter* devoted one-sixth of a page to what is described as a reaction "referred to only in technical chemical books." Its attempt to make the reaction better known is so full of errors that the Diels-Alder reaction is hardly recognizable.

Chemical and Engineering News revealed its business orientation by pointing out that this reaction does not belong to that "group of fabulous discoveries which almost at once spawn a host of big-tonnage chemicals." There follows, however, a full page of technically correct and informative text, including a description of the reaction, a variety of excellent samples of interesting applications, and a lively sketch of each chemist.

Biography

At the end of World War I and just before Poland regained its independence, Kurt Alder's father, Joseph August, a teacher, decided to move his family to Berlin so that they might retain their German citizenship. Alder completed his secondary education at the *Oberrealschule* and in 1922 began his study of chemistry at the University of Berlin, where Diels had studied in the late nineteenth century. These two chemists joined forces at the Christian Albrecht (later Kiel) University, where Alder took his doctorate in 1926. He remained at Kiel for ten years, first as Diels's assistant, then as reader, and later as professor of organic chemistry.

In 1936, Alder moved from the university to become research director of the Bayer Werke of the I. G. Farben-Industrie in Leverkusen, Germany. After four productive years of industrial research, Alder was appointed professor of chemistry at the University of Cologne and director of its Chemical Institute. He was dean of the faculty of philosophy in the year that he and Diels won the Nobel Prize.

Neither Diels nor Alder was in any way a controversial figure. They lived their lives in German university towns and devoted all of their professional energies to science. Diels had his family and music; Alder appears to have had no interest other than chemistry. One of his students said, "A fire burned within him. . . ."

World War II took a high toll from Alder, who continued his devotion to science even under the harshest conditions. Shortly after 1955, when he had joined seventeen other Nobel Prize winners in signing a letter in which they pleaded with the nations of the world to renounce war, Alder's body could stand no more. He died in 1958 at only fifty-five years of age.

Alder was honored by his profession and his university. He received the Emil Fischer Memorial Medal from the Association of German Chemists in 1938 and an honorary medical degree from the University of Cologne in 1950. In 1954, the University of Salamanca also awarded him an honorary doctorate.

Scientific Career

When Alder arrived at the University of Kiel, Diels already had several students working on an interesting series of organic, or carbon-containing, compounds, foreshadowing the chemistry that would bring them fame. These molecules possessed two electronic features that are of central importance to the chemistry now called Diels-Alder cyclization: two atoms that are held together, or bonded, by sharing two pairs of electrons, and one or more attached groups of atoms, which draw these electrons toward themselves. It happened that the particular molecules under study at this time involved nitrogen atoms, but this restriction is not necessary and would lead to a much less general and useful reaction.

The double-bond compound described had been shown to react under very mild conditions and in very high yield with the second compound vital for Diels-Alder chemistry—a diene. Even today this chemistry is often referred to as the diene synthesis, the name used in the Nobel Prize presentation. In general, the diene describes an organic compound that possesses two pairs of atoms, each held together by two pairs of electrons (two double bonds). Not all dienes are useful in Diels-Alder chemistry, only those in which the two double-bond pairs are attached by one single bond.

As this description of the electronic requirements of the Diels-Alder reaction became clearer through many individual experiments, Alder especially appreciated the highly specific nature of the chemistry. It is, in fact, this high degree of specificity that makes the reaction so generally useful. One of the most characteristic attributes of the molecules found in nature is that, while many subtle variations are possible and while each of these leads to a unique compound, one and only one of the structures fits exactly and usefully into nature's evolutionary pattern. The discovery and comprehension of these attributes of their chemistry is the task Diels and Alder embarked upon in 1928, when they published their first paper describing what they then referred to as syntheses of hydroaromatic compounds.

The term "aromatic" must be understood in order to appreciate the importance of Diels-Alder chemistry to the modern organic chemist. While many of the earliest compounds studied, such as oil of bitter almonds, possessed a pleasant fragrance, many others of similar chemical character are noted for their especially foul odors. Today chemists describe the aromatic character of molecules in electronic terms, especially those with alternating double and single bonds in a continuous cyclic structure. There are other complicating features of aromatic composition, but even this general description illustrates the relationship to Diels-Alder chemistry, which is strongly linked to such an electronic arrangement.

When a Diels-Alder cyclization or ring-forming reaction takes place, new bonds are formed between the starting compound having only one double bond and the one having two double bonds. For the latter, the new bonds are attached at the first and fourth atoms, the extremes of the four-atom system. This highly specific mode of bond formation always results in the formation of a ring of six atoms.

Another extremely common characteristic of the compounds in nature is the presence of rings having six atoms. Here again is evidence of the close relationship of Diels-Alder chemistry to the synthesis of the chemicals of nature. Some of the molecules that occur in nature contain the simplest and most elegant example of the aromatic compound—a six-carbon atom ring with three alternating single and double bonds. Prior to the discoveries of Diels and Alder, these naturally occurring structures were the only really useful starting point for the synthesis of other six-membered ring compounds. In their earliest publications, Diels and Alder spoke of hydroaromatic compounds, which are the natural consequence of the bonding in the product. Such molecules are related to an aromatic ring compound but lack one or two of its electron pairs.

The earliest success that Diels and Alder obtained was that of resolving the mode of the addition of the dienophile (compound containing one double bond) with the diene. Several examples of this chemical reaction had already been reported in the published literature, but the structure of the products obtained awaited correct interpretation. When a Diels-Alder reaction takes place, it is the six electrons of the double bonds that are redistributed. Four of these electrons are used to form the two new single bonds making the six-membered ring. The other two electrons form a new double bond in place of the single bond of the original diene. Thus, in this simplest example, the resulting six-membered ring is a hydroaromatic ring with one double bond, an aromatic ring in which two molecules of hydrogen have been added.

In contrast to his professor, Otto Diels, Alder had a deep interest in the details of exactly how the chemistry of a reaction takes place. In many respects this change of intellectual emphasis is characteristic of the times. In the nineteenth century, of which Diels is clearly a brilliant example, the study of organic synthesis stressed the exploration of the vast and uncharted possibilities of a particular method. In the first half of the twentieth century, imaginative young scientists were increasingly aware of the utility of seeking a more detailed understanding of what drives a reaction. Diels and Alder exemplify the very best in collaborators by complementing each other in this regard. Together they continually sought a broader range of compounds that were satisfactory participants in the diene synthesis. Under Alder's influence, they selected those examples that would shed the greatest illumination on the underlying nature of the chemistry. In his Nobel lecture, Alder presents clearly the beauty and utility of their work together. He first outlines in dramatic fashion the enormous range of possibilities these studies revealed. Then he presents a tour de force, difficult but understandable, of his lifelong efforts to enhance scientists' appreciation of the subtle details of this elegant reaction type.

The particular area in which Alder showed his greatest talents is stereochemistry, which, as the name implies, examines in detail the arrangement of molecules in space, the exact spatial arrangement of atoms within a given molecule. There is a great amount of evidence to support the belief that unless two molecular structures are exactly superimposable on each other, they represent different molecules possessing different properties. In many cases these differences are so small as to be nearly undetectable, but they are present.

Diels-Alder chemistry, like many important organic reactions, is capable of producing, in all but the simplest cases, a product that is really a mixture of stereoisomers, or molecules that are of identical composition but that differ in their molecular structure. It is noteworthy that Diels-Alder chemistry does not, unlike many other reactions, lead to mixtures of radically different product molecules. Alder showed in the course of many difficult and brilliantly executed experiments that these cyclizations, in fact, almost always lead to only a single stereoisomer.

While Alder and his students were carrying out these studies, he thought still more deeply about the details of the process. Toward the end of his Nobel lecture, he deals briefly with the evidence that the ring closure reaction must involve the presence of single or unpaired electrons. This idea was a powerful insight in a time when it had been widely admitted among organic chemists that such structures had no more than a hypothetical existence. While successors have modified and enlarged upon his speculations, these theories remain a very good approximation of modern thought. Interestingly, the Diels-Alder reaction remains one of the most widely studied and discussed of all chemical reactions, and it is not yet fully understood.

Alder's life was tragically brief, yet he managed, by an all-consuming sense of purpose, to make one of the most important contributions ever to the synthesis of organic chemical compounds. There are other methods for the preparation of six-atom ring compounds, but without exception they are decidedly less useful. Some are restricted to special applications, some need starting materials difficult to prepare, others require elaborate techniques and unusual reaction conditions. The Diels-Alder method has the great advantage of being almost universally applicable. Perhaps the best evidence for the exalted position of this chemistry now and in the future is the continuing large number of studies reporting new applications, novel variations, or new evidence of the mechanistic details of the reaction.

It is equally true that few synthetic chemical methods have had a more profound effect on the layperson than the Diels-Alder reaction. Alder himself pioneered the application of the reaction to the synthesis of artificial rubber. Along with Diels, he used it to develop methods for meeting the increasing demands of the emerging plastics industry for starting materials for the now all-too-common conveniences. It is hard to think of an area of organic synthesis in which the Diels-Alder cyclization has failed to play a leading role. Among those modern necessities that might be mentioned are the steroids, antibiotics, pesticides, vitamins, and color photography.

Bibliography

Primary

CHEMISTRY: "Über die Ursachen der Azoesterreaktion," *Justus Liebigs Annalen der Chemie*, vol. 450, 1926 (with Otto Diels); "Synthesen in der hydroaromatischen Reihe. I. Mittell. Anlagerungen von 'di-en' Kohlenwasserstoffen," *Justus Liebigs Annalen der Chemie*, vol. 460, 1928 (with Otto Diels); "Zur Polymerization cyclischer Kohlenwasserstoffen. I. Mittell. Die polymeren Formen des Cyclopentadiene," *Justus Liebigs Annalen der Chemie*, vol. 488, 1931 (with Gerhard Stein); "Über den sterinchen Verlauf von Additions- und Substitutionreaktionen. I. Zur Stereochemie der Diensynthese," *Justus Liebigs Annalen der Chemie*, vol. 514, 1934 (with Gerhard Stein); "Neuere Methoden der präparativen organischen Chemie. Die Methode der Diensynthese," *Chemie*, vol. 55, 1942; "Diensynthese und verwandte Reaktionen," in *Les Prix Nobel en 1950*, 1950 (*Diene Synthesis and Related Reaction Types*, 1964); "Neuere Entwicklungen der Diensynthese,"

Experientia, supp. 2, Fourteenth International Conference of Pure and Applied Chemistry, 1955.

Secondary

Abbot, David, ed. *The Biographical Dictionary of Scientists: Chemists*. New York: Peter Bedrick Books, 1984. Readable but brief biographical sketch with an excellent photograph. Reference to *The New York Times* article should be November 11 rather than 25.

"Diels-Alder Reaction Proves Potent Chemical Ally." *Chemical and Engineering News* 28 (1950): 4266. Short but good description of the importance of this chemistry. Only a few notes on Alder himself; its importance lies in the mention of his avocational interests.

Farber, Eduard. *Nobel Prize Winners in Chemistry, 1901-1961*. Rev. ed. New York: Abelard-Schuman, 1963. Interesting integration of Alder's life and science.

Finley, K. Thomas. "The Addition and Substitution Chemistry of Quinones" and "Quinones as Synthones." In *The Chemistry of the Quinonoid Compounds*, edited by Zvi Rappoport. New York: John Wiley & Sons, 1988. Quite technical, but gives a detailed picture of the vast amount of Diels-Alder chemistry that has been reported by chemists. The dienophile is restricted to quinones, which were among the earliest to be studied.

_____. "The Synthesis of Carbocyclic Compounds: A Historical Survey." *Journal of Chemical Education* 42 (October, 1965): 536-540. There is no biographical information here, but the Diels-Alder reaction is shown as an important tool in organic chemistry, and its place among other cyclization reactions is described.

Greene, Jay E., ed. *McGraw-Hill Modern Scientists and Engineers*. Vol. 1. New York: McGraw-Hill, 1980. A brief but well-written standard biography.

Ihde, Aaron J. "Kurt Alder." In *Dictionary of Scientific Biography*, edited by Charles Coulston Gillispie. New York: Charles Scribner's Sons, 1971. One of the very few English-language biographical sketches. Very readable, but places almost all of its emphasis on his scientific career. Contains an important bibliography of Alder's major written works and writings about him.

Mehta, Goverdhan. "Molecular Design of Compounds via Intermolecular Diels-Alder Reactions." *Journal of Chemical Education* 53 (September, 1976): 551-553. In spite of its title, this article explores a number of extremely interesting intramolecular Diels-Alder reactions. Quite technical but well worth the effort.

Nobelstiftelsen. *Nobel Lectures: Chemistry, 1942-1962*. New York: Elsevier, 1966. Reprints the Nobel lecture and presents standard biographical information.

K. Thomas Finley

1951

Chemistry
Edwin Mattison McMillan, United States
Glenn Theodore Seaborg, United States

Physics
Sir John Douglas Cockcroft, Great Britain
Ernest Thomas Sinton Walton, Ireland

Physiology or Medicine
Max Theiler, South Africa

Literature
Pär Lagerkvist, Sweden

Peace
Léon Jouhaux, France

EDWIN MATTISON McMILLAN
1951

Born: Redondo Beach, California; September 18, 1907

Nationality: American
Areas of concentration: Nuclear chemistry and nuclear physics

McMillan was a pivotal figure in the discovery of neptunium, the first element beyond uranium, and plutonium, a key element in the making of the atomic bomb (in construction of which he participated). His theory of the synchronization of electrical pulses and particles in accelerators led to a new class of these high-energy machines, making possible important advances in the study of fundamental particles

The Award

Presentation

Arne Frederik Westgren, Chairman of the Nobel Committee for Chemistry, was the representative of the Royal Swedish Academy of Sciences who delivered the presentation speech on December 10, 1951, before King Gustav Adolf awarded Edwin Mattison McMillan and Glenn T. Seaborg their diplomas, gold medals, and checks. In his address, Westgren took a historical approach in introducing the work that McMillan and Seaborg had done in discovering elements heavier than uranium (the transuranium elements). He began by noting that the Swedish chemist Karl Wilhelm Scheele had remarked in 1777 that it was futile to do further research on elementary bodies. Fortunately, even his Swedish followers ignored his advice, and Jöns Jakob Berzelius found several new elements: cerium in 1803, selenium in 1817, silicon in 1824, and thorium in 1829. In the course of the nineteenth century, chemists discovered many other elements, and in 1869 Dmitry Mendeleyev organized all the known elements according to their increasing atomic weights in a periodic table, an arrangement in rows and columns which left gaps for elements yet to be discovered. These gaps were soon filled, and by the twentieth century chemists knew that matter consisted of ninety-two elements, with the heaviest, uranium, numbered 92, at the end of the periodic table.

In the second decade of the twentieth century, the Danish physicist Niels Bohr considered the possibility of a series of elements beyond uranium, and he predicted that this series would be analogous to the lanthanides, the set of chemically related elements with atomic numbers 57 through 71 (often called the rare earth elements). Physicists tried to synthesize the transuranium elements in the 1930's by bombarding uranium with neutrons, but instead of making new elements, they serendipitously discovered that neutrons split, or fissioned, uranium nuclei. While investigating nuclear fission, Edwin McMillan, in collaboration with Philip Hauge Abelson, isolated element 93, later named neptunium, and obtained chemical proof that it really was a transuranium element. Westgren praised this discovery, "which opened a field of research in which vast and fundamentally important scientific and technical gains have been made."

Nobel lecture

McMillan delivered his Nobel lecture, entitled "The Transuranium Elements: Early History," on December 12, 1951. His talk, which centered on the circumstances leading to the discovery of neptunium and the identification of plutonium, began with a description of the great impact that nuclear fission had on his group at the University of California in the late 1930's. The discovery of the splitting of the atomic nucleus stimulated many scientists to do experiments with cloud chambers, counters, and cyclotrons. McMillan, caught up in the excitement, decided to do an experiment monitoring the fragments of a fissioning nucleus. He studied their range, the distance they traveled, by measuring their depth of penetration, first in a stack of thin aluminum foils and later in a stack of cigarette papers. As he expected, the force of fission propelled the various fragments into the stack of papers. He identified the radioactive fragments in the separated papers by their decay times and by chemical means. Unexpectedly, he found two radioactive products remaining in the paper that contained the uranium undergoing fission, one with a twenty-three-minute half-life (the time required for half the nuclei of an isotope to undergo radioactive decay) and another with a half-life of slightly more than two days.

The uranium in the target was predominantly uranium 238, an isotope with 92 protons and 146 neutrons in its nucleus. Addition of a neutron would form uranium 239, an isotope with 92 protons and 147 neutrons. McMillan ascribed the twenty-three-minute half-life to uranium 239, an isotope that had been known since 1936. He suspected that the two-day half-life was attributable to a new element beyond uranium, element 93, but to prove this required painstaking chemical work on a very small amount of material. At the time, most scientists believed that element 93, if it could be made, would have characteristics similar to those of rhenium, the element in the column directly above it in the periodic table. The isotope with the two-day half-life did not behave like rhenium, however, so McMillan decided to investigate the isotope's chemistry. This presented personal difficulties, for, as he remarked in his lecture, "in spite of what the Nobel Committee may think, I am not a chemist." Fortunately, Philip Abelson, a physical chemist with a good experimental knowledge of how to work with small amounts of chemical substances, came to Berkeley in 1940 for a vacation, and he and McMillan decided to collaborate. Using "carrier" techniques, they were able to separate the new element from the uranium and identify its distinctive chemical properties (a carrier is a readily obtainable substance having chemical properties similar to the radioelement available only in minuscule amounts). The key to solving the problem of identification was determining how certain chemicals reacted with the new element. These reactions suggested the element's strong resemblance to uranium, and in their paper, McMillan and Abelson noted that element 93 might be part of a second "rare earth" group of related elements starting with uranium. McMillan decided to call element 93 neptunium, after the planet Neptune, just as, 150 years earlier, Martin Klaproth had named uranium after the recently discovered planet Uranus.

Since neptunium 239 was radioactive and emitted electrons (beta particles), McMillan reasoned that the product of this decay would be a new element. To make adequate amounts of this element, he bombarded uranium with high-energy deuterons (a deuteron is an isotope of hydrogen whose nucleus contains both a proton and a neutron), and he produced what he surmised was an isotope of element 94. Again, he had the arduous task of proving that he had indeed made a new element. He performed some chemical experiments, finding that the new isotope was neither uranium nor neptunium. He was unable to participate in the final proof of what eventually came to be called plutonium, however, since he left Berkeley in November, 1940, to participate in the development of radar.

Critical reception

Edwin McMillan received the Nobel Prize at a time when the atomic bomb was having a profound social and political impact around the world. In their accounts, several newspapers and magazines explicitly noted the connection between the work of McMillan and the creation of the atomic bomb. For example, on November 16, 1951, *The New York Times* stated: "It was on the basis of this epoch-making work begun by Dr. McMillan and continued by Dr. Seaborg and his team-mates that the giant plutonium-producing nuclear reactors, furnishing vast quantities of plutonium for our atomic bomb stockpile, were built at Hanford, Wash., at an initial cost of $400,000,000." Although the Nobel Committee had previously awarded several prizes for discoveries related to the invention of the atomic bomb, committee members wished to separate the discoveries from the bomb and to encourage the peaceful uses of atomic energy. The award to McMillan and Seaborg must be seen in this context, for their discoveries in nuclear physics and chemistry were very much a part of both the promise and the threat of nuclear energy. The Nobel Committee viewed the world as passing into a new period, the atomic age, and they wanted to reward some of its chief architects, with the caveat that great dangers as well as great benefits were inextricably part of this new knowledge.

The importance of what the Nobel Committee was rewarding—the discovery of the transuranium elements—was obvious, and the prize to McMillan and Seaborg generated no controversy. In fact, the discovery of elements 93, 94, 95, 96, 97, and 98 was unique in history, and some writers stated that it is highly unlikely that so many elements will ever again be discovered in such a short time. Before McMillan and Seaborg did their research, the universe consisted of 92 elements; after them, chemists had an entirely new class of elements to study. According to William L. Laurence of *The New York Times*, these "superdetectives of the cosmos" provided a "postscript to Genesis" through their creation of the first synthetic elements heavier than uranium. Several newspapers noted the youth of the winners (McMillan was forty-four and Seaborg was thirty-nine) as well as the special circumstance that, for

The Nobel Prize Winners

the first time in the history of the awards, one institution, the University of California, produced two prizewinners in the same year.

Because the Nobel Prizes celebrated their fiftieth anniversary in 1951, some newspapers and magazines had articles appraising the benefits and drawbacks of the awards. Indeed, one of the common criticisms—the narrow disciplinary categories of physics, chemistry, and physiology or medicine—had import for the 1951 award in chemistry. McMillan was a physicist, and the Nobel Committee rewarded him by classifying him as a chemist. Nuclear chemistry is an interdisciplinary field, however, and the Nobel Committee, by its awards in 1951, emphasized the connection between chemistry and physics. John Cockcroft and Ernest Walton won the prize in physics for building the first machine to smash atoms, and McMillan and Seaborg won the prize in chemistry for using an atom-smasher to create the transuranium elements. Along with the criticism that there were no Nobel Prizes for biology and astronomy, an article in *The New York Times* on the history of the prizes also criticized the cumbersome mechanism for selecting the honorees. Despite these and other criticisms, most commentators praised the overall record of the Nobel committees for rewarding genuinely significant scientific achievements.

Internationally, the Nobel Prize to McMillan and Seaborg met with an overwhelmingly favorable reaction. For example, *The Times* of London, though giving most space and attention to the local heroes Cockcroft and Walton, warmly praised the award to McMillan and Seaborg. *Nature*, the well-known British journal of science, commended the Nobel Committee for directing the attention of the scientific world to "the most spectacular advance made in inorganic chemistry for a long time," namely, the extension of the periodic table from element 93, neptunium, to element 98, californium. Since this work involved a large group of collaborators, the prize to McMillan and Seaborg was also a tribute to the organization of scientific research at the University of California. The Radiation Laboratory at Berkeley, in particular, was seen as a paragon of what the big scientific laboratory should be.

Biography

Edwin Mattison McMillan was born in Redondo Beach, California, on September 18, 1907. His parents, Dr. Edwin Harbaugh McMillan, a physician, and Anne Marie (née Mattison), had both come from Maryland and were of English and Scottish descent. When their son was one year old, the McMillans moved to Pasadena, where Edwin received his elementary, high school, and college education. He received his B.S. degree from the California Institute of Technology (CIT) in 1928 and his M.S. in 1929. While at CIT, he wrote his first scientific paper under the direction of Linus Pauling, then a young postdoctoral student; he also went to Europe as a recipient of a travel prize. At the suggestion of Arthur Amos Noyes, one of the founders of CIT, McMillan enrolled in Princeton University in 1929 to pursue his doctoral studies. After completing his thesis on molecular beams, he was awarded a Ph.D. in 1932.

From the time of his doctorate, McMillan began a long association with the

University of California, Berkeley. He was a National Research Fellow there from 1932 to 1934, and when Ernest O. Lawrence founded the Radiation Laboratory in 1934, McMillan joined the staff as research associate. He became a member of the physics department in 1935, an assistant professor in 1936, and an associate professor in 1941. He married Elsie Walford Blumer, a daughter of the dean of the Yale Medical School, in Branford, Connecticut, on June 7, 1941, a marriage that eventually resulted in a daughter and two sons. His wife was the sister of Lawrence's wife, and McMillan and Lawrence were lifelong friends. During World War II, McMillan did national defense research, serving in the Radiation Laboratory of the Massachusetts Institute of Technology (1940-1941), at the United States Navy Radio and Sound Laboratory in San Diego (1941-1942), and in the Manhattan Project at Los Alamos, New Mexico (1942-1945).

After the war, he returned to the University of California, Berkeley, where he became a full professor in 1946. His postwar research centered on particle accelerators. He served as associate director of the Radiation Laboratory from 1954 to 1958, when he became director, a post he held until his retirement in 1973. Two years earlier, the laboratory had been renamed the Lawrence Radiation Laboratory, for its chief creator and inspiration.

Scientific Career

The nucleus, the center of the atom, was also central to McMillan's work in science. His two greatest contributions were in the field of nuclear physics. He helped discover the first two transuranium elements, neptunium and plutonium, by bombarding uranium nuclei with neutrons and deuterons. He later developed the theory of phase stability, which led to the creation of a new class of high-energy particle accelerators essential for probing the mysteries of the nucleus. For his work on the transuranium elements he shared with Glenn Seaborg the Nobel Prize in Chemistry in 1951; for his work on particle-accelerator theory, he shared with the Russian physicist Vladimir I. Veksler the Atoms for Peace Award in 1963.

McMillan's interest in physics began when he was a young boy in Pasadena. Fascinated with radio, he built high-frequency coils and read books about electronic theory. He also started attending weekly public lectures at the California Institute of Technology, which was within walking distance of his home. When he attended CIT, he majored in physics. In 1926, while only a sophomore, he collaborated with Linus Pauling on an X-ray study of lead and thallium. Some researchers believed that when lead and thallium were mixed at a certain composition and temperature, a compound formed, but Pauling was skeptical. McMillan, by taking X-ray photographs of various samples, proved that Pauling's skepticism was justified, since the powder photographs gave no evidence for the compound's existence. So impressed was McMillan by Pauling's straightforward and relaxed manner of teaching and conducting research that he consciously emulated Pauling as a model for his own lecturing and research.

While a graduate student at Princeton, McMillan had other influential teachers, in particular, Edward U. Condon and Eugene Wigner, both of whom taught him about the quantum mechanics of nuclear, atomic, and molecular physics. His doctoral work was in the field of molecular beams. The molecular-beam method, which became one of the most powerful techniques for studying the behavior of individual nuclei, atoms, and molecules, owed its origin to Otto Stern, a German physicist who fled to America after Adolf Hitler came to power. In one of his most important experiments, Stern passed a beam of neutral hydrogen molecules through an inhomogeneous magnetic field and measured the magnetic moment of the proton in these hydrogens. The result of this experiment was surprising, for it revealed that the magnetic moment of the proton (which, like the electron, behaves like a small spinning magnet) is two and a half times as large as would be expected if the proton were the same sort of particle as the electron. This experiment indicated the composite nature of the proton. In his work, McMillan studied how an electric field could exert a uniform deflecting force on a highly focused molecular beam.

Shortly before receiving his doctorate, McMillan met Ernest O. Lawrence, who was on a visit to Princeton. Lawrence persuaded McMillan to come to Berkeley, and thus began an important association with a man and a school that would continue throughout most of McMillan's career. By this time, Lawrence was well-known for his invention of the cyclotron, a device used to accelerate particles in a spiral path of increasing radius by means of a strong magnet and repeated applications of an oscillating electric field. During his two years as a National Research Fellow at Berkeley, McMillan did not work with the cyclotron but continued his studies of molecular beams by making measurements of the magnetic moment of the proton. When he joined Lawrence's group in 1934, a sophisticated cyclotron was already being used in a research program designed to explore new fields of deuteron reactions, induced radioactivity, and neutron production. McMillan improved the operation of this and other cyclotrons, and he used these machines to study nuclear reactions and their products. More specifically, he devised a method for bringing the particle beam outside the cyclotron for the first time (before, the beam had to be used inside the vacuum chamber of the cyclotron). To some, the beam looked like a death ray, and in fact it could cause harm to living things. Neutron beams were used, however, in experiments to benefit sick animals, a prelude to actual medical treatment of human patients. John Lawrence, Ernest's brother, was a medical doctor who was very influential in this work, but McMillan also played a role.

In 1935, Ernest Lawrence and McMillan bombarded aluminum with deuterons accelerated in a cyclotron and transmuted this element into nitrogen. As sole investigator, McMillan studied the gamma rays (high-energy X rays) accompanying artificial nuclear disintegration. In 1936, he suggested that the low-energy long-lived radiation often found in material removed from the Berkeley cyclotron could be caused by carbon-14, an isotope formed when the most widely dispersed carbon isotope, carbon-12, undergoes deuteron bombardment. When Martin D. Kamen, a biochemist, later established the existence and properties of the long-lived carbon-14 isotope, he acknowledged McMillan's earlier suggestion.

McMillan's most important work was done in the late 1930's and early 1940's, a time of great excitement in physics. In 1938, while trying to make new elements by adding neutrons to uranium, the German scientists Otto Hahn, Fritz Strassmann, and Lise Meitner produced instead the fission of uranium nuclei. The news of the discovery of fission reached Berkeley in late January, 1939, and shortly thereafter, McMillan devised an elegant experiment to explore the phenomenon by measuring how far the fragments of the split uranium nucleus would travel in matter. He did this initially with thin sheets of aluminum foil stacked together, but aluminum's own activation by neutron bombardment complicated half-life measurements, so he replaced the metal foils with cigarette papers treated with acid to remove any substances that might develop radioactivity under bombardment in the cyclotron. He stacked the treated papers in a pile and put a uranium-oxide-covered paper at one end. This pile served as a target in the cyclotron. When bombarded by neutrons, the uranium fissioned into fragments that penetrated into the paper stack, with various fragments stopping at different depths. Then McMillan took the papers apart and used a Geiger counter to measure the radioactivity in each paper.

The papers indeed contained the fragments that he was seeking, but the uranium-oxide covering contained something for which he was not looking, and this proved to be the most interesting. He found two radioactive substances on the uranium-oxide paper after neutron bombardment. One substance, with a half-life of twenty-three minutes, had been identified a few years earlier by Hahn, Strassmann, and Meitner as uranium 239. The other substance's half-life of 2.3 days could not be matched with any known isotope, and McMillan suspected that this substance might be an isotope of element 93. An investigation of the substance's chemical properties showed that it did not behave like the other elements in the same column of the periodic table. It behaved more like a rare earth, and McMillan assumed that was what it was—a rare earth fragment of a fissioned uranium nucleus and not a new element.

This result might have marked the end of the story, but the presence of the 2.3-day activity in the uranium layer bothered him. It behaved differently from the other fission fragments. McMillan was working at a time when previously reported trans-uranium elements had been convincingly discredited; despite this skepticism about transuranium elements, however, he found it increasingly difficult to believe that the 2.3-day activity was the result of a fission product, and early in 1940 he returned to the problem. He studied the activity chemically and found that the substance did not always crystallize or react as a rare earth would. Philip Abelson, his friend and former colleague, agreed with him that the 2.3-day activity was most likely attributable to a transuranium element, and they worked together to establish this opinion. McMillan made batches of irradiated uranium in the 60-inch cyclotron while Abelson pursued the chemistry of the transmuted element. He quickly established that the substance with the 2.3-day half-life had chemical properties different from those of any known element, though it did react much like uranium. Convinced now that they had identified element 93, they wrote a paper on their work.

McMillan had already decided to call the element neptunium, but he chose not to announce the name in their report.

After Abelson returned to Washington, McMillan decided to investigate the decay product of neptunium, for he suspected that another transuranium element was to be found. His reasoning was simple: The neptunium nucleus undergoes radioactive decay by emitting an electron, and this is accompanied by the transformation of a neutron into a proton, thereby creating an element with the atomic number of 94. It was one thing to suspect the presence of element 94; it was another thing to prove it. In his search for the new element, McMillan bombarded uranium with deuterons in the 60-inch cyclotron and found a distinct pattern of radioactivity in the product (alpha particles—helium nuclei—were emitted). Time pressures prevented him from making enough element 94 for chemical microanalysis, and when, in November of 1940, he was called into defense work, he handed over his research to Glenn Seaborg. With his collaborators, Seaborg completed the chemical proof of what he eventually called plutonium, after the planet Pluto, completing the planetary analogy that McMillan had used. Because of the military importance of plutonium, Seaborg and his coworkers withheld the announcement of their discovery until after the war.

McMillan's initial defense jobs were departures from what he had been doing at Berkeley. From November, 1940, until August, 1941, he was at the Radiation Laboratory of the Massachusetts Institute of Technology, where he was put in charge of the field testing of the United States' first airborne microwave radar. Then he was assigned to the Navy Radio and Sound Laboratory at San Diego, where he worked on sonar, the use of sound waves to locate objects under water. By the early 1940's, it had become obvious to scientists that plutonium, which had the capacity, under the impact of neutrons, to fission and fission again in a self-sustaining chain reaction, might be the material for an extremely powerful atomic bomb. General Leslie Groves, chief administrator of the atomic-bomb project, was looking for a scientific director, and he talked to Lawrence, who recommended McMillan for the position. J. Robert Oppenheimer also strongly approved of McMillan for the job, but Groves demurred, finally settling on Oppenheimer. In November, 1942, McMillan accompanied Oppenheimer on a trip to New Mexico to select a site for the atomic-bomb laboratory. On Oppenheimer's suggestion, and with McMillan's support, Los Alamos, a mesa about forty miles northwest of Santa Fe, became the site.

By April, 1943, Oppenheimer had assembled most of his scientific staff, of which McMillan was an important member. He had been a participant in the atomic-bomb project from the beginning. For example, he had participated in the special investigating committee on plutonium that Groves established to determine whether plutonium was a practical fissionable material for a bomb. At Los Alamos, McMillan worked with Seth Neddermeyer on implosion, a technique employing carefully shaped conventional explosives to bring enough plutonium together (the critical mass) for a sustainable chain reaction. McMillan also worked on the gun device that would bring two pieces of uranium 235 to critical mass. So secure did scientists feel about this mechanism that the uranium bomb was never tested before it was successfully used at Hiroshima. On the other hand, the plutonium bomb's implosion technique required a test, which Oppenheimer dubbed Trinity. McMillan was present at this first test of an atomic bomb, viewing it from a site 20 miles northwest of ground zero. He was impressed by the purple luminescence of the exploding cloud, a visible manifestation of the intense electrical excitation produced by the detonation.

While at Los Alamos, McMillan conceived the idea for a new type of cyclotron. By the early 1940's, cyclotrons had become so large and particles had been accelerated to such great speeds that Albert Einstein's prediction, in his theory of relativity, of the increase of mass with velocity began to have an effect. This increase of particle mass with velocity imposed a practical limit of about 25 million electron volts (MeV) on the conventional cyclotron (the electron volt is a measure of energy). The reason for the limit is that the increased mass of the orbiting particle causes it to take longer to complete each revolution in the cyclotron, and thus it falls out of rhythm with the fixed frequency of the oscillating electric impulses. In the spring of 1945, McMillan realized that if the frequency of the electric impulses could be varied in such a way that they stayed in phase with the decreasing orbital frequency of the particles, then an accelerator much more powerful than the conventional cyclotron could be built. He devised a way of synchronizing the accelerating particles with the electric impulses through the frequency modulation of the cyclotron voltage. He called his proposed machine the synchrotron, and he published his theory of phase stability in the September, 1945, issue of the *Physical Review*. Because of the lack of circulation of Soviet scientific journals, it was not until later that he learned that a Russian physicist, Vladimir Veksler, had independently come up with a similar idea in 1944.

When he returned to Berkeley from Los Alamos, McMillan began to build a synchrotron with $170,000 from the atomic-bomb project, a parting gift from Groves to Lawrence and McMillan. The gigantic machine, with its 184-inch magnet, became operational shortly after midnight on November 1, 1946, and immediately reached a beam energy of 200 MeV. By 1949, it was operating at 320 MeV. In addition to McMillan's Berkeley machine, synchrotrons were built at the Massachusetts Institute of Technology, Purdue, Cornell, and several other institutions. These and other particle accelerators were responsible for the discovery of many new elementary particles, which in turn created a revolution in ideas about the ultimate constitution of matter.

McMillan's later career centered on the construction and use of increasingly energetic accelerators. In the 1950's, he invented the bevatron, a synchrotron that accelerated protons to billions of electron volts of energy, and McMillan and his staff began thinking about the next step beyond the bevatron. In 1956 an Accelerator-Building Committee was formed to coordinate the planning of future machines. In his leadership role, McMillan constantly emphasized that experimenters and theorists must work together very closely in deciding what types of machines to build and how to interpret the results that were produced. Physicists needed high-energy accelerators to generate new particles, and some particle production was such a rare event that huge amounts of data needed to be collected and processed for a single discovery. All this was very expensive, and when McMillan became director of the Radiation Laboratory, he was forced to defend these costs. He argued that the knowledge gained was worth the expense, and he told the Atomic Energy Commission that it would be a tragic mistake for the United States to abandon its leadership in a field of physics in which it was preeminent.

Throughout his distinguished career, McMillan worked on problems that were destined to transform the world of physics: the transuranium elements, the atomic bomb, and particle accelerators. He did not plan these accomplishments, but his scientific curiosity led him to choose problems that, in the light of later developments, proved significant. His investigation of the ranges of recoil fragments of fissioning uranium nuclei led him to search for the transuranium elements, one of which—plutonium—had a dramatic effect not only on science but also on the world. During World War II, he discovered, with his colleagues, that the nuclear energy that physicists had discovered had awesome destructive power. Although he wanted to build and use accelerators for the aesthetic satisfaction that comes from adding to man's understanding of nature, the postwar funding for them often came from the military's belief that national security depended on supremacy in nuclear physics. In all of this, McMillan was a bridge between what Derek de Solla Price has called the "little science" of the prewar period and the "big science" that followed it. McMillan's early work with the cyclotron and his discovery of neptunium and plutonium were in the style of classic physics, with its modest budgets, small staffs, relatively simple apparatus, and inexpensive materials. Later, as director of the Lawrence Radiation Laboratory, he oversaw expensive accelerators, gigantic budgets, and large staffs. His work on new elements, the atomic bomb, and accelerators helped trigger the developments that led to a new age, and in this sense, his achievements have touched the life and altered the consciousness of every human being.

Bibliography

Primary

CHEMISTRY AND PHYSICS: "An X-Ray Study of the Alloys of Lead and Thallium," *Journal of the American Chemical Society*, vol. 49, 1927 (with Linus Pauling); "Radioactive Recoils from Uranium Activated by Neutrons," *Physical Review*, vol. 55, 1939; "Radioactive Element 93," *Physical Review*, vol. 57, 1940 (with P. H. Abelson); "The Synchrotron: A Proposed High-Energy Particle Accelerator," *Physical Review*, vol. 68, 1945; *Lecture Series in Nuclear Physics*, 1947 (with E. Segrè, E. Teller, F. Bloch, J. H. Williams, C. I. Critchfield, V. F. Weisskopf, and R. F. Christy); "Production of Mesons by X-Rays," *Science*, vol. 110, 1949 (with J. Peterson and R. White); *Experimental Nuclear Physics*, vol. 3, 1959 (with E. Segrè, G. C. Hanna, M. Deutsch, and O. Kofoed-Hansen); "The History of the Cyclotron," *Physics Today*, vol. 12, 1959; "Current Problems in Particles Physics," *Science*, vol. 152, 1966.

Secondary

Kevles, Daniel J. *The Physicists: The History of a Scientific Community in Modern America*. New York: Alfred A. Knopf, 1977. Although McMillan's work is mentioned only cursorily in this book, it provides an excellent analysis of the times, ideas, and institutions in which he participated. McMillan was very much a part of the generation of physicists that Kevles, a historian of science, analyzes—the scientists who came to professional maturity after World War I, mastered the atom, built the atomic bomb, and then brought the world into a new era. Since Kevles emphasizes scientists as social beings rather than as generators of complex scientific ideas expressed in advanced mathematics, the book can be understood and appreciated by the general reader.

Livingstone, M. Stanley. *Particle Accelerators: A Brief History*. Cambridge, Mass.: Harvard University Press, 1969. This monograph derives from lectures delivered at Harvard University in 1967 and 1968. Livingstone, who worked closely with Lawrence in the development of the cyclotron, deals with the history of accelerators from a personal viewpoint. Therefore, the book is not a systematic history of accelerators but an account of these machines as Livingstone experienced them. He gives a good idea of the most important developments from the 1930's to the 1960's. Requires no knowledge of advanced physics and mathematics and is well illustrated with photographs and diagrams.

Rhodes, Richard. *The Making of the Atomic Bomb*. New York: Simon & Schuster, 1986. This book has quickly become the classic account of how the atomic bomb was developed. In this well-written narrative, Rhodes tells, in abundant detail, how the bomb evolved from the new ideas of matter and energy conceived by physicists early in the twentieth century, through their discussions and amplifications of these ideas in universities and laboratories during the 1930's, to the actual construction and use of the atomic bomb in World War II. Rhodes analyzes McMillan's contributions at Los Alamos in the light of his larger themes. The book is illustrated with diagrams and sections of photographs.

Seaborg, Glenn T. *Man-Made Transuranium Elements*. Englewood Cliffs, N.J.: Prentice-Hall, 1963. This volume is part of the Foundations of Modern General Chemistry series, intended to be used by high school students who are beginning their study of physics and chemistry. Seaborg tries to make the discovery of the transuranium elements understandable and exciting for people with a knowledge of the basic principles of physics and chemistry, although the early chapters can profitably be read by those with even less preparation. The book is intended as an introduction, and to encourage further exploration by the reader, he appends a good list of references.

_____. *The Transuranium Elements*. New Haven, Conn.: Yale University Press, 1958. The Silliman Lectures that Seaborg gave at Yale University in 1957 are the source of this book. Seaborg presents a personal account of the discovery of the transuranium elements, in which he played a pivotal role. His approach, which is historical and general, is accessible to a wide audience. His emphasis is on the original experiments, which he describes in generous detail. He discusses McMillan's work on neptunium and plutonium in the early part of the book, which is profusely illustrated with charts, diagrams, and photographs.

Wilson, Robert R., and Raphael Littauer. *Accelerators: Machines of Nuclear Physics*. Garden City, N.Y.: Doubleday, 1960. Wilson and Littauer wrote this book for the Science Study series, which was instituted to give high-school students and the general public exciting accounts of fundamental topics in physics by expert scientists. Both Wilson and Littauer worked on accelerators at Cornell University, and their book gives lucid explanations on the principal types of particle accelerators. Wilson worked with Ernest O. Lawrence at Berkeley, and the book emphasizes Lawrence's role in the creation of the early atom-smashing machines. Diagrams and photographs help in analyzing the ideas behind the machines as well as their construction and operation.

Robert J. Paradowski

1951

Chemistry
Edwin Mattison McMillan, United States
Glenn Theodore Seaborg, United States

Physics
Sir John Douglas Cockcroft, Great Britain
Ernest Thomas Sinton Walton, Ireland

Physiology or Medicine
Max Theiler, South Africa

Literature
Pär Lagerkvist, Sweden

Peace
Léon Jouhaux, France

GLENN THEODORE SEABORG
1951

Born: Ishpeming, Michigan; April 19, 1912

Nationality: American
Area of concentration: Nuclear chemistry

Although Seaborg was awarded the Nobel Prize for his participation in the discovery of "not less than four more transuranium elements," as his work progressed, he was codiscoverer of all the elements from 94 to 102 on the periodic table and of element 106 as well. He also participated prominently in the discovery of several important isotopes

The Award

Presentation

On December 10, 1951, Arne Frederik Westgren, Chairman of the Nobel Committee for Chemistry of the Royal Swedish Academy of Sciences, presented winners Edwin M. McMillan and Glenn Theodore Seaborg to Sweden's King Gustav VI to have bestowed upon them the Nobel Prize in Chemistry, which they shared for their discoveries in the chemistry of the transuranium elements. Westgren's speech traced the history of rare earth elements to the late eighteenth century, when Scandinavians from Uppsala and Åbo had first become aware of them.

Westgren cited Dmitry Ivanovich Mendeleyev's formulation in 1869 of the periodic table of elements, in which the chemical characteristics of the elements occur regularly and periodically, indicating that because the table was so regular, the gaps that had to be filled in it were obvious. He then went on to tell how Niels Bohr's work on the structure of atoms caused scientists to realize that the positive charge in the nuclei of atoms and the number of electrons surrounding them rise by one for every increase in the series of elements.

In Bohr's time, the heaviest atom was uranium, number 92 in the table. Bohr speculated that a series of elements beyond 92 might exist, and it is with this group of transuranium elements that McMillan and Seaborg concerned themselves in their research. Westgren credited Seaborg with finding a whole row of new elements, studying their chemical characteristics, and, thus, making their atomic structures known. Westgren considered Seaborg's work to have extended the periodic table beyond the limits that nature seemed to have set.

Nobel lecture

Seaborg entitled his Nobel lecture "The Transuranium Elements: Present Status," clearly indicating that his work was not yet done and that the best he could do was to report on it up to the date of the lecture, December 12, 1951. The lecture, illustrated by slides, began where McMillan's Nobel lecture had left off, with a description of the work that led to the discovery of plutonium. Seaborg traced the beginning of this discovery to a day in the fall of 1940, when he suggested to a graduate student, Arthur C. Wahl, that he might take as his thesis problem a study of the tracer chemical properties of element 93, as yet unnamed.

The lecture in print occupies twenty-five pages, slightly more than two of them devoted to documentation. The lecture went on to explain how the discovery of element 94 proceeded from the discovery of element 93, detailing the complex experiments that Seaborg and his colleagues conducted using the cyclotron at the Lawrence Radiation Laboratory of the University of California at Berkeley.

Seaborg explained the importance of plutonium 239, a heavy isotope of plutonium that offered incredible possibilities for the generation of nuclear energy, along with the difficulty of producing it in quantity and of isolating it once it was produced. Its isolation was finally accomplished in 1942, after Seaborg had joined the Manhattan Project in Chicago at what was later named the Fermi Laboratory. It was after plutonium 239 had been isolated that scientists connected with the Manhattan Project turned their attention to synthesizing and identifying the next transuranium elements, whose existence had now been established.

The speech was graphically illustrated with pictures that showed the minute quantities with which Seaborg and his colleagues were working as they moved toward discovering the new elements after which they were questing. The turns down blind alleys resulted in their progress standing still at times, but they finally managed by reasoning and experimentation to move ahead, as was the case when they discovered element 96 in the summer of 1944, before they had isolated the preceding element, which was not clearly identified until some months later.

Seaborg paid full tribute for the discovery of elements 96, 97, and 98 to the people who operated the 60-inch cyclotron necessary to irradiate the materials with which Seaborg was working. He pointed out that five of the six transuranium elements discovered to that point owed their initial production to the Berkeley cyclotron. His speech ended with an overview of the discovery of each of the transuranium elements to date. He justified the listing of these elements where they occur in the periodic table rather than elsewhere by emphasizing that each element must occupy only one place in that table.

Critical reception

When the 1951 Nobel Prizes were announced in November of that year, it was revealed that the prizes in chemistry and physics would both be shared. Edwin McMillan, with whom Seaborg shared his award, was generally credited as the man who had done the initial pioneering work that led to Seaborg's discovery of numerous transuranium elements. Such statements were not made to diminish in any way the tremendous contribution Seaborg had made, but it was clearly established that his work was dependent on McMillan's earlier work.

The first report of the awards in *The New York Times* of November 16, 1951, was essentially factual, presenting in fairly understandable terms the essence of Seaborg's discoveries. The same paper took little notice of Seaborg's acceptance speech, briefly reporting instead on the social functions that accompanied the awards ceremony.

The Times of London devoted most of its attention to the British winners who shared the prize in physics, Sir John Cockcroft, who was English, and E. T. S. Walton of Ireland. They had worked as a team in Cambridge to devise a high-voltage machine that in 1932 smashed lithium atoms, the first time atoms had been divided into smaller entities. Cockcroft and Walton's work in nuclear physics certainly complemented that of Seaborg and McMillan in physical chemistry and pointed toward the atomic age. The British coverage expressed national pride at the physics award and gave brief, informative attention to the two American winners. Even *Time* and *Newsweek* magazines (November 26, 1951) gave top billing to the British team, although devoting an equal amount of space to the two American winners. *Life* magazine (November 26, 1951) ran pictures of the winners in both physics and chemistry and devoted a paragraph to their contributions.

The scientific community was a bit more profuse in its comments, expressing neither surprise nor serious dissatisfaction with the award. *Scientific American* in January, 1952, praised the work of both men, noting that the separation of plutonium from uranium marked the beginning of the nuclear age. Seaborg was not known as a theoretician essentially; he had not invented any significant research tools or techniques. To do so was not his forte. Following the leads of others, however, he was able to move beyond those who had invented the machines and perfected the techniques.

Biography

Born in the mining community of Ishpeming in Michigan's upper peninsula, not far from Lake Superior, to Herman Theodore Seaborg, a machinist, and his wife, Selma Olive Erickson, on April 19, 1912, Glenn Theodore Seaborg moved with his family to Home Gardens, south of Los Angeles, when he was age ten. His interest in literature exceeded his interest in science until the latter was sparked by a chemistry teacher at David Starr Jordan High School, from which he was graduated in 1929 as valedictorian of his class. He entered the new Westwood campus of the University of California at Los Angeles, which then had only four buildings, and received the bachelor of arts degree in chemistry from it in 1934. He continued his work in chemistry at the university's Berkeley campus, working closely with Gilbert N. Lewis, the renowned nuclear chemist. Seaborg completed the Ph.D. in 1937 and remained at Berkeley as a research associate and later as an instructor.

During World War II, Seaborg was on leave from the university to work in Chicago on the Manhattan Project. He returned to Berkeley in 1945 as professor of chemistry. The following year he was placed in charge of nuclear chemical research at the Lawrence Radiation Laboratory, and from 1954 to 1961 he was associate director of that facility. Seaborg served as a member of the Atomic Energy Commission's General Advisory Committee from 1945 until 1950. In 1958, Seaborg was appointed chancellor of the Berkeley campus of the University of California, a post he filled until 1961, when President John F. Kennedy appointed him to chair the Atomic Energy Commission, in which position Seaborg served until 1971, when he returned to Berkeley. After he retired in 1982, Seaborg served as director of the Lawrence Hall of Science and also joined the Graduate School of Education at the University of California's Berkeley campus because of his vital concern with science education.

Besides sharing the Nobel Prize in 1951, Seaborg was awarded the Thomas Alva Edison Foundation Award for the best book in science for youth in 1958 for *Elements of the Universe*. He won the Enrico Fermi Award of the Atomic Energy Commission in 1959 and the Charles Lathrop Parsons Award of the American Chemical Society in 1964. He became a decorated officer of the French Legion of Honor in 1973. He holds almost fifty honorary doctoral degrees from some of the most distinguished institutions of higher learning in the world.

Scientific Career

Glenn Seaborg was slow to move in the direction that would become his life's work. Showing no significant interest in science until he was well into secondary school, he decided, upon graduation, to pursue his bachelor's degree in chemistry, but his interest in the field lacked initial focus. Clearly he was bright and capable, but not until he was well into his graduate work at the University of California's Berkeley campus did he begin to focus on the variations of the isotopes of the elements, finally narrowing this concern to transuranium elements.

Seaborg's doctoral research concerned the way that fast neutrons interacted with lead. He learned early how the isotopes of lead change under bombardment from fast neutrons. After he received his degree, his work as a research associate enabled him to continue his work with isotopes, in the course of which he discovered new isotopes of many common elements. Isotopes are forms of the same element that differ because, although they all have the same number of protons, they are dissimilar in the number of neutrons they possess.

While Seaborg was still a graduate student, Enrico Fermi was seeking to develop new elements that were heavier than uranium, at that point (1934) the heaviest element yet discovered. Fermi added neutrons to the nucleus of uranium atoms. Otto Hahn, Fritz Strassmann, and Lise Meitner were conducting similar research and experimentation in Germany, and, in 1938, they discovered that the result was not the anticipated heavier elements, which had been called the transuranium elements, but rather a splitting of the uranium nucleus, which was accompanied by the release of incredible energy. This discovery was the first major step toward harnessing nuclear energy as an extremely dynamic power source.

Learning about these German experiments spurred Seaborg in his investigation of transuranium elements. The Lawrence Radiation Laboratory at Berkeley had the sophisticated equipment he needed for his research, including the 60-inch cyclotron necessary for the types of irradiation that he was doing. His colleague, Edwin

McMillan, with whom he was to share the Nobel Prize in Chemistry, had already observed that when he aimed neutrons at a uranium target, not all of the uranium nuclei that the neutrons struck produced fission.

The nuclei that did not undergo fission decayed by the emission of an electron that increased the atomic number of the uranium atom by one, thereby producing a new element. McMillan called this new element neptunium, after the planet Neptune, whose orbit lies beyond that of Uranus, for which uranium had earlier been named. Seaborg was at Berkeley when these discoveries were made and when the search for new elements was accelerating.

Seaborg and some of his colleagues discovered in 1941 that when neptunium, the new element, decayed further, it emitted beta waves as electrons. These increased by one the weight of neptunium, resulting in yet another element, with an atomic number of 94. Seaborg and his coworkers named this element plutonium, after the outermost planet in the solar system, and it was to prove crucial to the development of nuclear energy.

War was raging in Europe, and the United States was soon to be involved in it. Seaborg's work led to the production of the first atomic weapons, which, four years later, brought an end to the war with Japan. The most consequential discovery that Seaborg made in this period was that if he bombarded the new element, plutonium, with slow neutrons, plutonium 239 would undergo fission with the release of an unimaginable energy. It was atomic energy that fueled the first two of these bombs, one dropped on Hiroshima, the other on Nagasaki. Seaborg also found that the plutonium 233 isotope was fissionable, adding another element to the development of atomic power.

The work conducted in Germany in 1938 put Germany ahead in the race to develop atomic weaponry, and in 1939, when the report of that work was released, Albert Einstein and several of his scientific confreres warned President Franklin D. Roosevelt of the impending danger of this development. By 1942, the United States government, acting on this intelligence, had established the Manhattan Project; its mission was to explore fission and to develop weapons based on it. The thirty-year-old Seaborg was granted leave from his post at Berkeley to work in Chicago with the Manhattan Project.

In Chicago, Seaborg's chief responsibility was to head a project that would develop a chemical means of separating plutonium from uranium in quantities sufficient to use in building weapons, notably bombs. The main problem was that the necessary material existed in amounts measured in micrograms, or millionths of a gram. Seaborg's group discovered plutonium in very limited amounts in some other elements, but to do so they had to employ a new technique, known as ultramicrochemical analysis, to analyze the elemental materials with which they worked. By 1944, they had achieved their aim of accomplishing the large-scale separation of plutonium from uranium, and within a year they had enough plutonium to build the second atom bomb that the United States dropped on Japan.

As his work with the Manhattan Project proceeded, Seaborg continued his research on the heavier-than-uranium elements. His major stumbling block in this research was that only infinitesimally small amounts of the new elements resulted from the nuclear bombardment of the cyclotron. Illustrations accompanying Seaborg's acceptance speech in 1951 show amounts of these arcane substances, barely visible at a magnification of ten times, totally invisible to the naked eye.

Seaborg, using Mendeleyev's periodic table, could nevertheless predict quite accurately the chemical properties of the new elements he sought. Finding similarities between the radioactive elements actinium through plutonium, numbers 89 to 94 on the periodic table, and the lanthanide series, which is lighter, made it possible for Seaborg to predict 95 and 96, which he named americium and curium after he had completely identified them.

While he was still at work on the Manhattan Project, Seaborg was promoted to the rank of professor at Berkeley. He returned in 1946, the year after his promotion, and continued his work on transuranium elements, discovering those elements numbered 97 (berkelium), 98 (californium), 99 (einsteinium), 100 (fermium), 101 (mendelevium), and 102 (nobelium) on the periodic table, as well as another element, number 106, named unnilhexium. The instability of the elements with higher numbers on the periodic table makes them extremely difficult to work with. Whereas the half-life of the uranium isotope with the longest life is 4.5 billion years, the half-life of element number 106 is less than one second, making it virtually impossible to observe even with the most sophisticated equipment.

On his return to the University of California, Seaborg was drawn increasingly into administrative work, for which he had a particular gift. Well known as a patient, tactful scholar who never lost his temper, he served first as an associate director of the Lawrence Radiation Laboratory and, from 1958 to 1961, as chancellor of the Berkeley campus, a position from which he resigned to become head of the Atomic Energy Commission. As an administrator, Seaborg seldom gave commands; rather, he gently suggested, then gave his support. When he returned to Berkeley in 1971, Seaborg rejoiced in teaching and found particular satisfaction in teaching elementary courses in which he had sustained contact with undergraduates early enough in their careers that he might guide the best of them into science.

Seaborg's work employed chemical means of expanding humankind's knowledge of the physical universe by uncovering new transuranium elements. One result of such research was the discovery of fission, first in Germany and later in the United States. Fission offers a ready source of energy, and it is now commonly used for such peaceful purposes as providing electrical power that is not dependent upon a diminishing supply of fossil fuels. Nuclear energy, however, is not free from high risks, as the near meltdown at Three Mile Island in 1979 and the disaster at Chernobyl in 1986 have illustrated. These events have demonstrated that atomic pollution knows no geographic boundaries.

Seaborg, well aware of both the benefits and the risks of nuclear power, has dealt extensively in such books as *Education and the Atom* (1964), *Man and Atom: Shaping a New World Through Nuclear Technology* (1971), and *Kennedy,*

Khrushchev, and the Test Ban (1981) with the ethics as well as the methods and the material benefits of using such energy sources. Cognizant of the need for all people living in the nuclear age to understand science so that they can make intelligent decisions about the judicious use of the scientific advances that are constantly being made, Seaborg has devoted his retirement to helping train science teachers and to informing the public about matters related to science both as a beneficial and a potentially threatening force in their lives.

Bibliography

Primary
CHEMISTRY: *Comprehensive Inorganic Chemistry*, 1953 (with others); *The Actinide Elements*, 1954 (with Joseph J. Katz); *The Chemistry of the Actinide Elements*, 1957; *Elements of the Universe*, 1958; *The Transuranium Elements*, 1958; *Man-Made Transuranium Elements*, 1963; *Education and the Atom*, 1964 (with Daniel M. Wilkes); *The Nuclear Properties of the Heavy Elements*, 1964 (with Earl K. Hyde and Isadore Perlman); *The International Atom: A New Appraisal*, 1969; *Man and Atom: Shaping a New World Through Nuclear Technology*, 1971; *Nuclear Milestones*, 1972; *Primary Papers in Physical Chemistry and Chemical Physics*, 1978.
OTHER NONFICTION: *Oppenheimer*, 1969 (with others); "Glenn T. Seaborg," in Irvin Stone, ed., *There Was Light: An Autobiography of a University: Berkeley, 1868-1968*, 1970; *Kennedy, Khrushchev, and the Test Ban*, 1981 (with Benjamin Loeb); *Stemming the Tide: Arms Control in the Johnson Years*, 1987.
EDITED TEXTS: *The Transuranium Elements*, 1949 (with Joseph J. Katz and Winston M. Manning); *Production and Separation of U-233*, 1951 (with Leonard I. Katzin); *Transuranium Elements: Products of Modern Alchemy*, 1978.

Secondary
Bochm, George, A. W. "The AEC Gets a Different Kind of Scientist." *Fortune* 63 (April, 1961): 158-160, 230-241. Boehm's is one of the best general appraisals of Seaborg's work, both as a scientist and as an administrator, for the period it covers. The author writes with considerable feeling for his subject, adding many personal touches that make readers realize that they are reading about a flesh-and-blood person. Pictures are sparse but apt.
Madden, Charles F., ed. *Talks with Social Scientists*. Carbondale: Southern Illinois University Press, 1968. The material in this telephone interview is essentially concerned with Seaborg's view of society and with his thoughts about such matters as disarmament and atomic energy. The portion of the book devoted to Seaborg is a transcript of his interview with Professor Dorothy Carpenter of Stephens College in Columbia, Missouri, who ran interviews as a regular part of her course entitled Great Issues in Contemporary Society.
Nova: Adventures in Science. Reading, Mass.: Addison-Wesley, 1982. The essays in this book are based upon science programs aired over WGBH in Boston. The

writing is at a popular level. The information, though not deep, is accurate and interesting to read. Striking is the information given about the microscopic amounts of materials that Seaborg and his colleagues worked with. The earliest plutonium was so sparse that it was not perceptible by the naked eye.

Olsson, Nils William, and Christopher Olsson, eds. *Great Swedish Heritage Awards Night*. Minneapolis, Minn.: Swedish Council of America, 1984. Seaborg's is one of four portraits in this commemorative book marking the occasion of the council's awards. The writing is warm and unaffected. The discourse does not go deeply into Seaborg's scientific contributions, but rather commemorates him as a Swedish American who still spoke enough Swedish when he received the Nobel Prize that he was able to open his speech in that language.

Wasson, Tyler, ed. *Nobel Prize Winners*. New York: H. W. Wilson, 1987. This brief overview of Seaborg focuses essentially on his winning the Nobel Prize in Chemistry, explaining lucidly the scientific basis for the award. The article also contains a bibliography both of Seaborg's own writing and of writing about him. It has a picture of him as well.

R. Baird Shuman

1952

Chemistry
Archer John Porter Martin, Great Britain
Richard Laurence Millington Synge, Great Britain

Physics
Felix Bloch, United States
Edward Mills Purcell, United States

Physiology or Medicine
Selman A. Waksman, United States

Literature
François Mauriac, France

Peace
Albert Schweitzer, France

ARCHER JOHN PORTER MARTIN
1952

Born: London, England; March 1, 1910

Nationality: British
Area of concentration: Biochemistry

Martin helped develop the modern techniques of partition chromatography and gas chromatography, which have greatly simplified the task of preparing substances in their pure form. Martin himself used the method to separate the amino acids in proteins. The great advances in chromatography since World War II depend to a great extent on his technical innovations

The Award

Presentation

Swedish King Gustav VI Adolf presented the Nobel Prize in Chemistry to Archer John Porter Martin and cowinner Richard L. M. Synge on December 10, 1952, following the presentation speech by Arne W. K. Tiselius, a former Nobel Prize winner and a member of the Nobel Committee for Chemistry. Tiselius began by noting that a Nobel Prize may seem a major award for such a simple process as separating substances. He explained, however, that from the origin of chemistry, one of the most crucial needs has always been the isolating of substances and that, even in modern times, some of the most important discoveries have resulted from improved methods of separation.

The very first step in any chemical analysis is to prepare the material being studied in its pure state. Only then can it be successfully analyzed. Often the very first step, isolating the substance in its pure form, can be a major stumbling block, since so often the desired substance composes only a tiny fraction of the original matter. It is precisely here that Martin and Synge's method of filter-paper chromatography has proved to be of the greatest value. The process consists of using an appropriate liquid mixture, butyl alcohol and water, for example, to cause a drop of a solution on filter paper to separate into several new spots. The substance is held in individual parts by the water trapped by the paper while the alcohol moves freely, effecting "partitions" between the component substances—hence the name of the process.

Chromatographic analysis was discovered in 1906 by the Russian scientist Mikhail Tsvett, who used it to separate the pigments of green leaves. Even before Tsvett, a crude kind of chromatography existed using filter paper. What made Martin and Synge's method unique is not the chromatographic process or the filter paper analysis, but the process itself: partitioning a substance between liquids rather than on the surface of a powder. The incredible development of chromatography since their discovery has proved its importance.

Nobel lecture

On December 12, 1952, Martin delivered his Nobel lecture, entitled "The Development of Partition Chromatography." Martin began by announcing his intention to discuss the development of the method rather than trying to delineate its present situation or the work currently being done. His reason for taking this approach was a belief that recording the steps that lie behind a particular discovery may, if written soon enough after the events, serve as a guide and a stimulus to future investigations.

Martin observed that the technique of partition chromatography resulted from the combination of countercurrent solvent extraction and chromatography. He noted that the process is so simple that, had researchers been oriented in the correct direction, it could have been discovered a century earlier. There were different ambiences then, however, between the academic laboratory and industry. Whereas laboratory analysts saw little need for more efficient separation techniques, industry needed them because of the obvious economic advantages of large quantities simply prepared. Even after Tsvett's revealing work on chromatography, twenty-five years elapsed before laboratory researchers recognized the great advantages of the process. Martin noted that he and Synge were fortunate to be in the right place at the right time—when the demand for new methods was at its height.

Martin's interest in fractional distillation began while he was still a schoolboy. His first major application of his experiences was in the extraction of nonsaponified matter from saponified wheat germ oil. Then a sentence in an American paper led him to discover that two materials with similar coefficients of partition could be separated by using an extraction column. Unaware that he was duplicating experiments that had been done elsewhere, he assembled an elaborate machine to purify vitamin E, but, finding that his work had been preceded by that of another scientist, the results remained unpublished, and the machine was never used again.

After two years of studying the effects of vitamin B deficiencies on pigs, Martin began work with Richard Laurence Millington Synge on the separating of amino acids. Martin designed, and Synge had built, a complex—and troublesome—machine which was able to determine the fatty amino acids in wool. Martin tried to improve his machine but was unsuccessful. He turned to a new approach, which was essentially a chromatogram, and he and Synge went to work with enthusiasm. They finally succeeded in separating the acetyl amino acids. Other scientists had actually achieved partition chromatography first but found no applications for it and abandoned it. Joined by A. H. Gordon, Martin and Synge were unable to succeed in applying the method to other amino acids and turned their attentions to separating amino acids themselves rather than their acetyl derivatives.

An important breakthrough was achieved, after much painstaking work, when they adopted the filter-paper chromatographs of the dye industry. After extensive experiments with amino acids and the testing of a multitude of different solvents as partitioning agents, Martin, Gordon, and R. Consden discovered that their method was by no means confined to amino acids. It worked effectively on the simpler peptides, and they also used it to determine the structure of keratin, the forerunner of vitamin A. Other experimenters then entered the arena, and a number of new solvents and applications were rather quickly developed. Finally, Martin turned to the rapidly progressing field of gas-liquid chromatography, which he and Synge had proposed in their first paper on partition chromatography. Martin and A. T. James had recently been working on this method, which they found worked well on volatile substances.

Critical reception

Archer Martin's Nobel Prize recognized what might be termed more a technological advance than a scientific discovery. By redirecting the approach to separating one substance from a compound, he and Synge simplified the work of other researchers and, just as important, opened the door for the development of other separation techniques, such as gas chromatography. In fact, their method was quickly improved and not long thereafter superseded, although the initial impulse was still theirs.

Though in terms of scientific prestige, Martin and Synge's accomplishments might seem somewhat elementary, the award stimulated no negative response. *Science* duly noted the awarding of the prize but offered no further comment. *Nature*, in which their research had been published extensively, noted that these techniques of chromatography were in general use around the world and made possible major discoveries that would have been impossible only ten years earlier. Modifications in adsorption chromatography, elaboration of countercurrent extraction, and the creation of synthetic ion-exchange resins all resulted from the method of Martin and Synge, which was original in its simplicity, case of execution, and wide scope of application. Their invention of liquid-liquid chromatography, *Nature* said, "will be considered by future generations as one of the more important milestones in the development of chemical sciences."

The *British Medical Journal* actually provided a detailed three-page introduction to chromatography before congratulating the recipients and observing the extreme gift that the Nobel laureates had provided for themselves, their peers, and their successors. The article stated that even in 1952, "chromatography has provided one of the most powerful analytical tools at the disposal of chemical science," noting that its most significant application has been in the separation and identification of the amino acids. *Scientific American*, in its "Science and the Citizen" column, observed that all the chemistry and physics winners in 1952 were from the postwar generation of scientists and matter-of-factly explained how Martin and Synge's use of water to effect separation was an improvement over the earlier use of fats.

In the popular press, the practical applications received greater emphasis. *The New York Times* cataloged the substances with which the method worked particularly well—the sterols, blood and urine, hormones, vitamins, cholesterol—and noted that it was instrumental in the discovery of amino acids and the development of several new vaccines. The article traced the history of Martin and Synge's work on chromatography from the 1931 isolation of carotene in glass tubes packed with porous solids to their devising of paper chromatography which "has the advantage of simplicity, rapidity, and high resolving power." Seven months later, the newspaper rhapsodized even more about Martin's development of a machine to perform gas chromatography, suggesting that it may "alter basic researches" and calling its inventor "one of Britain's most famous chemists."

Biography

Archer John Porter Martin was born March 1, 1910, in London, the son of William Archer Porter, a physician, and Lillian Kate Brown Martin, a nurse. Following the traditional path of a member of the British upper middle class, he attended Bedford School from 1921 to 1929 and advanced to the University of Cambridge, where he intended to study chemical engineering but was led by Professor J. B. S. Haldane into specializing in biochemistry. As an undergraduate, he developed a method of detecting pyro-electricity by immersing crystals in liquid air and observing their attraction to a metal plate. After graduating from Cambridge in 1932, he accepted a position in the physical chemistry laboratory at Cambridge, where he worked on ultraviolet adsorption spectra. A year later, he moved to the Dunn Nutritional Laboratory to work under L. J. Harris and Sir Charles Martin on the isolation of vitamin E and the effects of vitamin E deficiency. He also worked on the effects of vitamin B_2 deficiencies on pigs. It was during his work on vitamin E that he used the solvent extraction and chromatographic techniques which formed the basis of his later developments in chromatography.

In 1938, Martin moved to the Wool Industries Research Association in Leeds, where he first worked with Richard L. M. Synge on the separation of amino acids and developed his approach to partition chromatography. On January 9, 1943, while at the Wool Industries laboratory, he married Judith Bagenal, a teacher, with whom he would have two sons and three daughters.

From 1946 to 1948, he headed the biochemistry division of the Boots Pure Drug Company's research department in Nottingham. In 1948, he joined the Medical Research Council at the Lister Institute and then moved to the National Institute for Medical Research, where, in 1952, he became head of the physical chemistry division. He served as a chemical consultant from 1956 to 1959, at which time he became director of Abbotsbury Laboratories in Hertfordshire, where he remained until 1970. He spent the rest of his active life in a variety of academic and consulting positions, which included professorships in The Netherlands, England, the United States, and Switzerland. Martin retired in 1983.

Scientific Career

The scientific career of Archer Martin is somewhat different from that of the stereotypical Nobel Prize winner. Instead of laboring in a university or sponsored facility, he spent much of his active career in industry, and, as a result, there is a pragmatic, applied-science orientation to much of his work. It is, therefore, not surprising that the work which contributed to his winning the Nobel and other prizes was the invention of techniques that made scientific investigation more efficient and was thus a direct gift to his fellow researchers around the globe: later Nobelists Frederick Sanger (1958) and Melvin Calvin (1961) used the method to work out the structure of insulin and the process of photosynthesis, respectively.

Born the only son and youngest child of a doctor and a nurse, Martin was encouraged to pursue a scientific career from childhood. In fact, he began his Nobel lecture by remembering the fractional distillation columns he built from coffee cans in his family's basement while he was a schoolboy. He prepared at the Bedford School in Bedford and entered Peterhouse at the University of Cambridge in 1929 as the recipient of the Exhibition at Peterhouse scholarship. At first, he professed an interest in chemical engineering—evidence perhaps of his practical nature—but also studied mathematics, physics, and mineralogy. As so often happens, it was the influence of an older professor which led to his final choice of career. As a student at Cambridge, he often attended the Sunday tea parties given by J. B. S. Haldane, famous for having rendered hydrogen safe for the workplace. As a result of the exposure to this noted researcher, Martin decided that his true path lay in biochemistry, and he concentrated his energies there. After receiving his baccalaureate degree in 1932, he stayed on as a research assistant in physical chemistry. In 1932, with Nora Wooster, he published his first scholarly paper: "Preparation and Mounting of Deliquescent Substances." This short paper, which details an original and convenient method developed to prepare crystals for study, shows that early in Martin's career he was interested in creating more efficient methods for separating and isolating substances for further study.

From 1933 to 1938, Martin worked in the Dunn Nutritional Laboratory at Cambridge, where he had the good fortune to study under a second noted researcher—whom he credits as being the greatest single influence on his career—Sir Charles Martin, who suggested that he join forces with Richard Synge in attempting to separate acetyl amino acids. In 1934, with several colleagues, Martin published a study of vitamin E prepared from wheat germ oil. In this experiment, he made an early attempt at separating substances by using a series of tubes with the material under analysis placed in the middle between columns of solvents that would flow over the material as the two liquids were exchanged. It was this kind of inventiveness that won for him the Grocer's scholarship for original research in medicine which he held from 1934 to 1936. He was awarded his M.A. in 1935 and the Ph.D. in 1936.

At about this time, Martin began his collaboration with Synge in pursuit of a method of separating amino acids in their acetyl forms. Synge, also a Cambridge-trained biochemist, had become interested in the analysis of proteins. He soon learned, however, that there were no satisfactory methods for separating the complex amino acids from within the protein hydrolysates. He experimented first with water and then with other solvents as partitioning agents, but was dissatisfied with the inefficiency of the method. Soon after Synge left Cambridge, Martin and Synge were united when they both accepted appointments to the Wool Industries Research Association laboratories in Leeds. It was here, while studying the composition of wool, the process of felting, and amino acids that the interaction between the theoretical Synge and the practical Martin was to bear its greatest results.

Martin's initial apparatus was not quite right for Synge's purposes, so they decided to build another machine. The new device, though cumbersome and fragile, was a first step in that it allowed them to determine the fattier amino acids in wool. Searching for a better method, Martin designed dozens of new machines, but none was practical enough to be constructed. At this point, Martin's genius for problem solving led him to a completely different approach: packing a tube with cotton and wool. By placing water below and chloroform above, Martin hoped to create many small separate streams of interchange. He was disappointed to find that the exchange was less effective than before. Tenacious to the extreme, Martin decided to move only one column at a time by running the chloroform down into water held in ground silica gel. Successful results were then obtained through the use of methyl alcohol, results that show separation by red bands on an orange column. This process was their first real step in the development of improved chromatography. Through much time-consuming research, Martin and Synge learned much but were never able to accomplish the separation as efficiently and accurately as they desired. They did, however, learn enough to formulate a theory of partition chromatography. The results of their research at this point were being published almost monthly in the British scientific journal *Nature*; most of the studies they reported involved amino acids in wool proteins.

Following results obtained by other researchers, and aided by A. H. Gordon, Martin and Synge turned their attention to the separation of amino acids themselves rather than their acetyl derivatives. Because a color indicator would not work with the amino acids, however, they returned to water as a solvent (they had earlier abandoned it because water would not cause a color change in the indicator). For their first attempt at separating amino acids, they adopted the filter-paper chromatography of dyestuff chemists. This technique led them to experiment with a large number of solvents in conjunction with water. A drop of the compound being analyzed would be placed on a small "tail" extending from a semicircular piece of filter paper. The end of the tail would be placed in a solution of water and butanol. After the water and butanol had covered the tail through capillary action, the paper would be dried and heated, and the separate amino acids could be identified. Since no one solvent would separate all the common amino acids, Martin and Synge tried passing an electric current through the substance before drying and gained some further results. Other experiments followed, and it was established that this relatively simple method, known as paper partition chromatography, was an efficient and effective method for separating amino acids—it was in many ways a starting point for the stunning achievements in protein chemistry in the subsequent thirty years.

It was soon established that partition chromatography worked equally well with other substances. Synge, who had moved to the Lister Institute, determined the order of amino acids in peptides; Sanger used similar methods in his Nobel Prize-winning analysis of insulin, and many researchers began applying the process in different ways. Martin continued his work with Gordon and R. Consden. After solving a problem caused by an excess of copper in the atmosphere of their laboratory, they made it possible to do an analysis of any amino acid and to perform hundreds of such analyses simultaneously.

Although the Nobel Prize was awarded to Martin and Synge for the development of partition chromatography, in his Nobel lecture Martin revealed a new method developed with his associate, A. T. James, which was to prove even more important in the development of modern chemistry: gas chromatography. Though Martin and Synge had suggested the possibility ten years earlier in their first published paper, no one had risen to the challenge, so it fell to Martin and James to develop a method that would work with volatile substances. After failing to achieve fractional crystallization with the liquid column method, they substituted an inert gas such as nitrogen, helium, or argon for the usual liquid.

The final machine, unveiled in 1953, consisted of an 11-foot tube packed with celite. The ends of the tube passed through containers of liquid indicators that changed color according to the substances passing through them. The amounts and types of fractionated materials were then graphed on a revolving drum. Martin and James found that, whereas the number of components that can be separated with the earlier packed column is twenty to thirty, several hundred can be separated using gas. In conjunction with liquid chromatography, this method has had hundreds of applications in all areas of organic chemistry, including the separation of hydrogen and deuterium isotopes. It has been used in biomedical research, clinical and drug screening, petroleum cracking, and by all the industries that make use of petroleum derivatives.

In 1952, Martin became head of the Physical Chemistry Division of the National Institute for Medical Research at Mill Hill, London. In 1956, he returned to industry, becoming a chemical consultant, and in 1959 was named director of Abbotsbury Laboratories Ltd., a position he held until 1970, when he became a consultant for the Wellcome Institution. During this period, beginning in 1964, he held an overlapping series of academic appointments: from 1964 to 1974 as Extraordinary Professor at Eindhoven Technological University in The Netherlands; from 1973 to 1978 as Medical Research Council Professorial Fellow of Chemistry at the University of Sussex; from 1974 to 1979 as Robert A. Welch Professor of Chemistry at the University of Houston; and from 1980 until his retirement in 1983 as visiting professor at the École Polytechnique Fédérale de Lausanne. Since then, he has lived in Cambridge with his wife.

In addition to the Nobel Prize, Martin's career has been filled with honors. After being named a Fellow of the Royal Society in 1950, he was awarded the Berzelius Gold Medal of the Swedish Medical Society in 1951, presented the John Scott Award in 1958, and awarded the John Price Wetherill Medal and America's Franklin Institute Medal in 1959. In 1960, he was made Companion of the British Empire; in 1963, he won the Leverhulme Medal. In 1969, he was given the Kolthoff Medal, and in 1971 the Callendar Medal. In 1972, he was presented the Japanese Order of the Rising Sun and given the Achievement Award of the Worshipful Company of Scientific Instrument Makers. He was named an Honorary Fellow of the University of Cambridge in 1974, and the University of Connecticut gave him the Randolf Major Medal in 1979. In 1985, he was awarded Austria's Fritz Pregl Medal. He was awarded honorary doctorates from the universities of Leeds, Glasgow, and Urbino.

In a sense, Martin is more an inventor than a researcher; his career shows the results of a pragmatic nature presented with the need for simplified solutions to everyday problems. Instead of devoting himself to the analysis of a particular substance, Martin applied himself to the development of methods that made the tasks of others easier. He is, therefore, a man known better inside his profession than outside. His accomplishments are not so much the stuff of news conferences or television specials as of the everyday life of the working scientist. Martin could not have envisioned the incredible growth that chromatography would undergo or its widespread use in so many areas of science and industry. What he did recognize was the immediate need for more efficient methods, so he went into the laboratory and invented them. As a result, the methods of chromatography have become as common in the laboratory as titration, distillation, and spectrometry. In presenting Martin with its prestigious Leverhulme Medal, the Royal Society recognized his "inventiveness, imagination, and resourcefulness" in combining disparate observations into "sound general methods of extraordinary and sweeping range."

Bibliography

Primary

BIOCHEMISTRY: "Preparation and Mounting of Deliquescent Substances," *Nature*, vol. 129, 1932 (with Nora Wooster); "Absorption Spectrum of Vitamin E," *Nature*, vol. 131, 1934 (with T. Moore and Marion Schmidt); "Volatile Aldehydes Liberated by Periodic Acid from Protein Hydrolysates," *Nature*, vol. 146, 1940 (with R. L. M. Synge); "A New Form of Chromatogram Employing Two Liquid Phases," *Biochemical Journal*, vol. 35, 1941 (with R. L. M. Synge); "Protein Chromatography in the Study of Protein Constituents," *Biochemical Journal*, vol. 37, 1943 (with A. H. Gordon and R. L. M. Synge); "Partition Chromatography," *Annual Reports of Progress in Chemistry*, vol. 45, 1949; "The Chromatographic Fractionation of Ribonuclease," *Biochemical Journal*, vol. 49, 1951 (with R. R. Porter).

Secondary

"Basis of Chromatography." *British Medical Journal* 2 (November 15, 1952): 1087-1088. The editors of this journal decided to take the space to introduce its readers to the concepts of chromatography before announcing the Nobel Prize for 1952. It is a brief but historically interesting introduction to chromatography as it existed in 1952, observing, for example, that among the achievements of the method was the demonstration that leaves contain their autumn pigment even in spring.

Farber, Eduard. *Nobel Prize Winners in Chemistry: 1901-1961*. Rev. ed. New York: Abelard-Schuman, 1963. Farber's update of his 1953 catalog of Nobelists is a useful, if elementary, introduction to the bases for the awards. The material itself is essentially a condensation of the recipients' Nobel lectures.

Gritter, Roy J., James M. Bobbit, and Arthur E. Schwarting. *Introduction to Chromatography*. 2d ed. Oakland, Calif.: Holden-Day, 1985. This book is an exemplary introduction to chromatography. The first edition of 1968 observed that the world of chemical research was becoming ever more dependent on chromatography as a tool. The second edition restates this, with all the advantage of hindsight, and updates the incredible advances in the field. Despite the proliferation of books on chromatography, this text should be the beginning point for any serious student of the subject.

Novotny, Milos V. "Chromatography." In *McGraw-Hill Encyclopedia of Science and Technology*. 6th ed., vol. 3. New York: McGraw-Hill, 1987. While by no means as complete as the Gritter text, this presents an admirable condensation of the plethora of chromatographic techniques in a limited, ten-page entry.

Sherwood, Martin. *The New Chemistry*. New York: Basic Books, 1974. This book, though written solely for the layperson, is a surprisingly lucid and rational account of many of the techniques that have been developed by chemists since World War II. It includes a brief but accurate introduction to chromatography and its use in conjunction with mass spectrometry.

Daniel J. Fuller

1952

Chemistry
Archer John Porter Martin, Great Britain
Richard Laurence Millington Synge, Great Britain

Physics
Felix Bloch, United States
Edward Mills Purcell, United States

Physiology or Medicine
Selman A. Waksman, United States

Literature
François Mauriac, France

Peace
Albert Schweitzer, France

RICHARD LAURENCE MILLINGTON SYNGE
1952

Born: Liverpool, England; October 28, 1914

Nationality: British
Areas of concentration: Physical chemistry and biochemistry

Synge developed new methods for separating and analyzing molecules, especially proteins and sugars. His most notable contribution was partition chromatography, in which molecules are separated from one another between two different liquids moving over a surface composed of silica, starch, or cellulose

The Award
Presentation

Professor Arne W. K. Tiselius, the 1948 Nobel laureate in chemistry and a member of the Nobel Committee for Chemistry, presented the Nobel Prize in Chemistry to Richard Synge and Archer Martin on December 10, 1952. Tiselius began his presentation speech with an overview of the applications of chemistry to the study of life, placing special emphasis upon the need for improved separation techniques to isolate important molecules from living organisms. Among the most important biological molecules would be proteins, nucleic acids (such as deoxyribonucleic acid and ribonucleic acid), carbohydrates (sugars), and lipids (fats).

Richard Synge and Archer Martin developed filter-paper chromatography, also known as partition chromatography. A complex mixture of molecules is placed at one end of the filter-paper strip. The same end is dipped into an alcohol-water solution, which is drawn vertically up the dry filter paper by capillary action— much as a candle's wick draws fluid to fuel a flame. As the alcohol-water solution is drawn up the filter paper, so are the molecules of the complex mixture. The molecules in the complex mixture are separated based upon each molecule's attractiveness for the paper and for either the alcohol or the water. The end result is a series of spots on the filter paper, each spot representing a single type of molecule isolated from the starting complex mixture.

Partition chromatography had made several important contributions to biochemistry by 1952. Synge and Martin had used the method to study the chemical structure of antibiotics and amino acids. Frederick Sanger used the technique to determine the structure of insulin, a protein hormone that helps to regulate the amount of sugar in the bloodstream. Sanger and others would eventually receive Nobel Prizes for discoveries using Synge and Martin's partition chromatography.

Nobel lecture

Richard Synge delivered his Nobel lecture, entitled "Applications of Partition Chromatography," on December 12, 1952. His lecture followed that of his colleague and cowinner, Archer Martin. Synge's speech consisted of two parts: first, a description of how he came to work with Martin, and second, a discussion of partition chromatography and its biochemical importance.

As a research student at the University of Cambridge under the supervision of N. W. Pirie, Synge became interested in glycoproteins, substances that are part protein (for example, amino acids) and part carbohydrate (for example, sugars). Additional work with Dr. D. J. Bell and Dr. A. Neuberger stimulated his interest in separating substances, particularly in the separating of a glycoprotein into its constituent sugars and amino acids. Through Dr. Hedley R. Marston, an adviser to the International Wool Secretariat, Synge obtained a studentship for developing new separation techniques. The studentship brought about his association with Archer Martin, who was studying the same problem.

Partition chromatography involves the separation of molecules between different phases of solutions; that is, the separation of molecules between different types of liquids (such as alcohol versus water or chloroform versus water). For example, in a chloroform-water separation, the mixture that is to be separated is placed in a chloroform-water solvent. Chloroform and water are immiscible; that is, they do not readily mix. Therefore they separate into two phases, one above the other (as oil and water do). The molecules in the mixture will either favor chloroform or water and will separate accordingly, based upon each molecule's physical and chemical properties.

Synge and Martin applied this separation procedure to paper chromatography. The mixture to be separated is spotted at one end of a paper strip. This same end is dipped into the chloroform-water solvent, which is drawn up the paper "wick" by capillary action. Certain molecules of the mixture remain in the water phase, which adheres to the paper. Other molecules remain with the chloroform, the mobile phase, which freely moves up the paper. The net result is separation of molecules.

A very important application of the method was amino acid separation. A protein consists of a long chain of amino acids. Synge and Martin proposed that if a protein is cut into a series of overlapping fragments of varying lengths (for example, one fragment with amino Acids A-B-C-D-E-F-G, another fragment with amino acids A-B-C-D, another with C-D-E-F, and so on, followed by separation of the fragments by partition chromatography, and finally followed by amino acid identification, then the correct amino acid sequence of the protein could be determined. Synge and Martin used this approach to determine the structure of the antibiotic gramicidin-S. Furthermore, Frederick Sanger (1958 and 1980 Nobel chemistry laureate) applied the approach to insulin, and Stanford Moore and William H. Stein (1972 Nobel chemistry laureates) applied the approach to ribonuclease. Synge quoted from early work by these biochemists during his lecture.

Besides its important applications to the determination of protein amino acid sequences, Synge stressed the applications of partition chromatography to the analysis of other biological molecules, including nucleic acids, carbohydrates, and lipids. To enhance partition chromatography, Synge emphasized the use of radioactively labeled molecules in the separation process, an approach which would later be used by several Nobel chemistry laureates.

Critical reception

The awarding of the 1952 Nobel Prize in Chemistry to Richard Synge and Archer Martin continued a strong trend in the Royal Swedish Academy of Sciences toward recognizing the chemical separation of molecules. In Arne Tiselius' presentation speech to the two Britons and in several other Nobel chemistry presentations, reference was made to the Dutch term for chemistry, "scheikunde," or "the art of separation." It was notable that the torch was passed from one separation chemist to two others; Tiselius was the 1948 Nobel chemistry laureate for his development of two separation techniques, electrophoresis and adsorption analysis. Furthermore, Synge had studied in Tiselius' laboratory in 1946-1947, and the two had since collaborated on several research papers.

Synge and Martin were profiled in the world press, including *The Times* of London, *Newsweek*, and *Time* magazine. The November 17, 1952, issue of *Time* cited Martin, age forty-two, and Synge, thirty-eight, for their method of studying "complicated molecular structures." The November 17, 1952, issue of *Newsweek* highlighted the pair for their method of "segregating confused chemicals." While their discovery, like many scientific achievements, received little more than a footnote from the press, it had major implications for biochemistry.

The Swedish Academy's decision was well received worldwide. At the time of the award, Synge and Martin's partition chromatography method was in wide use among biochemical scientists. Furthermore, the applications of partition chromatography were extensive in biomedicine and industry. It was used in the determination of the amino acid sequences of the proteins insulin by Sanger and of ribonuclease by Moore, Stein, and Christian Anfinsen. It was also being used by Melvin Calvin, the 1961 Nobel chemistry laureate. Partition chromatography would later be used again by Sanger and Walter Gilbert for the nucleotide-sequencing of the DNA molecule, an achievement for which both would receive Nobel Prizes in 1980. Rarely, in fact, has such a simple technique spawned so much discovery.

The analysis of molecules using paper chromatography had been used for nearly a century; the reliability of the method, however, had been poor until Synge and Martin's invention of partition chromatography. Its discovery helped revolutionize biochemistry and continues to be a cornerstone of biochemical analysis.

Biography

Richard Laurence Millington Synge was born on October 28, 1914, in Liverpool, England. His parents were Laurence Millington Synge and Katherine Charlotte Swan. After studying classics and science at Winchester College, he entered Trinity College of the University of Cambridge in 1933, where he successfully completed Part I (physics, chemistry, and physiology) and Part II (biochemistry) of the Natural Sciences Tripos. He continued at Cambridge as a research student in Sir

Frederick G. Hopkins' Biochemical Laboratory from 1936 to 1939. He transferred to the Wool Industries Research Association in Leeds in 1939.

After receiving his doctorate from Cambridge in 1941, he continued at Leeds as a biochemist until 1943, when he became staff biochemist at the Lister Institute of Preventive Medicine in London. He also married Ann Stephen in 1943. They had seven children: Jane, Elizabeth, Matthew Millington, Patrick Millington, Alexander Millington, Charlotte, and Mary.

Synge served as director of the Department of Protein Chemistry at the Rowett Research Institute in Bucksburn, Aberdeen, Scotland, from 1948 to 1967. He was then biochemist with the Food Research Institute in Norwich, England, from 1967 to 1976. He served as Honorary Professor in the School of Biological Sciences, University of East Anglia, from 1968 to 1984. He received the John Price Wetherill Medal from the Franklin Institute in 1959. He was a member of the Royal Irish Academy, the Royal Society of New Zealand, the American Society of Biological Chemists, and the Phytochemical Society of Europe.

Scientific Career

Richard Synge began his studies of molecular separation as a research student in Sir Frederick Hopkins' Biochemical Laboratory at the University of Cambridge. Under the supervision of N. W. Pirie, he began studying the chemical properties of glycoproteins. Work with Dr. D. J. Bell stimulated his interest in separating glycoproteins into their carbohydrate and protein components. His first successful extraction of carbohydrates from glycoproteins came with the chloroform extraction technique developed by Dr. A. Neuberger of the University College Hospital in London.

In 1938, with the help of Dr. Hedley R. Marston of the CSIR Nutrition Laboratory in Adelaide, South Australia, Synge began work studying the amino acid composition of wool. He received funding from the International Wool Secretariat. He successfully separated amino acids using Neuberger's chloroform-water phase separation technique. At the same time, Dr. Archer Martin, also supported by the International Wool Secretariat at the Wool Industries Research Association at the University of Leeds, had developed an instrument for purifying vitamin E. Synge joined Martin at the University of Leeds in 1939.

Working together, Synge and Martin combined their interests in biochemical molecules and separatory techniques for isolating molecules from one another. The result of their efforts over the next two years was partition chromatography, a simple technique based upon chemical principles known for more than a century. Martin, in his 1952 Nobel lecture, described partition chromatography as a combination of chromatography with countercurrent solvent extraction. Developed by the Russian biochemist Mikhail Tsvett in the very early twentieth century, chromatography involved the separation of molecules moving across a specially prepared surface, on which some molecules were slowed down more than others because of their different chemical properties. Countercurrent solvent extraction involved the separation of molecules between two unmixable liquids, with the molecules favoring one liquid over the other.

Although partition chromatography could have been developed in the nineteenth century, it was the acceleration of chemical knowledge and the need for more advanced separatory methods in both medicine and industry in the early 1940's that ignited its development. Partition chromatography, as developed by Synge and Martin, involved the application of a complex mixture to a specially prepared solid substance, the chromatography adsorbent. This adsorbent could be a fine paper such as cellulose, a column packed with starch, or a column filled with tiny grains of silica. The complex mixture would separate into its various molecules as it flowed over the column; each molecule would separate from the others as it would be slowed down by the solid adsorbent at a different rate from each of the other molecules.

To improve the separation of molecules from the complex mixture as it moved over the solid surface adsorbent, the countercurrent solvents were added. For example, two liquids that tend to separate from each other when mixed were used (for instance, chloroform and water or butyl alcohol and water). The solid surface adsorbent, such as starch, cellulose, or silica, will have a high attractiveness for water, and therefore will have a high attractiveness for molecules which interact better with water than with either chloroform or butyl alcohol. The remaining molecules, which interact better with chloroform or butyl alcohol, will move more freely along the solid surface adsorbent.

Thus, partition chromatography successfully separates the molecules of a mixture based upon how much each molecule is retarded, or slowed down, by the surface adsorbent and upon whether each molecule prefers to interact with water or the other solvent—chloroform, butyl alcohol, and so on. Once the procedure is completed, the solid chromatography adsorbent surface will consist of a linear set of groupings of molecules. Those molecules which interact strongly with both water and the surface adsorbent move the shortest distance along the chromatography column. Those molecules which weakly interact with water and adsorbent move farther along the column.

Each molecule can be identified based upon its color; if the molecule is colorless, it can be identified based upon its reactivity with chemicals, ultraviolet light, infrared light, and so on. In the case of paper chromatography, a molecule can be cut from the paper for further testing.

For paper chromatography on cellulose, the complex mixture is spotted at one end of a strip of cellulose paper, which is dipped into the two-phase (for example, chloroform-water) countercurrent solvent. As the chloroform-water solvent is wicked up the paper strip, the molecules of the complex mixture are pulled along as well. Some molecules are retarded by the cellulose more than others. Furthermore, some molecules prefer the water phase over the chloroform phase; because the water strongly interacts with the cellulose, these molecules are further slowed by the cellulose. Those molecules which have more attractiveness for chloroform and less attractiveness for the cellulose move farther along the cellulose strip.

Synge and Martin applied partition chromatography to the separation of a variety of substances, including proteins, amino acids, sugars, and fatty acids. They publicly demonstrated the method and its applications to the Biochemical Society on June 7, 1941, at the National Institute for Medical Research in London. The method was well accepted and rapidly became adopted as a valuable tool for the molecular separation of a variety of substances, especially proteins, during the 1940's, Synge used the technique to complete his doctoral dissertation, analyzing the chemical properties of the amino acids of wool.

Chromatography's most important role was its analytical usefulness, particularly in the determination of protein structure. A protein consists of a long chain of amino acids, of which there are approximately twenty different types found in the proteins of all living organisms on earth. These twenty different amino acids are arranged in different orders in different proteins, thereby making each protein type unique. For example, all ox insulin proteins are a chain of fifty-one amino acids. The fifty-one ox insulin amino acids consist of the twenty amino acid types arranged in a specific order. Obviously, many amino acid types occur more than once.

If a protein, such as insulin, is cut into fragments of varying amino acid lengths (amino acids A-B-C-D-E, A-B-C, C-D-E-F, D-E-F-G, and so on), followed by partition chromatography and identification of fragments, then the amino acid sequence of the protein can be determined. If a protein's amino acid sequence is known, then its structure and function can be understood. Frederick Sanger applied this approach to the determination of the amino acid sequence of insulin, for which he was awarded the 1958 Nobel Prize in Chemistry. Synge and Martin, along with R. Consden and A. H. Gordon, used the technique to determine the amino acid sequence and structure of the antibiotic gramicidin-S. Stanford Moore and William H. Stein, along with Christian Anfinsen, applied the method to the protein ribonuclease, for which all three were awarded the 1972 Nobel Prize in Chemistry.

After developing the partition chromatography method in the early 1940's, Synge and Martin continued to refine and improve its applications. With paper chromatography, they and others developed two-dimensional chromatography, by which a complex mixture is first separated into its component molecules in a linear direction, followed by turning the paper strip on its side and running the separated molecules sideways. The result is not a simple strip with a linear series of separated molecules, but a square sheet with molecules in various places. The resolution, or separability of molecules, is much improved with this approach, because the molecules are separated in two different directions.

Synge and Martin, as well as other biochemists, experimented with the use of radioactive "markers" in the separation process. For example, to mark a protein, one uses a radioactive atom (radioisotope) of an element commonly found in proteins, such as sulfur-35. The radioactive proteins are separated by paper chromatography, the paper is exposed to X-ray film, and the result is a photograph, termed a radioautograph, of the separation. This method was extensively used by

1961 Nobel laureate Melvin Calvin for tracing the incorporation of carbon from carbon dioxide into glucose during photosynthesis in plants. It was later very useful to Walter Gilbert and Frederick Sanger for DNA sequencing.

In 1946-1947, Synge worked with 1948 Nobel chemistry laureate Arne Tiselius at the Institute of Physical Chemistry in Uppsala, Sweden. Tiselius was deeply interested in separatory methods, specifically electrophoresis and adsorption analysis. After assuming the position of director of the Department of Protein Chemistry at the Rowett Research Institute in 1948, Synge devoted his research to adsorption analysis and partition chromatography of large proteins, specifically antibiotics and enzymes involved in metabolism.

Applying his own methods and those learned from Tiselius, Synge used three techniques for isolating amino acids from rye grass: partition chromatography, electrophoresis through a diaphragm cell, and ion-exchange chromatography—the latter a technique by which molecules are separated based upon their interactions with various electrically charged atoms (ions). Being an excellent analytical chemist, he was interested in comparing the positive and negative qualities of each approach. He used these methods to study the protein, carbohydrate, mineral, and acid content of plant juices. He extended these studies to the effects of plant juice molecules on the microorganisms which inhabit the intestines of ruminants (animals such as cattle, and sheep that consume plants and require intestinal bacteria to aid in digestion).

Synge maintained that various plant juice molecules were stimulators of bacterial growth. He performed two-dimensional paper chromatography on the molecules of various bacterial species that inhabit the intestines of ruminants. He argued that a high incidence of diaminopimelic acid in certain bacteria, including *Ruminococcus flavefaciens*, made this molecule a prime candidate for being a growth factor for these microorganisms.

After he received the 1952 Nobel Prize, Synge continued working with various separation methods for biological molecules. With D. L. Mould, he experimented with the separation of sugars using electrokinetic ultrafiltration, a process by which the sugar molecules are separated on a chromatography membrane suspended in an electric field. The process proved to be useful for the isolation of sugars during various stages of metabolism. Synge later refined the procedure to develop a method for separating proteins based upon their molecular weights.

Synge and J. C. Wood used paper chromatography and electrophoresis to study the properties of amino acids found in rye grass, most of which were found to associate with acidic compounds. With Mary Youngson, he used radioactively labeled amino acids to study the proteins of rye grass. Synge and E. P. White used partition chromatography to isolate sporidesmin, a toxin produced by the fungus *Sporedesmin bakeri* that is responsible for facial eczema in sheep and other ruminants. They determined an approximate molecular weight for the toxin.

Through all of his work, Richard Synge, like his colleagues Martin and Tiselius, was devoted to the development of improved methods for the separation of molecules. Also like his predecessors, he was very conscious of the applications of these methods to human welfare—in medicine, agriculture, and industry. Partition chromatography served both as an important separatory tool and as an important analytical tool. Its development was the stimulus for many later breakthroughs in molecular analysis, especially those involving proteins and nucleic acids, the two principal molecules of life.

Bibliography

Primary
CHEMISTRY: "Partition Chromatography," *The Analyst*, vol. 71, 1946; "Methods for Isolating Amino-Acids: Aminobutyric Acid from Rye Grass," *Biochemical Journal*, vol. 48, 1951; "Non-protein Nitrogeneous Constituents of Rye Grass: Ionophoretic Fractionation and Isolation of a 'Bound Amino-acid' Fraction," *Biochemical Journal*, vol. 49, 1951; "Applications of Partition Chromatography," Nobel lecture, in *Les Prix Nobel*, 1952; "Note on the Occurrence of Diaminopimelic Acid in Some Intestinal Micro-organisms from Farm Animals," *Journal of General Microbiology*, vol. 9, 1953; "Separation of Polysaccharides Related to Starch by Electrokinetic Ultrafiltration in Collodion Membranes," *Biochemical Journal*, vol. 58, 1954 (with D. L. Mould); "Experiments on Electrical Migration of Peptides and Proteins Inside Porous Membranes: Influences of Adsorption, Diffusion and Pore Dimensions," *Biochemical Journal*, vol. 65, 1957; "Preparation of Some Derivatives of Gramicidin S," *Biochemical Journal*, vol. 65, 1957; "Bound Amino Acids in Protein-free Extracts of Italian Ryegrass," *Biochemical Journal*, vol. 70, 1958 (with J. C. Wood).
HISTORY OF SCIENCE: "A Retrospect on Liquid Chromatography," *Biochemical Society Symposium*, no. 30, 1969.

Secondary
Farber, Eduard. *Nobel Prize Winners in Chemistry, 1901-1961*. Rev. ed. New York: Abelard-Schuman, 1963. An informative reference, this book presents short synopses of the first sixty-one years' winners of the Nobel Prize in Chemistry. Each laureate is discussed with a biographical sketch, description of the individual's scientific work, and the importance of the work.
Goodenough, Ursula. *Genetics*. New York: Holt, Rinehart and Winston, 1974. This undergraduate genetics textbook provides a comprehensive and clear presentation of nucleic acids and proteins. Includes discussions of important methodologies, including chromatography, that have contributed to the current knowledge of biochemistry, molecular biology, and genetics.
Pecsok, Robert L., L. Donald Shields, Thomas Cairns, and Ian G. McWilliam. *Modern Methods of Chemical Analysis*. New York: John Wiley & Sons, 1968. This upper-level undergraduate chemistry textbook provides a comprehensive, indepth coverage of all aspects of modern analytical chemical techniques. The book includes several chapters covering the various types of chromatography,

including paper chromatography and partition chromatography.
Pharmacia Fine Chemicals. *Affinity Chromatography: Principles and Methods*. Uppsala, Sweden: Author, 1983. This reference manual provides a very detailed description of various chromatographic methods, including summaries of experimental set-ups and applications. The work is intended for the serious biochemist.
Stryer, Lubert. *Biochemistry*. San Francisco: W. H. Freeman, 1975. Stryer's textbook is a classic biochemistry book for undergraduates. It is very clearly written, with excellent diagrams and illustrations. The chapter on protein structure includes concise explanations of electrophoresis and chromatography.
Tinoco, Ignacio, Jr., Kenneth Sauer, and James C. Wang. *Physical Chemistry: Principles and Applications in Biological Sciences*. Englewood Cliffs, N.J.: Prentice-Hall, 1978. This physical chemistry textbook is designed for advanced undergraduates and graduate students. It provides a rigorous discussion of analytical chemistry techniques and their applications to biochemical analysis. It includes a mathematical treatment with some calculus.

David Wason Hollar, Jr.

1953

Chemistry
Hermann Staudinger, West Germany

Physics
Frits Zernike, The Netherlands

Physiology or Medicine
Fritz A. Lipmann, United States
Sir H. A. Krebs, Great Britain

Literature
Sir Winston Churchill, Great Britain

Peace
George C. Marshall, United States

HERMANN STAUDINGER
1953

Born: Worms, Germany; March 23, 1881
Died: Freiburg im Breisgau, West Germany; September 8, 1965
Nationality: German
Area of concentration: Macromolecular chemistry

Resisting the tide of opinion prevalent in the 1920's, Staudinger theorized that polymers are composed of macromolecules that can grow to enormous size and that produce atomic chains rather than a ring structure. This theory helped launch the plastics industry and led to later DNA research

The Award

Presentation

Professor Arne Fredga, a member of the Nobel Committee for Chemistry of the Royal Swedish Academy of Sciences, presented the seventy-two-year-old Hermann Staudinger to King Gustav VI of Sweden to be awarded the Nobel Prize in Chemistry on a cold Thursday, December 10, 1953. Fredga noted that the first enunciation of atomic theory dated to Democritus of Abdera, a Greek philosopher of the fifth century B.C.

He then traced the development and significance of atomic theory in more recent times. He identified molecules as chemical compounds consisting of atoms of two or more elements linked together to form chains or more complex structures. Fredga emphasized the minuteness of molecules by pointing out that the number in a liter of water would be expressed by a twenty-six-digit number.

Having covered much of the background that had led Staudinger to his important work with polymers and to his articulation of a theory based on the existence of macromolecules, Fredga said that significant researchers contemporary with Staudinger considered his theories unacceptable and challenged them at every turn. Staudinger persisted in his conviction that chemical molecules can reach substantial sizes and that when they do, they act differently from regular (small) molecules. These macromolecules, as Staudinger called them, form high polymers when the anticipated ring closure fails to occur. This theory has provided the basis for synthesizing materials such as rubber, cellophane, nylon, and other products of modern civilization.

Fredga emphasized that, although Staudinger provided the plastics industry with its theoretical underpinnings, he did not become involved in the commercial aspects of macromolecular research, preferring to continue his purely scientific investigations in the field.

Nobel lecture

Hermann Staudinger delivered his Nobel lecture, entitled simply "Macromolecular Chemistry," on December 11, 1953. He sought to elucidate the new features that his macromolecular theory had introduced into organic chemistry. The address was detailed, highly technical, and extensively documented. Its intended audience was specialists in organic chemistry, for whom Staudinger's discourse is clear and well sequenced. The lecture was illustrated profusely with figures and diagrams, most of which would prove daunting to nonspecialists.

In a useful, easily understood chart, Staudinger separated those macromolecular substances that occur naturally—hydrocarbons such as rubber, polysaccharides such as cellulose, polynucleotides such as nucleic acid, proteins, enzymes, lignins, and tans—from those synthesized through polymerization (polystyrene, buna), polycondensation (bakelite, nylon), and polyaddition (polyurethane). On the same chart, he identified such conversion products of natural substances as vulcanized rubber, rayon, cellophane, and leather.

Staudinger explained how macromolecular compounds occur naturally in proteins, enzymes, and nucleic acids. These compounds also occur in polysaccharides and rubber; they can be synthesized as plastics and as artificial fibers such as nylon and polyester. Staudinger, who arrived at his revolutionary theory of macromolecules through his unremitting use of pure logic, noted that these compounds result from the addition of carbon atoms, which are then bound by their chief valences. He classified all molecules with a molecular weight of ten thousand or more as macromolecular, imposing no upper limit on their possible size and stating that macromolecules with molecular weights reaching several millions have been observed.

Staudinger devoted a considerable portion of his address to capsulizing relevant molecular research that had preceded his own as well as some that was carried on simultaneously with it. He recognized generously the contributions of other scientists. If he harbored any lingering rancor over the disbelief that large segments of the scientific community initially expressed about his theory, no suggestion of it occurred in his address, which was a model of propriety and professional decorum.

An understanding of viscosity is essential to an understanding of macromolecular chemistry, and Staudinger delved into this matter in considerable, highly technical detail. The most significant point he made in this discourse was that the viscosity of macromolecular substances in solution is unstable and changeable because minute amounts of low-molecular substances are enough, in the presence of the oxygen available in the atmosphere, to decompose chains of macromolecules, thereby causing extreme changes in their viscosity.

Staudinger concluded by noting the implications of macromolecular chemistry for research into biological processes, suggesting that a growing knowledge of the field may yield information about the nature of the building blocks that living cells require to create matter. This suggestion implies that the puzzle of life may indeed one day be solved through an increased understanding of the field that Staudinger, who positioned macromolecular chemistry hierarchically between cytology and low-molecular organic chemistry, first opened to investigation.

Critical reception

Perhaps the popular reaction to Staudinger's being awarded the Nobel Prize is best exemplified by *Newsweek*'s (November 16, 1953) headline, "Better Late Than Never." The *Newsweek* article presents some details about Alfred Nobel's holograph will, digressing to say that the will was so flawed that, had it been probated in France rather than Sweden, it would likely have been invalidated.

Newsweek notes that Alfred Nobel's real wish seemed clearly to be to recognize promising young scientists and writers who, through winning the prize, would be relieved of financial pressures so that they could continue to make significant contributions to society. The article then points out that the laureates in physics and chemistry for 1953 were sixty-five and seventy-two years old respectively. *Newsweek* might also have noted, but did not, that the laureate in literature for the same year, Winston Churchill, was seventy-nine.

Staudinger generally received more recognition upon announcement of the prize than other comparable laureates have received. Perhaps this response was the natural reaction of a public that by 1953 dressed in nylon and polyester and drove on tires made from synthetic rubber; people could easily observe the commercial manifestations of Staudinger's work. For whatever reason, Staudinger received favorable press coverage, usually with one or more photographs, in such publications as *Time* (November 16, 1953), *Scientific American* (December, 1953), *Science News Letter* (November 14, 1953), and *The Rotarian* (March, 1954).

Official news of the award first came to the United States in *The New York Times* of November 5, 1953, which devoted considerable space to Staudinger and ran a picture of him. The article had a Horatio Alger quality, emphasizing the skepticism with which the scientific world had viewed Staudinger's theory of macromolecules and presenting the laureate as an underdog who finally gained worldwide recognition. When *The New York Times* (December 11, 1953) reported the actual awarding of the prizes the following month, it focused attention on the prize in literature and ran a full commentary, including the text of Churchill's address, read for him in his absence by Lady Churchill. The article did little more than list the other laureates by name and field.

The *Science News Letter* emphasized the practical value of Staudinger's work, linking his research to synthetic fibers, plastics, and rubber products deemed crucial to modern existence. It credited Staudinger with discovering, in 1930, the relationship between molecular weight and viscosity.

Time credited Staudinger with demonstrating that, in organic compounds containing large groups of atoms, a definite pattern exists and that those compounds that do not form rings can easily consist of thousands of atoms connected in specific patterns. They are not, as previously thought, mechanical groupings of small molecular aggregations.

Newsweek quoted an unidentified chemist as regretting the fact that Staudinger received the Nobel Prize as a final recognition before death, indicating that the award would have had more meaning to him earlier. If Staudinger himself shared that view, he certainly never revealed it.

Much of the press made a special point of mentioning that Staudinger, who could have grown enormously wealthy had he concentrated on the commercial aspects of his work, remained ever the scientific scholar, standing apart from the business world that would have assured his fortune. Several articles emphasized that this giant of a man—he stood six feet, four inches tall—was a patient teacher and a tireless researcher. He lectured in a whisper, gesturing nervously as though unsure of himself. He reveled in other people's scientific successes as well as in his own.

Biography

Hermann Staudinger was born into an intellectual family on March 23, 1881. His father, Franz, was a neo-Kantian philosopher; his mother, Auguste Wenck Staudinger, was an intellectually energetic woman. Completing his secondary education at the *Gymnasium* in Worms, Staudinger began his university studies at the University of Halle, then transferring to the technical university in Darmstadt after his father was appointed to a teaching position there.

The young Staudinger was extremely interested in botany and wished to study it. His parents, however, thought that he needed a strong foundation in chemistry if he were to succeed in botany, so, following their advice, he pressed on in chemistry, going to the University of Munich, then back to Halle to finish his degree, which he received in 1903 after completing a dissertation on the malonic esters of unsaturated compounds.

His next research, leading to his *Habilitation* (teaching degree) in 1907, was on highly reactive ketenes, a subject on which he produced more than fifty articles as well as a book, published in 1912. He joined the faculty of the technical institute at Karlsruhe in 1907 and remained there for five years before he moved to the Eidgenössische Technical Institute in Zurich. He taught there until 1926, when he was invited to teach at Freiburg, replacing Heinrich Wieland, winner of the 1927 Nobel Prize in Chemistry. The following year he married Madga Woit, daughter of a famed physiologist, who became her husband's collaborator in much of his work. He remained at Freiburg until his retirement in 1951.

In retirement, Staudinger directed the Research Institute for Macromolecular Chemistry, established in the 1940's to replace the department he had headed at Freiburg. He continued as director until 1956, when he resigned to pursue his own research and writing for the nine years that remained to him; he died on September 8, 1965.

Scientific Career

The chemistry of polymers, with which Hermann Staudinger became intimately involved, is one of the more difficult areas of chemical research, and if Staudinger had not already realized this, his friends in the scientific community reiterated it to him time and again when he was in the process of deciding upon his major field of chemical research. Nevertheless, during the early days immediately after he received his doctorate, Staudinger, who was working with Johannes Thiele at Strasbourg, discovered ketenes, highly reactive forms of ketone; they were to have a profound effect on his life and on his future work.

Staudinger's renowned work on ketenes resulted in his being appointed to the faculty of the technical institute at Karlsruhe. There he worked with Karl Engler, who had a close connection with the German chemical company Badische Anilin und Sodafabrik (BASF), which was trying to find a way to synthesize rubber because rubber prices had become outrageously high in Germany.

Within three years, Staudinger had discovered a means of synthesizing isoprene, the basic ingredient of natural rubber. Simultaneously, he was continuing his research in ketenes, refining his 1907 study for publication in 1912. At that time, prevailing scientific wisdom stipulated that rubber was composed of a loose connection of rings, each with two or more isoprene atoms. The small molecules were thought to be fixed by weak bonds that formed aggregates called micelles. Staudinger, now teaching in Zurich, worked on a variety of projects during World War I, trying, among other things, to discover the chemistry of the aroma and taste of coffee so that it could be synthesized in a wartime Germany whose coffee supply had been cut off. He carried out this research with Tadeus Reichstein, a 1950 Nobel laureate in physiology or medicine, who was then his student. He was also at work on making synthetic paper and a number of other products.

By 1917, Staudinger's broad range of research in synthesizing had led him to the conclusion that the aggregate theory used to explain the viscosity of rubber was incorrect. In pursuing this conclusion, based at this point more on logic than on the huge amounts of experimental research it would take to prove it, he was embarking tentatively and quite alone on a course that most scientists of his day saw little reason to pursue; they were convinced that the data were in and that the aggregate theory convincingly explained natural rubber.

Staudinger's daring explanation, which deviated so drastically from the accepted one, was that in natural rubber one finds a stable molecule consisting of a chain of isoprene units joined by primary bonds. He postulated that the molecules contained thousands of atoms. Under experimental conditions they do not easily form rings, as small molecules do. He soon devised the name macromolecules to identify his new discovery, which would soon result in a new branch of organic chemistry.

By 1920, Staudinger's ideas were developed enough to generate a macromolecular theory of polymers. By this time, Staudinger had established a strong reputation as an organic chemist, and his venturing into a field in which increasing experimentation and publication seemed yearly to be validating the credibility of the aggregate theory was not easy for him. Being a true scientist, however, he could not rest on his reputation alone and ignore the truth of his own experimental findings. He persisted in the face of harsh, sometimes shrill, criticism from renowned leaders of the scientific community.

The decade from 1920 to 1930 was a full one for Staudinger. He persisted in conducting the experiments that would in time vindicate him, but the road to proof was arduous. Recalling experiments of a nineteenth century French chemist, Marcelin Berthelot, Staudinger found the seeds of something that would disprove the aggregate theory, which stated that the aggregate was held together by an attraction between the double bonds in their rings. If these double bonds were dispelled by the introduction of hydrogen atoms, the result should be liquid hydrocarbon. Berthelot, however, had used this method of reducing rubber, and the result was a solid, not the liquid it should have been. Staudinger replicated the experiment and produced Berthelot's results.

Wishing to avoid the complexity of experimenting with natural polymers, Staudinger began to work with synthetics, notably polystyrene and polyoxymethylene, demonstrating that, as with similar members of the series, the viscosity of their solutions was arranged in a serial order. In 1924, 1925, and 1926, Staudinger presented his findings at notable scientific meetings, but he lured few advocates to his side. Indeed, opposition rose from every quarter, but his reputation as an organic chemist remained strong enough that in 1926 he was offered the position Heinrich Wieland had vacated at Freiburg in 1924, when he went to the University of Munich to direct the Baeyer Laboratory. That Wieland's position at Freiburg remained unfilled for two years suggests that Staudinger was not the university's first choice.

Once at Freiburg, Staudinger wanted to build on the work that Theodor Svedberg and Robin Fåhraeus were doing with the ultracentrifuge in measuring the equilibrium of sedimentation of oxy- and carbonylhemoglobin. Their work provided a basis to substantiate the existence of high-molecule compounds, similar to the macromolecules Staudinger was pursuing, in the chemistry of proteins. The use of an ultracentrifuge presented a key to Staudinger's being able to pursue his work, but in 1929, the Notgemeinschaft der Deutsche Wissenschaft denied his request for funds to purchase this necessary equipment.

Refusing to be defeated by this setback, Staudinger continued his work in viscosimetry and ultimately evolved Staudinger's law, establishing the relationship between specific viscosity and molecular weight. Meanwhile, Staudinger had other researchers examine the shape of macromolecules in solution, and his theory was further supported by studies in X-ray crystallography indicating that the symmetry of crystals was attributable to ropelike bundles of chains stretching toward the axes of fibers beyond the one-unit cell.

At about the same time, research conducted in the United States by Wallace H. Carothers resulted in polymerization achieved by a process of condensation that produced water that could be measured accurately, yielding information about the number of residues in the polymer. Clearly, the theory of macromolecules was beginning to gain credence as such research proliferated.

By the time he was beginning his work at Freiburg, Staudinger began to be extremely concerned with the biochemical implications of his research, and almost thirty years later he would emphasize these implications in the concluding paragraphs of his Nobel lecture. He realized that important life processes were intimately associated with the high polymers in the form of proteins and enzymes.

Within the next decade, he came to realize that every macromolecule contains genetically a definite structural organization that the tools then available to organic chemists were not sensitive enough to assess. What Staudinger was moving toward was the identifying processes that would result in the discovery of ribonucleic acid (RNA) and deoxyribonucleic acid (DNA), an understanding of which leads scientists closer to the point of understanding the origin of human existence as well as the existence of all organic matter.

Although the commercial implications of Staudinger's work were enormous, the progress he made toward unraveling the RNA/DNA puzzle represents his greatest scientific contribution. During the 1940's, Staudinger's work went into decline; he began to lose perspective, which resulted in his finding macromolecules where there were none. He thought he had found them in bacteria, although earlier experimentation by reputable chemists had proved quite conclusively that a bacterium cannot be a macromolecule.

It is doubtful that he understood how nucleic acids transfer information to proteins or how they store information. His failure to understand these important concepts limited severely the validity of much of his later work. His earlier work was slow to gain recognition, because those who supported the aggregate theory continued to be quite articulate, and their arguments constantly threw shadows upon Staudinger's most important discoveries. Much of what he postulated could not be proved scientifically until more sensitive measuring devices were available than those that were then in common use.

As a result, the Nobel Committee recognized Staudinger long after his greatest contributions had been made and at a time when his scientific career was in decline. Staudinger's career, as well as those of his wife and many of his colleagues, had received a substantial setback when most of the chemistry institute at Freiburg was destroyed in 1944 by Allied bombings of the university. Staudinger's most significant postwar contribution was his founding in 1947 of *Makromolekulare Chemie* (macromolecular chemistry), a journal he edited for some years, which was devoted to his specialized field. This journal was a much fuller version of the *Journal für makromolekulare Chemie* (journal of macromolecular chemistry) that Staudinger founded and edited for the two years of its existence, 1943 to 1945.

Bibliography

Primary
CHEMISTRY: *Die Ketene*, 1912; *Über Polymerisation*, 1920; *Anleitung zur organischen qualitätiven Analyse*, 1923; *Die hochmolekularen organischen Verbindungen, Kautschuk und Cellulose*, 1932; *Organische Kolloid Chemie*, 1940; *Makromolekulare Chemie und Biologie*, 1947.
AUTOBIOGRAPHY: *Arbeitserinnerungen*, 1961 (*From Organic Chemistry to Macromolecules*, 1970).

Secondary
Olby, Robert C. "Hermann Staudinger." In *Dictionary of Scientific Biography*, vol. 13, edited by Charles Coulston Gillispie. New York: Charles Scribner's Sons, 1976. Although this brief introduction to Staudinger is directed at nonspecialists, it tends to become quite technical in its explanation of his work and contributions. Nevertheless, it provides a fine succinct overview of Staudinger and his work.

_____. "The Macromolecular Concept and the Origins of Molecular Biology." *Journal of Chemical Education* 47 (1970): 168-174. This article provides a good overview of the field in which Staudinger was a pioneer. The article is somewhat technical but less so than Olby's book (see following entry). It provides a reasonable starting point for the reader who is willing to put forth some effort.

_____. *The Path to the Double Helix*. Seattle: University of Washington Press, 1974. Olby writes for a scientific audience. Chapters 1 and 2 are of particular interest to readers wishing to know more about Staudinger's contributions to research in macromolecular organic chemistry. Not an easily accessible book for the beginner, although it is probably the best book in its field.

Schlessinger, Bernard S., and June Schlessinger, eds. *Who's Who of Nobel Prize Winners*. Phoenix, Ariz.: Oryx Press, 1986. This is a succinct bibliographical guide to winners of the Nobel Prize. Intended primarily for librarians, the book is also serviceable to general researchers who need help in locating sources.

Wasson, Tyler, ed. *Nobel Prize Winners*. New York: H. W. Wilson, 1987. Despite its brevity, this review of Staudinger's career covers the most salient aspects of his work and offers the reader with little background in chemistry a good place to begin. The prose is lucid and direct.

R. Baird Shuman

1954

Chemistry
Linus Pauling, United States

Physics
Max Born, Great Britain
Walther Bothe, West Germany

Physiology or Medicine
John F. Enders, United States
Thomas H. Weller, United States
Frederick Robbins, United States

Literature
Ernest Hemingway, United States

Peace
Office of the U. N. High Commissioner for Refugees

LINUS PAULING
1954

Born: Portland, Oregon; February 28, 1901

Nationality: American
Areas of concentration: Structural chemistry and molecular biology

Pauling helped develop the modern science of molecular structure by using X-ray and electron-diffraction techniques to determine the detailed architecture of minerals, gas molecules, and such complex biological molecules as hemoglobin and antibodies. Throughout these studies, the nature of the chemical bonds holding these structures together was his principal theme

The Award

Presentation

Gunnar Hägg, a chemical crystallographer and a member of the Nobel Committee for Chemistry, represented the Royal Swedish Academy of Sciences in delivering the presentation address on Friday, December 10, 1954, before King Gustav VI gave the Nobel medal and scroll to Linus Pauling. In his address, Hägg surveyed the early history of research on the chemical bond and analyzed how Pauling's work was a fitting culmination of its development. He appropriately began with the Swedish chemist Jöns Jakob Berzelius, who proposed early in the nineteenth century that chemical forces were electrical and that chemical combination resulted from joining electropositive and electronegative atoms (the dualistic theory). Since Berzelius' theory was unable to explain certain organic molecules or even how two hydrogen atoms could unite to form a molecule, it was abandoned, and by the end of the nineteenth century, chemists had realized that chemical bonds existed in several varieties.

Gilbert Newton Lewis, who became Pauling's friend and inspiration, characterized one variety, the covalent bond, as "*the* chemical bond" and described it as a shared pair of electrons. Pauling used the insights of quantum mechanics to elucidate more deeply this and other types of bonding in molecules and crystals. Because chemical bonds are present in most substances, inorganic as well as organic, Pauling's career was diverse, ranging over vast areas of chemistry, physics, biology, and medicine. In all these fields, he chose to work "on the frontiers of science," and his pioneering discoveries stimulated fruitful scientific work throughout the world.

Nobel lecture

On Saturday afternoon, December 11, 1954, Pauling delivered his Nobel lecture, entitled "Modern Structural Chemistry." It revealed the clarity of thought and simplicity of presentation that made him a popular lecturer at the California Institute of Technology. He began his Nobel address by paying tribute to the pioneers of structural theory: to Edward Frankland, who first stated explicitly that atoms had definite combining powers (the doctrine of valence); to Archibald Scott Couper and Friedrich August Kekulé, who independently suggested that the carbon atom could form four bonds and link with other carbon atoms in chains; and to Alexander Mikhailovich Butlerov, who proposed that a compound's molecular structure determined its properties.

With the discovery of the electron at the end of the nineteenth century, several scientists tried to develop an electronic theory of the chemical bond (the bond that holds atoms together in molecules), but it was G. N. Lewis who advanced the idea that electrons could be shared between atoms in such a way that these electrons could contribute to the stability of both atoms. Pauling used Lewis' concept of the electron-pair bond in his quantum mechanical discussions of molecular structures and properties. Before Pauling's work, physicists could not explain how a carbon atom could form four equivalent bonds, since quantum mechanics described carbon as having two kinds of outer electron orbitals (called s and p), which never mixed. Pauling showed how the interchange (or resonance) energy of two electrons could lead to the mixing or hybridizing of the two pure orbitals. In this way, the carbon atom could form four equivalent tetrahedral bond orbitals, each a hybrid of the s and p orbitals. This concept of hybridization allowed Pauling to explain not only the chemical properties of carbon compounds but also the magnetic properties of complex inorganic substances.

Toward the end of his lecture, Pauling turned his attention to the coordination theory of crystal structure that he had developed in the late 1920's. He had used this theory to predict possible structures for ionic compounds. Basically, his method involved using certain rules to select one atomic arrangement among various possible ones. For example, in the silicates, he assumed that each metal atom divides its valence equally among the ions that are coordinated about it. More specifically, in a crystal of topaz—a compound of aluminum, silicon, oxygen, and fluorine—a tetrahedron of four oxygen atoms surrounds each silicon atom, and an octahedron of four oxygen atoms and two fluorine atoms surrounds each aluminum atom. The silicon has normal single bonds, but the aluminum is involved in half bonds. Pauling made excellent use of this concept of fractional bonds in the field of metals and alloys. He concluded his lecture by predicting that the greatest use of these new structural ideas would be in the elucidation of the structures of proteins, nucleic acids, and other complex substances, a prediction that proved to be correct.

Critical reception

Linus Pauling received the Nobel Prize in Chemistry at a time when his political activism had got him into passport difficulties with the U.S. State Department. In the late 1940's and early 1950's, he had spoken out often and with increasing effectiveness against nuclear weapons. This alarmed certain members of Congress and the State Department: In 1952, he was three times denied a passport to travel to

European scientific meetings, and on October 1, 1954, he was refused even a limited passport to travel to India, where Prime Minister Jawaharlal Nehru had invited him to attend the dedication of an institute for scientific research.

Formal announcement of his Nobel Prize reached Pauling during a trip, just before he was to give a lecture at Cornell University. Pauling was very pleased with the annoucement. The reaction of Cornell's scientific community was enthusiastically favorable, and this highly positive reaction would be matched by that of scientists all over the world, as was later demonstrated in an article by Maurice L. Huggins for *Chemical and Engineering News*, wherein he noted that Pauling had "doubtless contributed more than any other living chemist to the understanding of chemical phenomena." After Cornell, Pauling and his wife traveled to Princeton, where he took time from his lectures to speak with reporters about his award. When asked if he would be allowed to go to Sweden to accept the prize, he replied: "I don't think there will be any trouble. Nazi Germany once caused trouble for its Nobel Prize winners, but I would not expect the United States to do so."

Pauling may have been certain that he would get a passport, but documents obtained under the Freedom of Information Act reveal that his passport became the subject of debate among concerned officials of the State Department. Some believed that Pauling would be likely to hurt the United States by his words abroad. After discussion, however, most agreed that a refusal of Pauling's passport would have "a disastrous effect for the U.S. on public opinion all over Europe and particularly in the Scandinavian countries." Pauling's previous request for a passport to travel to Sweden and around the world was in the possession of the State Department, and in a memorandum to J. Edgar Hoover about this request, an official noted that there was no evidence that any of Pauling's previous actions warranted the conclusion that he acted under the "direction, domination or control . . . of the Communist movement." According to the memorandum, Pauling's actions were those of "an imprudent and foggy-minded left winger" rather than a Communist sympathizer. The denial of his passport would result in "adverse reaction at home and abroad," with consequent harm to the United States. These arguments proved convincing, and Pauling was given his passport.

Though the details of the State Department debate were unknown to reporters, similar points cropped up in articles about Pauling's Nobel Prize. For example, *The New York Times* of November 4, 1954, discussed the scientific and political aspects of the award in separate articles. In the article on the award itself, the Nobel citation was interpreted as honoring Pauling, a chemist's chemist, for his discovery of the structure of proteins. A separate article, "Pauling Was Under Fire," discussed the charges of Senator Joseph McCarthy concerning Pauling's "leftist associations." Even newspapers in Pauling's home state of Oregon were torn between pride at his richly deserved scientific honor and questions about his political activities, but as one of these newspapers stated, the Nobel Prize is awarded not for political contributions but for scientific ones. Similarly, *Newsweek*, *Time*, and other popular magazines felt compelled to comment on the political as well as the scientific issues raised by Pauling's award. *Newsweek* of November 15, 1954, for example, noted with approval the "timeless honor" that had been bestowed on the "ebullient, prolific head" of the chemistry division at the California Institute of Technology, but it also discussed his passport difficulties and the U.S. Public Health Service's denial in 1953, on "loyalty" grounds, of his request for a $40,000 grant for blood and protein investigations.

In Europe, the reaction to Pauling's award was not so schizophrenic. Swedish reporters commented that Pauling was "definitely the most popular of the American Nobel Prize winners," and he was given an enthusiastic ovation following his speech at the Nobel banquet. Reporters interpreted this ovation as both a tribute to Pauling and a demonstration by the Swedes of what they considered an inadmissible intrusion of "McCarthyism" into the field of intellectual freedom. American officials closely followed Pauling's activities in Sweden, and one reported to Washington that the fears of the State Department were "groundless," because Pauling had made no statement that could "in any way be considered prejudicial to the United States or injurious to its prestige." Despite these assurances, the State Department continued to worry about Pauling's influence and the reaction of the foreign press, and during his trip around the world, officers at various embassies in India, Japan, and other countries monitored his movements and speeches. The American embassy in Japan sought to minimize his effect on the Japanese press and people by successfully interfering in his attempt to get an audience with the emperor. Despite these efforts to control his activities in Asia, Pauling managed to deliver more than fifty speeches, and the reaction of the press and people in these countries was overwhelmingly favorable.

Biography

Linus Carl Pauling, the first of three children and the only son of Herman Pauling, a pharmacist, and Lucie Isabelle (née Darling), was born in Portland, Oregon, on February 28, 1901. He received his early education in Condon, an arid Western town in the Oregon interior, and in Portland, where his father died in 1909. Herman's death created severe difficulties for the family. Linus became a shy adolescent who spent most of his time reading and doing chemical experiments in his basement laboratory. He took all the courses in science and mathematics available to him at Washington High School, and at Oregon Agricultural College (now Oregon State University) he majored in chemical engineering. He was forced to leave college for a year to help his mother financially, but he was able to graduate summa cum laude in 1922.

He began his graduate work at the California Institute of Technology (CIT), but after a year he returned to Oregon to wed Ava Helen Miller, who had earlier been his student in Corvallis. She came back with him to Pasadena, where he pursued studies in physical chemistry, leading to a doctorate in 1925. After a brief period as a National Research Fellow, he spent a year and a half on a Guggenheim Fellowship in Europe, doing postgraduate research with some important theoretical physicists, most notably Arnold Sommerfeld at the University of Munich. Upon his return to California in 1927, Pauling began a career as teacher and researcher at CIT that would last for thirty-six years. During World War II, he interrupted his research to work on government projects. He discovered an artificial substitute for blood serum, for example, and invented an oxygen detector that found wide use in submarines and airplanes. For these and other achievements, he was awarded the Presidential Medal for Merit.

After the war, his Nobel Prize in Chemistry brought heightened public awareness of his stature, and he used this in his efforts to bring about an end to nuclear tests. In 1958, he and his wife presented to the United Nations a petition signed by more than eleven thousand scientists from around the world. For his efforts on behalf of world peace, he was awarded the Nobel Peace Prize for 1962 on October 10, 1963, the date that the Nuclear Test Ban Treaty went into effect. During the mid-1960's, Pauling was a staff member at the Center for the Study of Democratic Institutions in Santa Barbara, but within a few years he began to miss his deep involvement in scientific research, and in 1967 he became a professor of chemistry at the University of California in San Diego, where he remained for two years before becoming a professor at Stanford University, his last academic position. To pursue his interest in molecular medicine, he founded in 1973 the institute that now bears his name, the Linus Pauling Institute of Science and Medicine. This research center was the scene of much of his work in the 1970's and 1980's.

Scientific Career

Structure has been the central theme of Pauling's scientific work. From his adolescence, when, as a collector of minerals, he wondered about the connection between their structures and such properties as hardness and luster, through his college years, when he began to think about the chemical bond, he had a deep faith in the atomic theory and its implication that atomic arrangements must in some way be responsible for how materials behave. As a graduate student at CIT, he enthusiastically adopted X-ray crystallography as a technique for exploring the atomic architecture of crystals. In 1925, he was quick to grasp the implications of quantum mechanics for chemistry, and during his studies in Europe he was able to apply this new technique to some important chemical problems, such as the theoretical prediction of the properties of ionic crystals.

With his studies in Europe completed, Pauling returned to CIT in 1927 to begin a career that moved progressively from structural determinations of simple gas molecules and complex crystals to such extremely complex biological materials as hemoglobin, antibodies, and other proteins. One of Pauling's earliest successes was his discovery of the chief principles underlying the structures of ionic crystals. In the late 1920's and early 1930's, he and his collaborators determined the structures of many silicate and sulfide minerals. Along with Lawrence Bragg, he helped to transform the structural chemistry of the silicates from one of the least understood to one of the best understood branches of chemistry. Pauling used his extensive knowledge of bond distances and bond angles to derive what came to be called his "coordination theory" of crystal structures. Many crystallographers had tried to determine the atomic arrangement of a crystal's unit cell (its basic structural unit) by rigorously eliminating all but one of the possible arrangements, but most scientists took this approach without analyzing whether the possible arrangements were chemically reasonable or whether they were in agreement with known interatomic distances and atomic sizes. Pauling developed rules, based on his vast knowledge of chemistry, to select the best atomic arrangement from among all the possible ones.

In 1930, as a result of a meeting with Herman Mark in Germany, Pauling became interested in electron diffraction. In this technique, electrons are scattered by the electric field of the positively charged nuclei of gas molecules, providing an excellent way to determine directly such quantities as the distance between atoms. Pauling and his chief collaborators, Lawrence Brockway and Verner Schomaker, improved Mark's technique and collected essentially new information on substances such as benzene and cyclohexane. These many determinations of structures by both X-ray and electron diffraction aided Pauling's theoretical work. For example, he found a way to assign to elements numbers which represented their power of attracting electrons in a covalent bond, their so-called electronegativity. Pauling used his electronegativity scale, which was widely adopted by chemists, to determine the amount of ionic and covalent character in various chemical bonds.

A central idea in Pauling's theoretical considerations during the 1930's was resonance. He had used the interchange, or resonance, energy of two electrons in his treatment of bond hybridization. In resonance, the true state of a chemical system is neither of the component quantum states but some intermediate one, caused by an interaction which lowers the energy. This idea of resonance was a major factor in Pauling's development of the valence-bond theory, in which he proposed that a molecule could be described by an intermediate structure that was a resonance combination or hybrid of other structures. His classic study, *The Nature of the Chemical Bond and the Structure of Molecules and Crystals* (1939), provided a unified summary of his experimental and theoretical studies, and it was responsible for valence-bond theory's dominance of chemistry in the 1940's and 1950's.

The arrival of Thomas Hunt Morgan, the famous geneticist, at CIT in the late 1920's stimulated Pauling's interest in biological molecules, and by the mid-1930's he was performing successful magnetic studies on hemoglobin, whose striking red color and property of combining reversibly with oxygen appealed to him. He found that a magnet attracted hemoglobin from venous blood, whereas it repelled hemoglobin from arterial blood. Since hemoglobin is a protein molecule, interest in this molecule led naturally to a more general interest in proteins, and with Alfred Mirsky, Pauling published a paper on protein structure in which he and Mirsky proposed that the protein molecule, a chain of amino-acid groups, is coiled into a specific configuration stabilized by hydrogen bonds and weak intermolecular forces. Denaturation then consists in the breakage of these bonds and the assumption of a more random configuration by the molecule.

On one of Pauling's visits to the Rockefeller Institute for Medical Research in New York City to visit Mirsky, he met Karl Landsteiner, the discoverer of blood types, who became Pauling's entrée into another field—immunochemistry, or the study of antibody-antigen reactions. Antibodies are protein molecules that are made by specialized cells in response to invasion of the body by antigens, foreign substances such as viruses, bacteria, and toxins. Pauling's first paper on antibody structure apeared in 1940. During World War II, he and his colleagues succeeded in altering the chemical structure of certain blood proteins known as globulins to produce the first synthetic antibodies.

At the end of the war, as a result of an encounter with William Castle, a coworker on the Bush Report (an attempt to plot the path of science in the postwar period), Pauling became interested in sickle-cell anemia. When he learned that the red blood cells of patients with this hereditary disease became sickle-shaped only in venous blood, with its low oxygen content, he immediately postulated that the sickling was caused by a genetic defect in the globin portion of the cell's hemoglobin. Three years later, he and Harvey Itano were able to prove that a defect in the protein portion of hemoglobin was indeed responsible for the disease.

While a guest professor at the University of Oxford in 1948, Pauling returned to a problem that had occupied him in the late 1930's: the three-dimensional structure of proteins. By folding a paper on which he had drawn a chain of linked amino acids, he discovered the alpha helix, a cylindrical, coil-like configuration of amino acids connected by hydrogen bonds. The key to his solution of the problem was his knowledge that all atoms in the bonding group (called the "peptide bond") were in the same plane. This put serious constraints on possible structures and led naturally to a helical configuration. The most significant element of Pauling's structure was its nonintegral number of amino acids per turn of the helix. Pauling and Robert Corey published a description of the alpha helix in 1950, and this structure was soon verified experimentally.

During the early 1950's, Pauling became interested in deoxyribonucleic acid (DNA), and in February, 1953, he and Corey published a structure for DNA that contained three strands, twisted around one another in ropelike fashion. Shortly thereafter, James Watson and Francis Crick proposed the double helix, which proved to be correct. Watson and Crick had the advantages of access to X-ray photographs taken by Rosalind Franklin and of freedom to attend various international scientific meetings. Pauling's passport difficulties hampered him in both regards. Nevertheless, he was very pleased with the structure, and as Watson stated in his account of the discovery, *The Double Helix* (1968), he and Crick would not have made their discovery without Pauling's prior work and his stimulation as a competitor.

In the late 1950's, Pauling was best known to the public for his campaign against the testing of nuclear weapons. He did not view this activism as unrelated to his scientific career, because he used scientific arguments to inform the public of the dangers that these tests posed for human life throughout the world. Other scientists disagreed with his reasoning. Edward Teller, the architect of the hydrogen bomb, for example, was an advocate of nuclear testing who believed that small amounts of radiation might even be beneficial. Pauling, on the other hand, believed that radiation from the debris of these tests was causing birth defects and creating cancers in many people. Teller and Pauling debated the subject of fallout on television in February, 1958; neither convinced the other to modify his position.

During the 1960's, the field of molecular medicine began to take up more of Pauling's time. Through his work on antibodies and sickle-cell anemia, he had become convinced that molecular size and shape were the important factors in biological reactions. In this period, he founded the new field of orthomolecular medicine, whose central idea is that substances normally present in the body can be manipulated to help treat certain diseases. In the light of later developments, perhaps the most significant occurrence in the 1960's was a letter Pauling received in 1966 from Irwin Stone, an industrial chemist who had a deep interest in vitamin C. Stone held that the minimum daily allowance for this vitamin proposed by the Food and Nutrition Board of the National Research Council was far too low for many people, and because he wanted Pauling to live a long and healthy life, he suggested that he take large amounts, or megadoses, of this vitamin.

Pauling and his wife followed Stone's advice, and they noticed an increased feeling of well-being and an especially striking decrease in the incidence of colds. This experience sent Pauling prospecting through the scientific literature for information on the protective effects of vitamin C against the common cold. From reading the published evidence, he came to a conclusion that was at odds with most authorities: Vitamin C, provided it is taken in large enough amounts, has a beneficial effect in helping the body fight off colds. The eventual outcome of his research was a book, *Vitamin C and the Common Cold* (1970). It became a best-seller and caused a huge increase in vitamin C sales throughout the United States. The book also embroiled Pauling in yet another controversy. Many nutritionists and medical doctors found his views unfounded, irresponsible, and even dangerous, but Pauling claimed that studies done both before and after publication of the book confirmed his views.

In the early 1970's, Pauling became interested in using vitamin C for the treatment of cancer, largely through his contact with the Scottish physician Ewan Cameron. Their collaboration resulted in a book, *Cancer and Vitamin C* (1979), in which they marshaled evidence for the effectiveness of vitamin C against cancer. In the 1980's, Pauling obtained financial support to have his ideas tested in his own laboratory as well as in the laboratories of the Mayo Clinic. Workers at the Linus Pauling Institute obtained positive results in animal studies, but researchers at the Mayo Clinic obtained negative results in two studies with human patients, so the controversy remained unresolved. In his book *How to Live Longer and Feel Better* (1986), Pauling attacked the first Mayo Clinic study because researchers had used heavy doses of highly toxic anticancer drugs along with the vitamin C. According to Pauling, these drugs damage the immune system and consequently interfere with the action of vitamin C. He criticized the second Mayo Clinic study for the short period that researchers gave the cancer patients vitamin C and for their suppressing the information that patients who died had long since been deprived of vitamin C. Pauling concluded that what the Mayo Clinic studies showed was that "cancer patients should not stop taking their large doses of vitamin C."

Throughout his career, Pauling has liked to work on the frontiers of knowledge, and many of his greatest discoveries have occurred in the areas between disciplines—between chemistry and physics, chemistry and biology, chemistry and medicine. Despite his involvement in several controversies, most scientists have recognized the overwhelming importance of his contributions, and he has been honored throughout the world with the most prestigious awards of institutions, professional organizations, and governments. His structural vision helped to transform not only chemistry but also physics, biology, and medicine. Pauling pushed the frontiers of these fields to a greater level of understanding, where physics, chemistry, biology, and medicine all merge, allowing scientists to see more clearly the apparently unlimited richness of the material world.

Bibliography

Primary

CHEMISTRY: *The Nature of the Chemical Bond and the Structure of Molecules and Crystals: An Introduction to Modern Structural Chemistry*, 1939; *General Chemistry*, 1947; *College Chemistry*, 1947; *The Architecture of Molecules*, 1964 (with Roger Hayward); *The Chemical Bond*, 1967; *Chemistry*, 1975 (with Peter Pauling).

PHYSICS: *The Structure of Line Spectra*, 1930 (with Samuel Goudsmit); *Introduction to Quantum Mechanics, with Applications to Chemistry*, 1935 (with E. Bright Wilson, Jr.).

BIOLOGY: *Molecular Structure and Biological Specificity*, 1957.

MEDICINE: *Vitamin C and the Common Cold*, 1970; *Orthomolecular Psychiatry: Treatment of Schizophrenia*, 1973 (with David Hawkins); *Vitamin C, the Common Cold, and the Flu*, 1976; *Cancer and Vitamin C*, 1979 (with Ewan Cameron); *How to Live Longer and Feel Better*, 1986.

PEACE: *No More War!*, 1958; *Neue Moral und internationales Recht*, 1970.

Secondary

Edelstein, Stuart J. *The Sickled Cell: From Myth to Molecules*. Cambridge, Mass.: Harvard University Press, 1986. In this book, Edelstein, a biochemist, tries to summarize what is known about the historical and cultural roots of sickle-cell anemia and the molecular details of how it attacks humans. He discusses both Pauling's work on hemoglobin and sickle-cell anemia and his own experiences in Africa, where he conducted field work among the Igbo of Nigeria.

Judson, Horace Freeland. *The Eighth Day of Creation: Makers of the Revolution in Biology*. New York: Simon & Schuster, 1979. The story of molecular biology told mainly in the words of the people who created it. Judson interviewed Pauling, and he presents a good account of Pauling's work on proteins and nucleic acids. Originally serialized in *The New Yorker*, this book is intended for general audiences.

Olby, Robert. *The Path to the Double Helix*. Seattle: University of Washington Press, 1974. Intended for a scientifically sophisticated readership, Olby's book is the best historical account of the discovery of the double helix. The book contains an excellent discussion of the discovery's background as well as of the discovery itself. Olby analyzes Pauling's role in the discovery through a treatment of Pauling's research on both the alpha helix and DNA.

Pauling, Linus. "Fifty Years of Progress in Structural Chemistry and Molecular Biology." *Daedalus* 99 (Fall, 1970): 988-1014. This article represents the most extensive autobiographical reminiscences that Pauling has written. He emphasizes his scientific work, but the account is historical and general and can be understood by the reader with little scientific knowledge. This article is also available in a book, *The Twentieth Century Sciences: Studies in the Biography of Ideas*, edited by Gerald Holton (New York: W. W. Norton, 1972).

Rich, Alexander, and Norman Davidson, eds. *Structural Chemistry and Molecular Biology: A Volume Dedicated to Linus Pauling by His Students, Colleagues, and Friends*. San Francisco: W. H. Freeman, 1968. A festschrift for Pauling in honor of his sixty-fifth birthday. Many of the articles are specialized and technical, but a substantial number are historical and general. For example, J. H. Sturdivant's article, "The Scientific Work of Linus Pauling," provides a good overview of Pauling's achievements in structural chemistry and molecular biology.

Watson, James. *The Double Helix*. New York: Atheneum, 1968. Pauling attacked this personal account of the discovery of the structure of DNA when it first appeared for what he saw as its errors and distorted view of science. Nevertheless, it provides insight into the way some scientists view modern research. It is best read in connection with corrective commentaries and reviews, as have been provided in *The Double Helix: A Norton Critical Edition*, edited by Gunther S. Stent (New York: W. W. Norton, 1980).

White, Florence Meiman. *Linus Pauling: Scientist and Crusader*. New York: Walker, 1980. This short biography is intended for young persons ten years of age and older, but because it was written with the cooperation of Linus and Ava Helen Pauling, it contains some interesting anecdotes and insights into the human side of its subject.

Robert J. Paradowski

1955

Chemistry
Vincent du Vigneaud, United States

Physics
Willis Eugene Lamb, Jr., United States
Polykarp Kusch, United States

Physiology or Medicine
Axel Hugo Theorell, Sweden

Literature
Halldór Laxness, Iceland

Peace
no award

VINCENT DU VIGNEAUD
1955

Born: Chicago, Illinois; May 18, 1901
Died: White Plains, New York; December 11, 1978
Nationality: American
Areas of concentration: Organic synthesis and molecular biology

Du Vigneaud investigated the role of sulfur in biologically important compounds such as the polypeptide hormones insulin, oxytocin, and vasopressin. From these investigations he discovered the importance of the methyl group and its migration from one molecule to another in living organisms. He synthesized the first polypeptide hormone, oxytocin

The Award

Presentation

Arne Fredga, a professor of organic chemistry at the University of Uppsala in Sweden and a member of the Royal Swedish Academy of Sciences, presented the academy's citation to Vincent du Vigneaud in December, 1955. Professor Fredga, who synthesized organic compounds containing sulfur and studied their optical activity, was personally familiar with the aversion chemists have to compounds of sulfur, which often have very unpleasant odors. In his address, he cited Professor du Vigneaud for ignoring this unpleasant fact as well as ignoring the traditional barriers between organic and biological chemistry. As a result, du Vigneaud made significant contributions to the understanding of how molecules behave in animals. Du Vigneaud's accomplishments centered on a study of polypeptide hormones, which are small molecules related to proteins and which have important biological functions. From a study of insulin, du Vigneaud demonstrated the important role that sulfur plays in fixing the shape or structure of molecules with biological activity. In his study of biochemicals containing sulfur, he studied cystine and cysteine, which are amino acids that contribute significantly to holding proteins and hormones together in their correct shapes. If the two sulfur atoms that form the important disulfide bridge are broken, then proteins and hormones lose their structure and no longer function biochemically.

Although hormones are produced in many organs of animals, du Vigneaud concentrated on those produced by a small, bean-sized organ in the body called the pituitary gland. These hormones are very significant in regulating biological activity in animals, and they only function when the molecules have exactly the correct composition and shape. Two studed by du Vigneaud are especially important. Oxytocin is responsible for initiating birth by causing the uterus to contract; it also stimulates milk production or lactation. Vasopressin is important in controlling blood pressure and regulating kidney function. Discovering the structure and function of these compounds was an important advance made for science and society by du Vigneaud. As final proof that he had determined the correct structure, he succeeded in synthesizing one of them, oxytocin. This was the first time that a polypeptide hormone had been synthesized.

It was not a simple task, since each of the eight amino acid molecules that make up oxytocin had to be put in the correct sequence and the correct arrangement with respect to left- and right-handedness. In his final step in his successful synthesis of oxytocin, he coupled the two sulfur atoms together, thereby causing the ring to form and to make the oxytocin molecule.

Professor du Vigneaud's study of hormones also led him to investigate the reactions that allow a small, one-carbon component called the methyl group to move from one place to another on molecules in living systems. Biochemical reactions that add or remove carbon atoms are crucial for living systems, and du Vigneaud studied these reactions. He also worked with biotin, which was also called vitamin B_7 and H, with penicillin. His achievements in all these areas led to a better understanding of the importance of chemical structure to biological function.

Nobel lecture

In his Nobel lecture, "A Trail of Sulfur Research from Insulin to Oxytocin," delivered on December 12, 1955, Professor du Vigneaud traced the research that culminated in the synthesis of the hormone oxytocin. This trail covered thirty years of research, and, like much scientific research, it is a story of one success leading in unanticipated ways to the next. Vincent du Vigneaud did not begin his life of scientific research with the goal of understanding the function of sulfur in biological compounds, but one important teacher and a sequence of research successes led logically to this end result. The trail of sulfur that ran through du Vigneaud's research became obvious in retrospect.

His scientific career began with a study of the important hormone insulin, which is produced in the pancreas gland. This hormone is responsible for regulating the sugar in blood, and a deficiency of this hormone causes diabetes. He moved from studying this relatively large hormone to studying the much smaller and simpler polypeptide hormones produced by the posterior lobe of the pituitary gland. The presence of sulfur in all these substances unifies the various parts of his research career. In much scientific research, temporary side projects can provide keys which turn out to be central to solving the main problem later; this happened in du Vigneaud's career at least twice. In order to obtain enough oxytocin to determine the structure of this compound, he needed to use a technique called countercurrent distribution to extract enough of the hormone from the pituitary glands of hundreds of thousand of hogs and cows. He learned this technique while working on the synthesis of penicillin, which was an ancillary project he undertook during World War II. The second side project that later proved essential to his synthesis of oxytocin was the use of sodium dissolved in liquid ammonia to reduce molecules. This technique provided the key final step in the synthesis of oxytocin.

With enough pure oxytocin available, he could test biological activity and begin the analysis that was necessary to determine the structure of the polypeptide. He showed that the pure, extracted material did exhibit the biological activities of inducing contractions in the uteri of rats and of inducing milk production. This important step was necessary to demonstrate that it was oxytocin acting alone that was responsible for these biological activities.

Using this material, he systematically searched for the structure of oxytocin. By deliberately breaking chemical bonds with reagents of known behavior and by preparing chemical derivatives, he was able to deduce the structure of oxytocin, discovering that it was composed of eight amino acids in a particular sequence. Once the correct sequence was known, a confirming proof consisted of actually making the compound from much simpler ones. Since the beginning reagents and final products of an organic synthesis are known, the structure is said to have been definitely proved if the natural and synthetic compounds have the same physical and chemical properties.

Professor du Vigneaud said that his research group put the eight amino acids together in the correct sequence, but to complete the synthesis of oxytocin there was a final problem. Of the eight amino acids in oxytocin, six form a ring that contains exactly twenty atoms. This ring is held closed by two sulfur atoms in a disulfide bond. By employing the reduction technique using sodium in liquid ammonia, he succeeded in closing this small ring and completing the first totally synthetic production of a polypeptide hormone. Du Vigneaud concluded his lecture by stating that the discovery of the structures of oxytocin and vasopressin would "undoubtedly open the door" for a better understanding of these hormones that would benefit the pharmacologist and clinician as well as the biochemist.

Critical reception

The presentation of the Nobel Prize in Chemistry to Vincent du Vigneaud was received positively by both the scientific community and the general public. The scientific community recognized thirty years of concerted and significant research in the structure and function of molecules, and it recognized the experimental difficulties that had been overcome in finally achieving the synthesis of oxytocin. The general public recognized this achievement as further reinforcement of the notion that science was on the verge of solving many of the most troublesome problems of biology. *The New York Times* reported on December 7, 1955, that du Vigneaud himself looked forward into the future with confidence and excitement. In this period, many biochemical compounds had been discovered, and their structures and functions remained mysterious and unknown. Du Vigneaud likened his work to that of a terrestrial explorer who had just opened up a new continent. There was much yet to be done, but he had shown the way and demonstrated that it could be done. Further, unlike the previous year's Nobel laureate, Linus Pauling, the 1955 recipient did not publicly espouse political causes.

In this period of optimism, *The New York Times* reported in the same article on December 7, 1955, that he "forecast still greater discoveries dealing with the structure of proteins." Du Vigneaud even speculated that viral proteins would have their structures and functions determined. He did anticipate that such work would take decades; in this period of optimism he may not have realized the amount of work or the extent of time that would be required. The important relationship between the chemical structure of molecules and their biological function was recognized at the time of the Nobel Prize; this relationship has remained a central theme of biochemistry, pharmacology, and medicine.

As an educational administrator as well as a researcher in biochemistry, du Vigneaud remained concerned about encouraging young people to enter careers in science. He lamented at the time of the Nobel award that the field of biochemistry was named as a branch of chemistry. For many people, chemistry implies difficulty bordering on the impossible, and he believed that this preconception might drive talented young people away from the field.

Biography

Vincent du Vigneaud was born in Chicago, Illinois, on May 18, 1901. His father was an inventor and a machine designer. Like so many other young scientists, he began his research in chemistry and biology as a child in a small laboratory in the family basement. Fortunately for mankind, Vincent succeeded in working with gunpowder without having a major accident and failed in his attempts to develop a super-large strain of rat.

Du Vigneaud entered the University of Illinois at Urbana in 1918 and studied organic chemistry. He completed a B.S. degree in that field in 1923 and stayed on at the university to work with the noted professor of organic chemistry C. S. Marvel. He completed an M.A. degree a year later, in 1924. It was during this year of further study that he was introduced to biochemistry through a class that he took. Soon after completing that degree, he married Zella Zon Ford on June 12, 1924. They eventually had a son, Vincent, and a daughter, Marilyn Renée.

He worked in organic chemistry for six months after graduation at the Jackson Laboratory of the E. I. du Pont de Nemours Company. After that, he spent a year as an assistant biochemist at the Philadelphia General Hospital; simultaneously, he was on the staff at the University of Pennsylvania Graduate School of Medicine. It was during this year that he appreciated the importance of clinical work. He now had the background in both organic chemistry and medicine that would form the essential foundation of his scientific career.

In 1925, the new School of Medicine at the University of Rochester opened. He went there in that year and began his work with insulin, which culminated in 1927 with a thesis and Ph.D. degree. He was awarded a National Research Council Fellowship to continue his studies at The Johns Hopkins University School of Medicine. In 1928, he went to the Max Planck Institute in Dresden, Germany, where he had an opportunity to study under Max Bergmann, who had been a student of one of the great founders of modern chemistry, Emil Fischer. There du Vigneaud studied amino acids and peptides, which are the biologically important building blocks of the hormones he would continue to study.

Upon leaving Germany after one year, he studied in the United Kingdom at both the University of Edinburgh and at University College in London. He returned to the United States in 1929 and accepted a position on the faculty at his alma mater, the University of Illinois. In 1932, he accepted the position of full professor and head of the Department of Biochemistry at the School of Medicine at George Washington University. In 1938 he moved to New York City, where he occupied the same position at the Cornell University Medical College. He stayed there twenty-nine years, until 1967. Upon leaving the Medical College, he moved to Ithaca, New York, where he was appointed a professor of chemistry at Cornell University. During this last part of his career, he maintained an active research program with postdoctoral fellows in the new laboratories on the sixth floor of the chemistry research building. He retired from this position in 1975.

Throughout his career he lectured widely, and he was invited to present some of the most prestigious lectures. He gave the Liversidge Lecture at the University of Cambridge in England, was a visiting lecturer in Switzerland in 1947, and gave the Messenger Lectures at Cornell University in 1950. Du Vigneaud died on December 11, 1978.

Scientific Career

A concern that consistently runs through the career of Vincent du Vigneaud is a quest to understand the relationship between the structure and the function of biologically active molecules. To be successful in this search he needed to gain experience both in organic chemistry and in biology and medicine. Organic chemistry focuses on the structure of molecules, and the biological functions are important for clinical studies: His career was a combination of these two areas.

His early studies at the University of Illinois involved organic chemistry. There he had opportunities to learn the purification, analytical, and synthetic techniques used in determining the structures of compounds that contain carbon. During his work on his first graduate degree in organic chemistry, he took a course in biochemistry from Professor H. B. Lewis. This course and its teacher influenced the subsequent direction of his research, for it stimulated his interest in biological molecules and the emerging area of biochemistry. This interest was further stimulated by the year that he spent in Philadelphia involved in clinical research. As an assistant to Dr. W. G. Karr, he published a paper in 1925 in the *Journal of Biological Chemistry* on the rate of disappearance of *d*-glucose from the blood. This work began his interest in insulin.

With his move to the newly opened Medical School at the University of Rochester, he began to narrow the field of his study to concentrate on the sulfur found in insulin and other related compounds. He discovered that sulfur formed a disulfide bridge, and in this way it held two parts of the molecule together. This disulfide bridge is essential for polypeptide hormones to maintain their shapes, or structures. When the disulfide bridge is broken, the molecule loses its biological activity. This process is called denaturation. From his studies at Rochester, he published many papers on insulin. The biological activity of insulin was the subject of a paper published in 1927 on the ability of glucose, the sugar in the blood, to inactivate insulin. Other papers followed on the clinical and medical aspects of the compounds that he studied. He published papers on such diverse biochemical activities as the growth-promoting properties of cystine, the metabolism of sulfur-containing compounds, the inactivation of purified insulin, glutathione, and the availability of tryptophan.

At The Johns Hopkins University, du Vigneaud succeeded in isolating from pure crystalline insulin that part of the molecule that contains the sulfur, and he found that it was the amino acid cystine. He showed that insulin is made up only of amino acid groups. It was also at The Johns Hopkins University that he encountered a problem: At that time there was no known way to combine cystine at its acid end with another amino acid. This problem initiated an auxiliary project on methods of synthesizing organic compounds to overcome this difficulty. While studying the chemical reactions of cystine, du Vigneaud discovered that a novel method of reduction could be used on this molecule. This was the beginning of his use of sodium metal dissolved in liquid ammonia. This reaction, more than twenty years later, would prove to be a crucial step in his successful synthesis of oxytocin.

After studying insulin at Rochester, Baltimore, Philadelphia, and Washington, D.C., he continued those studies upon becoming head of the biochemistry department at the Cornell University College of Medicine in New York City in 1938. He summarized the importance of insulin studies to biochemistry in a paper entitled "The Role Which Insulin Has Played in Our Concept of Protein Hormones and a Consideration of Certain Phases of the Chemistry of Insulin," which was published in 1938 in *Cold Spring Harbor Symposia on Quantitative Biology.*

This was also the beginning of his studies on a new vitamin, biotin, which also came to be known as vitamin B_7 or H. This was one of several ancillary challenges that he studied during his career. Biotin not only is available in the normal human diet but also is produced by the bacteria found in the intestines. His results from the studies of growth promotion in yeasts and bacteria were published in papers in 1942 entitled "Growth Stimulating Effect of Biotin for Diphtheria Bacillus in the Absence of Pimelic Acid" and "Yeast-Growth Promoting Effect of Diaminocarboxylic Acid Derived from Biotin." His paper "Structure of Biotin" was published in the *Journal of the American Chemical Society* in 1942.

This was also the period in which he encountered the phenomenon of small pieces of organic molecules that can move about from one molecule to another. These mobile methyl groups contain only one carbon atom, and they are as small a molecular grouping as can be found in organic chemistry. In spite of their small size, they are important in biochemical processes. To assist in better understanding the chemical and biochemical events that occurred, he quickly adopted techniques using the radioisotopes that became available at the end of World War II. Du Vigneaud published a paper, "The Transfer of Methyl Groups from Methionine to

Choline and Creatine," in 1940 in the *Journal of Biological Chemistry.*

While this biochemical and clinical work was proceeding at Cornell Medical Center, Professor du Vigneaud continued increasing his techniques of synthesizing organic molecules related to the ones he was isolating from natural sources. Often these were available only in amounts too small to allow a structure determination. This problem was solved with a technique he learned while engaged in the synthesis of penicillin during World War II. Penicillin, an antibiotic in great demand during the war, was obtained through the extraction of mold cultures that provided only a small amount of the antibiotic. The artificial synthesis of this antibiotic would greatly increase the amounts available. From this war-related research, du Vigneaud learned of the extraction and purification technique called countercurrent distribution. After the war, he successfully applied this technique to obtain the needed quantities of natural hormones, including oxytocin.

This synthetic work with oxytocin culminated in a series of four papers published in 1954 in the *Journal of the American Chemical Society.* He also reported on the "Synthesis of the Cystine Peptides in Oxytocin" in 1955 in a *Special Publication of the Chemical Society (London).* He published approximately one hundred scientific papers describing the results of his research before receiving the Nobel Prize. As with so many other Nobel laureates, the number of his scientific papers decreased after he received the prize. He did not, however, stop his research.

After leaving the biochemistry department at the Cornell University Medical Center in New York City in 1967, after twenty-nine years of productive research and academic leadership, du Vigneaud continued his research in the chemistry department at Cornell University in Ithaca, New York. His research team consisted of postdoctoral research fellows. He continued working on the peptide hormones and synthesized the retro versions, which are the molecules assembled with the order of the amino acids exactly reversed from the natural one. This was part of a continuing effort to study the resulting biochemical functions of these newly synthesized compounds and to relate their structure to function. Although many additional compounds have been studied and synthesized since du Vigneaud showed that it could be done with oxytocin, his demonstration that function is dependent on structure remains an abiding principle of biochemistry.

Bibliography

Primary

CHEMISTRY: "The Role Which Insulin Has Played in Our Concept of Protein Hormones and a Consideration of Certain Phases of the Chemistry of Insulin," *Cold Spring Harbor Symposia on Quantitative Biology,* vol. 6, 1938; "Identity of Vitamin H with Biotin," *Science,* vol. 92, 1940; "The Transfer of Methyl Groups from Methionine to Choline and Creatine," *Journal of Biological Chemistry,* 1940; "Structure of Biotin," *Journal of the American Chemical Society,* vol. 64, 1942; "Dimethyl and Monomethyl-aminomethanol in Transmethylation Reactions," *Journal of Biological Chemistry,* vol. 164, 1946; *A Trail of Research in Sulfur*

Chemistry and Metabolism and Related Fields, 1952; "Synthesis of the Cystine Peptides in Oxytocin," *Special Publication of the Chemical Society (London)*, no. 2, 1955; "A Trail of Sulfur Research from Insulin to Oxytocin," *Les Prix Nobel*, 1955; "The Organic Chemical Approach to the Study of the Chemical Functional Groups of Oxytocin to Its Biological Activities," *Proceedings of the Robert A. Welch Foundation, Conference on Chemical Research*, vol. 8, 1965.

Secondary

Candee, Marjorie Dent, ed. *Current Biography Yearbook, 1956*. New York: H. W. Wilson, 1956. In the biography of du Vigneaud, published the year after he won the Nobel Prize, the main events in his life and career are listed.

Farber, Eduard. *Nobel Prize Winners in Chemistry, 1901-1961*. Rev. ed. New York: Abelard-Schuman, 1963. Presents a brief biography, followed by excerpts from du Vigneaud's Nobel lecture and a note on the importance of the work.

"Lasker Awards for 1948." *American Journal of Public Health* 38 (December, 1948): 1717-1719. Du Vigneaud was one of the winners of this award from the American Public Health Association, and this article mentions his contributions, including transmethylation, vitamin, and penicillin work.

Moritz, Charles, ed. *Current Biography Yearbook, 1979*. New York: H. W. Wilson, 1979. This gives an obituary article on du Vigneaud, with a short biography.

The New York Times, December 12, 1978: 23. An obituary on du Vigneaud, discussing his career and Nobel Prize-winning work.

Smith, John J., ed. *Americana Annual, 1956*. New York: Americana Corp., 1956. This entry describes his prizewinning work and presents a biographical sketch.

Patrick G. Barber

1956

Chemistry
Sir Cyril Norman Hinshelwood, Great Britain
Nikolai Semenov, Soviet Union

Physics
William Shockley, United States
John Bardeen, United States
Walter H. Brattain, United States

Physiology or Medicine
Werner Forssmann, West Germany
Dickinson Richards, United States
André F. Cournand, United States

Literature
Juan Ramón Jiménez, Spain

Peace
no award

SIR CYRIL NORMAN HINSHELWOOD
1956

Born: London, England; June 19, 1897
Died: London, England; October 9, 1967
Nationality: British
Area of concentration: Chemical kinetics

Hinshelwood investigated the mechanisms of chain reactions involving free radicals and the inhibiting effects of drugs on the growth of bacterial cells. His work involved branching chain reactions and the activation energy needed to initiate unimolecular (one-molecule) reactions

The Award

Presentation

Arne Ölander, a member of the Nobel Committee for Chemistry of the Royal Swedish Academy of Sciences, presented Cyril Norman Hinshelwood and Nikolai Semenov as corecipients for the 1956 Nobel Prize in Chemistry. In his address, he reviewed some early contributions to the theory of chemical reaction kinetics. In the 1880's, Svante Arrhenius of Sweden and Jacobus Henricus van't Hoff of The Netherlands proposed that for reaction to occur between two molecules, they must collide violently enough to weaken or break some of the bonds in the molecule, so that the atoms can rearrange to form new molecules. In 1913, the German chemist, Max Bodenstein, proposed the idea of a chain reaction. This means that, when two molecules collide violently, or when a single molecule absorbs light energy of the proper frequency and wavelength, highly reactive, unstable molecules may be formed as well as stable final products. Known as "free radicals," these can then react readily with the parent molecules to produce further reactive species. Thus, a single free radical can cause a great number of molecules to react in chain fashion. The Dutch physicist Hendrik Anthony Kramers and the Danish chemist Jens Anton Christiansen further proposed that if more than one free radical were produced in a reaction, a branching chain could be initiated, leading to an explosion. In careful studies of the pressure and temperature dependence of the reactions between phosphorus and oxygen, and between hydrogen and oxygen, Hinshelwood and Semenov showed that low and high pressure regions existed in which reaction did not occur at all. In intermediate regions, both reactions take place explosively. They interpreted these reactions successfully in terms of the branching chain mechanism proposed by Christiansen and Kramers earlier. They went on to show that chain mechanisms can be used to interpret a wide variety of chemical reactions, including the combustion of hydrocarbons. Hinshelwood also found that some reactions proceed by both a chain and a nonchain mechanism.

Nobel lecture

On December 11, 1956, Hinshelwood delivered his Nobel lecture, which was entitled "Chemical Kinetics in the Past Few Decades." He chose to adopt a very personal tone in recalling the "lines of thought and . . . the accidents" that influenced the development of his own career in chemistry. He mentioned how, as a young chemist, he was fascinated by the mysteries of chemical change.

His interests were directed toward two ends: first, the discovery of new homogeneous reactions, particularly those of single molecules (known to chemists as unimolecular reactions), and second, the study of factors that make surface catalysis a preferred mechanism. Most unimolecular reactions turned out to be complex. Their study, however, revealed that molecular collisions play an important role in communicating energy to molecules, and that the activation energy is dominant in determining the reactivity of a molecule. The activation energy is that minimum amount of energy which the molecule requires before it can react. To the collisional theory, Hinshelwood added the assumption that the rotational and vibrational motions within the molecule can contribute to the energy required for reaction to occur.

In the mid-1920's, the chain theory of propagation was proposed to account for the hydrogen-oxygen thermal reaction, the oxidation of hydrocarbons, and a departure from the Einstein rule in the photochemical reaction between hydrogen and chlorine. These reactions showed dependence on three factors: the size of the reaction vessel, the presence of inert gases, and the presence of sensitizers and inhibitors.

Bodenstein showed that reaction occurs at the surface under certain conditions. Semenov and Hinshelwood explained the upper and lower explosion limits for the phosphorus-oxygen and the hydrogen-oxygen reactions in terms of a chain-branching mechanism. Chain-branching was controlled below the lower limit by destruction of the chain carriers at the surface of the reaction vessel. At the upper explosion limit, chain-branching is suppressed by three-body collisions. (At low pressures, three-body collisions are infrequent, and at high pressures, destruction at the surface is unimportant.)

In the early 1930's, after the suggestion was made that free radical chain mechanisms might play a role in the thermal decomposition of hydrocarbons, Francis Owen Rice and Karl Herzfeld proposed theoretical reaction schemes for hydrocarbon decomposition reactions based on free radical mechanisms. Supporting evidence soon came from the use of small concentrations of nitric oxide, a molecule with one unpaired electron. It is capable of combining easily with free radical species, thus interrupting the chain process. Through the use of nitric oxide and other inhibitors, it became clear that nearly all thermal decompositions occur by free radical mechanisms.

Most of the substances that exhibited first order kinetic behavior (the type of behavior on which unimolecular reaction rate theory was originally based) were shown to decompose by chain mechanisms rather than by simple unimolecular processes. The thermal decomposition of butane, however, seemed to be an exception. It was not completely suppressed even by the addition of high concentrations of inhibitors. This behavior was interpreted in terms of parallel, nonradical, unimolecular process for three main reasons: Several different inhibitors gave the same limiting value; added inert gases accelerated the reaction by the same amount as they did in the uninhibited reaction; and the kinetics of the "residual" reaction showed peculiarities common to other unimolecular reactions. Semenov and his colleagues held that the residual reaction could be explained in terms of "free-radical like" surface valences, which act in a way similar to that of free radicals in the gas phase.

There were theoretical problems to be dealt with in the interpretation of the basic rate equation. At high pressures and temperatures, a steady state concentration of activated molecules exists—molecules, that is, with sufficient energy to undergo reaction unimolecularly. The critical step is the accumulation in one special bond of enough energy to rupture it. In this case, the frequency factor should be of the order of magnitude of a single molecular vibration. Yet there are examples in which it is orders of magnitude larger. This suggests that energy can be mobilized from the internal vibrations and rotations of the molecule. Thus, there may be many different energy states of the molecule from which final transformation may take place.

Organic chemists became interested in relating structural changes within the molecule to the values of the frequency factor and the activation energy. They also sought to relate changes in the values of these rate factors to electron displacements within the molecule. The quantum mechanical theory of valency has been particularly fruitful in interpreting this kind of behavior.

Finally, one might ask why the multiplicity of reactions in the living cell is an essential condition for the phenomenon of life to be possible at all. The individual chemical reactions seem to function within the living cell to create life in much the same way as the variety of instruments in an orchestra do to create the symphony. Thus, the study of chemical kinetics seems to be profoundly significant in understanding the processes of life itself. The limits of its applicability seem to be completely unforeseeable.

Critical reception

Considering Hinshelwood's extensive contributions to the development of experimental and theoretical chemical kinetics, the notices of his selection for the Nobel Prize in Chemistry in most of the news media were rather perfunctory. *Chemical and Engineering News* reported it laconically, as did *Time*, *Newsweek*, and *U.S. News & World Report*, giving little more than the names and notice of why the award was given jointly to him and Semenov. Even the November 2, 1956, issue of *The New York Times* contented itself with some rather pedestrian comments: "They were cited as having contributed about equally in showing a quarter of a century ago that molecules, like people, may congregate peaceably or explode in violent chain reactions depending on their environment and provocation." The article went on to add that "behind the official language was a long series of experiments that paved the way for more efficient automobile engines and the modern plastics industry." A rather suggestive remark followed, stating that "whether their work with molecules pointed the way to controlled atomic chain reactions is a widely debated point."

The Times of London, was, if anything, even more succinct. It merely commented in its November 2, 1956, issue that "the prize was awarded for their researches into the mechanism of chemical reactions." It was probably the rather esoteric character of their contributions as far as the ordinary reader was concerned that was responsible for the brief notices that they received in the public press. At this time, too, the press was filled with news of the Hungarian Revolution and of concern about nuclear testing. Further, the work for which Hinshelwood and Semenov received the Nobel Prize had been largely accomplished in the late 1920's and early 1930's, which by 1956 was considered by many to be "ancient history." It supported some of Hinshelwood's own observations about the greater importance attributed by the records of history to political events than to the contributions of men of science and letters. Speaking of the founders and early members of the Royal Society, on the occasion of its tercentenary on July 19, 1960, he had this to say about them: "Their labours were largely unknown to their contemporaries, they are but perfunctorily recorded by historians, and yet they have ended by transforming the face of the globe and the life of humanity."

Biography

Sir Cyril Norman Hinshelwood was born in London on June 19, 1897, the only son of Norman Macmillan Hinshelwood and Ethel Francis (née Smith). After his father died in Canada in 1904, his mother brought him to London, where she took a flat in Chelsea. He was educated at the Westminster City School and won a Brackenbury scholarship at Balliol College, University of Oxford, in 1916. Instead of entering the college at once, he went to work as a chemist at the Explosives Supply Factory at Queensferry. In January, 1919, he went to Balliol College, and he held a research fellowship there in 1920. The following year he became a tutorial fellow of Trinity College, where he did research and taught until 1937. In that year, he was elected Dr. Lee's Professor of Chemistry, following the retirement of Frederick Soddy. From 1938 on, he became more and more interested in the application of chemical principles to the study of the adaptability of bacteria to changes in their environment.

In 1949, he was knighted by George VI, King of Great Britain. His interest in the Latin and Greek classics was lifelong, and was reflected in the fact that he served as president of the Classical Association in 1958-1959 at the same time that he was serving as president of the Royal Society. Hinshelwood's aesthetic interests dated back to his childhood. He loved beauty in all its forms, literature, music, and the arts. He was a collector of Chinese porcelains and Eastern carpets. He knew eight languages, including Latin, Greek, Russian, and Chinese, and was fluent in French, German, Italian, and Spanish. In 1968, the year after his death, an exhibit of one hundred of his paintings was sponsored by Goldsmiths' Company, to whose court he had been elected in 1960, and to which he left a sizable legacy because of his admiration for what they did to relieve human suffering. One of his finest occasional papers was his centenary essay on Dante's imagery in the *Divina Commedia* (1308-1321; *The Divine Comedy*). He enjoyed classical music, especially the music of Beethoven and Mozart. He retired in 1964 to the Chelsea flat that his mother had acquired in 1904. He also continued to act as a consultant to many industrial organizations, and he served on the committees of many cultural and scientific organizations. He died peacefully on October 9, 1967.

Scientific Career

Cyril Hinshelwood's first exposure to the mysteries of chemical change came during World War I. In 1916, he received a Brackenbury scholarship to Oxford. Instead of accepting it immediately, however, he went as a chemist to the Explosives Supply Factory at Queensferry. There he found opportunities to develop his innate gift for research and was promoted to assistant chief laboratory chemist. He became fascinated with the dependence of chemical changes on the energy and environment of molecules.

In January, 1919, he began his scholarship at Balliol College, and he completed the shortened war degree course with such distinction in 1920 that he was elected to a research fellowship at Balliol. The following year, he became a tutorial fellow of Trinity College. During his undergraduate years, he published three papers on solid state chemistry, written during the time he spent at Queensferry. He taught and engaged in research at Trinity College until 1937, when he was appointed Dr. Lee's Professor of Chemistry at Oxford to succeed Frederick Soddy (winner of the 1921 Nobel Prize in Chemistry).

By the early 1920's, his interests shifted to the elucidation of the kinetics of gas phase reactions by means of molecular kinetic theory, to which attention had been directed by Lord Rayleigh and Irving Langmuir just prior to the war. Walther Nernst prophesied in 1921 that he and his colleagues in Berlin would "settle this whole business of gas reactions within a year." By 1926, with publication of *The Kinetics of Chemical Change in Gaseous Systems*, Hinshelwood accomplished the first stage in the development of a scientific theory of gas phase reaction kinetics. This first stage consisted of "gross over-simplification, reflecting partly the need for practical working rules, and even more a too enthusiastic aspiration after elegance of form," as he later expressed it in his presidential address to the Royal Society in 1957. The third edition of his work, published in 1933, came close to realizing the second stage of the theory, "when the symmetry of the hypothetical systems is distorted and the neatness marred as recalcitrant facts increasingly rebel against uniformity." These drily witty descriptions characterize the elegance with which Hinshelwood commanded the English language, an elegance rarely found in the scientific literature. A third stage of the theory, he concluded, is still in the making, the stage in which "a new order emerges, more intricately contrived, less obvious, and with its parts more subtly interwoven, since it is of nature's and not of man's contriving."

This book remains a classic in the literature of chemical kinetics. It was a model of clarity and covered the field of chemical kinetics with a fresh insight. In the process of preparing for it, he mastered calculus and intensively studied Sir James Jeans' classic work, *The Dynamical Theory of Gases* (1904). At this time, kinetic theory was able to give a reasonable interpretation of the reaction between two or three molecules, that is, bimolecular and termolecular reactions. The energy needed for such reactions to occur (the activation energy) could be acquired by collision between molecules with kinetic energies sufficiently in excess of the average kinetic energy of the molecules of the system. A very small fraction of the total number of collisions in unit time are energetic enough to cause reaction.

The problem of unimolecular reactions drew the attention of kineticists at this time. These reactions are characterized by the fact that the rate of the reaction is independent of pressure—that is, of the concentration of reactant molecules present in the system. Thus, they seemed to be independent of collisions either with other molecules or with the surface of the reaction vessel.

Two rival theories bid for attention. Frederick Alexander Lindemann, later Viscount Cherwell, suggested that the molecules were dependent on gaining energy by collisions. Once the molecules gained enough energy to react, however, time was then needed before this energy was distributed within the molecule in such a way as to produce the excited state from which reaction could occur. He therefore predicted that the rate would be pressure-dependent at sufficiently low pressures, where collisions were too infrequent to maintain an equilibrium concentration of excited molecules. Another theory proposed that the rate of unimolecular reactions depended upon the steady absorption of radiant energy from outside the system.

Between the publication of his first papers on solid state chemistry and the second edition of his book, Hinshelwood and his pupils explored a wide range of gas phase reactions, both in the presence and absence of surface catalysts, in which various aspects of this theory were tested. Included among this work were studies of the kinetics of decomposition of nitrous oxide, phosphine, chlorine monoxide, ammonia, hydrogen iodide, acetone, and a number of aldehydes, ethers, and ketones, as a function of temperature, pressure, added gases, surface to volume ratio, and the presence of catalysts. Working over a wide range of reactions, he was able to focus on the significant features of each reaction system. He consistently used simple, if occasionally hazardous, experimental techniques. On one occasion he evaporated chlorine monoxide, an explosive substance, by warming up the container in his hand—an action dangerous in the extreme. Yet neither he nor any of his colleagues ever experienced a serious laboratory accident.

Of particular significance were kinetic studies of the hydrogen-oxygen reaction, an apparently simple chemical process. It was in the study of this reaction that his work came in touch with that of Nikolai Semenov, with whom he shared the Nobel Prize in Chemistry in 1956. Walther Nernst first proposed a chain mechanism to account for the high quantum yield of the hydrogen-chlorine photochemical reaction. The chain mechanism assumed that a single active molecular species, known as a free radical, could go on to cause reactions in many stable molecules, reactions sometimes numbering in the millions and tens of millions. These highly reactive free radicals required relatively little activation energy in order to react when compared to that required by stable molecules. The hydrogen-oxygen reaction could only be explained in terms of such a chain mechanism.

This system, however, as well as the phosophorus-oxygen system that had been studied earlier by Semenov and his colleagues, had some unique features that the simple chain mechanism of Nernst could not completely explain. They both exhibited pressure and temperature regions where controlled reaction occurred, as well as other regions in between where the reaction took place explosively. Hinshelwood and Semenov were able to account for these phenomena successfully by assuming a "branching chain" mechanism. That is, more than one free radical species is formed in the course of a single reaction step, creating a rapid increase of free radicals and leading to an explosive situation. At low pressures, these radicals diffuse rapidly to the surface, where they are destroyed. At high pressures, they are removed by three-body deactivating collision processes, which also break the chain.

In 1936, after he had assumed the Dr. Lee's Professorship at Oxford, Hinshelwood became interested in the study of the chemical kinetics of living cells. Every cell depends upon a complex of interlocking chemical reactions, each with its own specific enzyme catalyst. He chose to consider the problem of how certain bacteria adapt to changes in nutrients, and to the presence in their environment of substances initially poisonous to them. He reasoned that in addition to the process of natural selection and the occurrence of mutant strains, organisms can adapt by subtle changes in this complex interlocking system of chemical reactions, and that these changes can even be reversible. The first ten years of work in this area were collected in a book of great originality, *The Chemical Kinetics of the Bacterial Cell* (1947). This was followed in 1966, the year before his death, by his last work, coauthored with A. C. R. Dean, *Growth, Function, and Regulation in Bacterial Cells* (1966). It was a brilliant summary of the progress made in his quest to understand "how the main characteristics of life, in its physical manifestations," as exhibited by unicellular organisms, "emerge from the interplay of the laws of nature."

He was active until the day of his death in service to the scholarly community, as well as to cultural and civic interests. He served as a member of several advisory councils on scientific matters to the British government. He was elected Fellow of the Royal Society in 1929 and served as its president from 1955 to 1960, delivering the society's tercentenary address in 1960. In 1956, he shared the Nobel Prize in Chemistry with his lifelong friend, Nikolai Semenov, for their "research into the mechanics of chemical reactions," particularly their work on branching chain reactions. He also served as president of the Chemical Society (1946-1948) and as president of the Faraday Society (1961-1962). Among his many awards were the Lavoisier Medal of the Société Chimique de France; the Davy, Royal, Copley, and Leverhulme medals of the Royal Society; the Faraday and Longstaff medals of the Chemical Society; and the Guldberg Medal of Oslo University (1952). He received numerous honorary degrees from universities both in the United Kingdom and abroad and held honorary memberships in the major scientific societies of the world. He was knighted in 1948 and appointed to the Order of Merit in 1960.

After his retirement in 1964, he remained active as a consultant to industrial organizations, as a valued member of the Arts Council, chairman of the council of Queen Elizabeth College, London, chairman of the scientific advisory committee of the National Gallery, and chairman of the education committee of the Goldsmiths' Company. He died at home on October 9, 1967, still at the peak of his powers.

Bibliography

Primary

CHEMISTRY: "Homogeneous Reactions," *Chemical Reviews*, vol. 3, 1926; *Thermodynamics for Students of Chemistry*, 1926; *The Kinetics of Chemical Change in Gaseous Systems*, 1926; *The Reaction Between Hydrogen and Oxygen*, 1934 (with A. T. Williamson); *The Chemical Kinetics of the Bacterial Cell*, 1946; "The More Recent Work on the Reaction Between Hydrogen and Oxygen," *Proceedings of the Royal Society*, vol. A188, 1946; *The Structure of Physical Chemistry*, 1951; *Growth, Function, and Regulation in Bacterial Cells*, 1966 (with A. C. R. Dean).

Secondary

Bowen, Edmund John. "Sir Cyril Hinshelwood, 1897-1967." *Chemistry in Britain* 3 (1967): 534-536. This is an appreciation and evaluation of the life and work of Hinshelwood which appeared at his death. As an Oxford colleague, Bowen writes from firsthand knowledge of Hinshelwood. It is an excellent account of the development of his professional interests, with many personal details. A photograph of Hinshelwood heads the article. Contains no bibliography or index; the main references are to Hinshelwood's books.

Farber, Eduard. *Nobel Prize Winners in Chemistry, 1901-1961*. Rev. ed. New York: Abelard-Schuman, 1963. This book presents a brief biographical sketch, a description of Hinshelwood's work, and a note on the significance of the work. The description of the work consists of excerpts from Hinshelwood's Nobel lecture.

Hartley, Harold. "Sir Cyril Norman Hinshelwood." In *The Dictionary of National Biography, 1961-1970*, edited by E. T. Williams and C. S. Nicholls. New York: Oxford University Press, 1981. Hartley was Hinshelwood's research director at Oxford in the early 1920's, and he writes from a close personal relationship with Hinshelwood. He stresses his wide-ranging aesthetic interests in languages, music, and painting. The only two references are to Bowen's article and to an article in *The Times* of London at the time of Hinshelwood's death.

Hinshelwood, Cyril N. "Tercentenary Address of the President." *Proceedings of the Royal Society* A257 (1960): 421-430. Hinshelwood's abiding interest in the history of science is clearly revealed in this tercentenary address, delivered as the outgoing president of the Royal Society. He describes the variety of character and interests of the founding members of the Royal Society, then assesses the initial reception given to the newly founded society—a mixture of high praise and contemptuous scorn. He shows that this reception is essentially no different from that accorded science in the modern world.

Thompson, Harold W. "Cyril Norman Hinshelwood." *Biographical Memoirs of the Fellows of the Royal Society* 19 (1974): 374-431. This presents by far the most comprehensive biographical account of Hinshelwood's life and work. Thompson was closely associated with Hinshelwood in some of his most important work on unimolecular reactions. It is an excellent appreciation of Hinshelwood's thought on a wide variety of topics, including philosophy and the relations between science and the humanities. Includes a complete bibliography of Hinshelwood's writings, which number more than 425.

Ernest G. Spittler

1956

Chemistry
Sir Cyril Norman Hinshelwood, Great Britain
Nikolai Semenov, Soviet Union

Physics
William Shockley, United States
John Bardeen, United States
Walter H. Brattain, United States

Physiology or Medicine
Werner Forssmann, West Germany
Dickinson Richards, United States
André F. Cournand, United States

Literature
Juan Ramón Jiménez, Spain

Peace
no award

NIKOLAI SEMENOV
1956

Born: Saratov, Russia; April 15, 1896
Died: Moscow, Soviet Union; September 5, 1986
Nationality: Soviet
Area of concentration: Chemical kinetics

Semenov was instrumental in developing a chain reaction theory to explain the combustion of certain gases. Understanding the mechanism of such reactions has been important in the development of efficient internal combustion engines and of plastic polymers, and it laid the groundwork for understanding chain processes in nuclear reactions

The Award

Presentation

Nikolai Semenov, together with Sir Cyril Norman Hinshelwood of the United Kingdom, received the 1956 Nobel Prize in Chemistry from King Gustav Adolf of Sweden. The presentation address was delivered by Professor Arne Ölander, member of the Nobel Committee for Chemistry of the Royal Swedish Academy of Sciences.

In his award speech, Ölander noted that the first Nobel Prize in Chemistry was awarded to Jacobus Henricus van't Hoff of the Netherlands for researches into the laws of chemical dynamics. The discoveries of Semenov and Hinshelwood built upon the foundation laid by van't Hoff and Svante Arrhenius, who, at the beginning of the twentieth century, demonstrated that chemical reactions take place when molecules of two substances collide with sufficient force—that is, that chemical reaction rates are dependent on the kinetic energy of molecules. In 1900, Max Planck showed that a quantum of light could interact with a molecule, causing a chemical reaction. In 1913, Max Bodenstein, a German chemist, postulated a theory of chain reactions whereby a single chemical reaction (in this case a light-initiated reaction) gives rise not only to the stable end products of the reaction but also to an unstable product capable of initiating a chemical reaction at a lower collision velocity. Christiansen and Kramers elaborated this to include nonphotochemical reactions and suggested the possibility of branched chain reactions.

Semenov and his Russian colleagues, investigating the combustion of phosphorus vapor and oxygen at different relative concentrations and in different sizes of vessels, discovered that the results were inexplicable according to classical combustion theory but agreed with the assumption that a branched chain mechanism was involved. Then Semenov in the Soviet Union and Hinshelwood in England turned their attention to the more complicated reaction involved in the combustion of hydrogen with oxygen and ultimately to complex organic reactions. The speech concluded with an example of the industrial importance of chain-reaction combustion theory: the manipulation of octane rating in order to avoid explosion in high-pressure internal combustion engines.

Nobel lecture

Semenov delivered his Nobel lecture, entitled "Some Problems Relating to Chain Reactions and to the Theory of Combustion," on December 11, 1956. He began with a historical introduction and a description of some of his own early experimental work on combustion theory, leading up to the critical experiments on phosphorus ignition and chemical chain reactions. He then outlined some examples of chain reactions, illustrating the effects of molecular structure and vessel surface phenomena, and concluded with descriptions of ongoing research in his laboratory, particularly in the field of petroleum chemistry.

Combustion and explosion are chemical reactions accompanied by the liberation of heat and various kinds of motion in gases. In the latter years of the nineteenth century, van't Hoff and Arrhenius formulated a physical theory to explain these processes. In a simple chemical reaction, two molecules interact to produce two or more molecules of different chemical structure. In order for this to occur, chemical bonds between atoms in the original molecule must be broken, and new chemical bonds must form to produce the resulting molecules. One source of the energy needed to break these bonds is the kinetic energy of the molecules themselves, which in turn is a function of the temperature of the reacting substances. For combustion to occur, the heat liberated by bond formation in the end products of the reaction must be greater than the heat required to initiate the reaction. As the reacting mixture heats up, collisions of sufficient energy to break bonds become more frequent; the reaction is thus self-propagating until some limiting factor (such as heat absorption by the walls of the container or a declining concentration of reactants) stops it.

Combustion theory has been of great practical importance to industry since its inception because it is essential to considerations of efficiency and safety in any process involving either combustion or combustible substances. Semenov and his coworkers, beginning in the early 1920's and continuing parallel to their work on branched chain reactions in the late 1920's and 1930's, investigated several problems relating to the simple kinetic model of combustion. One ingenious demonstration of the importance of turbulence on flame propagation involved showing that the rate of flame propagation in a carbon monoxide/air mixture in a tube increased a thousandfold when a spiral wire was introduced on the inner surface of the tube. They also investigated the phenomenon of detonation—the ignition of a gas mixture caused by the increased heat created when the gas is compressed.

By the early 1920's, chemists had noted a number of combustion phenomena that did not seem to fit Arrhenius' model. In the Soviet Union, Chariton and Valta investigated the combustion of phosphorus vapor and oxygen. This reaction was anomalous in that an explosive reaction occurred at intermediate concentrations of oxygen but had both a definite upper and lower limit for oxygen concentration;

moreover, mixtures at the threshold value might remain stable indefinitely, but they were exquisitely sensitive to perturbation. Bodenstein, the foremost authority on chemical kinetics of the day, dismissed the findings as impossible and suggested that experimental error had occurred, but Semenov went on to show that the results did agree with a branched chain reaction model.

Chemical chain reaction theory depends on the role of "free radicals" in chemical reactions. A free radical is an atom or a polyatomic fragment of a molecule that has an unpaired electron in its outer electron shell. It has no net electrical charge, but because atoms combine into molecules in such a way as to form complete outer electron shells, free radicals are more highly reactive than stable molecules—that is, a less energetic collision is required to cause a chemical reaction between a free radical and a molecule than to cause a chemical reaction between two molecules. A reaction between a free radical with an odd number of electrons and a molecule with an even number of electrons must have at least one free radical as one of its end products. An unbranched chain reaction occurs if each subsequent reaction produces only one free radical. Such a mechanism had already been postulated in the case of certain photochemical reactions. In the case of phosphorus vapor (and, as it turns out, many other combustion processes) every free radical/molecule interaction produces three free radicals, resulting in a rapidly escalating explosive chain reaction. Chain termination occurs when radicals recombine, join a molecule to form an inactive particle, or are adsorbed on the vessel wall. The ability of surfaces to alter markedly the rate of chain reaction processes is of considerable industrial importance. Surfaces that promote the formation of free radicals, thereby initiating chains, catalyze reactions; surfaces (or impurities) which adsorb free radicals can be used to decrease the speed of the reaction. Cyril Hinshelwood was instrumental in developing the theory of upper limits and chain termination in the case of the reaction of hydrogen and oxygen to form water vapor.

Chain reactions with degenerate branching constitute an important subclass of chain reaction. In this case the initial reaction is a straight chain reaction, but one of the molecules formed contains a bond with low dissociation energy (a peroxide bond, for example), so that the molecular intermediate tends to break down into free radicals. Many hydrocarbon oxidation processes involve degenerate branching.

As Hinshelwood demonstrated, chain reactions and simple kinetic reactions obeying Arrhenius' law are not mutually exclusive processes. Because a chain initiation reaction requires a higher initial energy than a simple collision reaction between two molecules, both processes may occur in the same reaction mixture, and simple reactions may predominate under some circumstances.

Semenov concluded his lecture as he had begun it, by emphasizing the international nature of chemical research. He said that the chain theory would have to be applied more extensively to studies of hydrocarbon cracking and direct oxidation processes. In order to achieve further successes, he said, "the mutual endeavors of learned men in every country" would be needed to explain chemical and biological processes "to the benefit of peaceful development and the well-being of mankind."

Critical reception

The 1956 Nobel Prizes in all fields, and especially in the sciences, generated relatively little interest in the press. This was partly a result of the fact that the individuals and accomplishments being honored were not particularly controversial or prominent in the public eye at the time. More important, November, 1956, was a time of twin acute international crises: the Anglo-Egyptian conflict over the Suez Canal and the Russian invasion of Hungary. The ruthless suppression of the Hungarian uprising by the Soviet Union cast a shadow on East-West relations which extended beyond the political sphere and dampened any enthusiasm Western scientists might have shown for the first Soviet scientist to be awarded a Nobel Prize. Although Semenov was able to travel to Stockholm to receive his award and was courteously received by the Nobel Committee, the cancellation of the customary ceremonial banquet because of the Hungarian crisis must have made him aware of the tension and anti-Soviet sentiment that existed.

Coverage in *The Times* of London (November 2 and December 11, 1956) understandably emphasized the role of Hinshelwood and mentioned only that Semenov was the first Soviet recipient of the prize. A somewhat longer article in the November 2 issue of *The New York Times* described the discoveries of the two men and their importance and stressed that both Hinshelwood and Semenov were instrumental in developing the theory. In an article entitled "Prizes for Teams," *Time* magazine commented on the joint nature of the effort and noted that, although their laboratories were 1,300 miles apart, the two men were friends and correspondents and collaborated on the work.

In the Soviet Union, Semenov occupied a unique position as the first Soviet Nobel laureate and the only Russian citizen to have received a Nobel Prize in Chemistry. In a country that values scientists and scientific research particularly highly, such a position confers exceptionally high social status and brings substantial monetary rewards as well. The Nobel laureate in the Soviet Union is more of a celebrity than his or her counterpart in the West; most educated Russians are familiar with the names of their laureates in the sciences, while Americans are familiar only with those individuals who have become controversial, usually in a context other than their prizewinning discovery. Soviet Nobel laureates are also insulated from the blatant invasion of privacy that can make celebrity status a trial in the West.

Biography

Nikolai Semenov was born in Saratov, in central Russia, on April 15, 1896 (April 3 according to the Old Style Russian calendar), the son of Nikolai Alexandrovich Semenov and Elena Dimitrievna Semenova. After attending secondary school, he enrolled in the physics faculty of Petrograd University, where he became closely associated with A. F. Ioffe. During his university career he first became interested in the problem of ionization of gases, a field which continued to interest him into the 1920's. He was graduated in 1917, the year of the Russian Revolution, and during the troubled period of the Civil War taught as a lecturer at the University of Tomsk in western Siberia.

In 1920, he was appointed lecturer at the Petrograd (later Leningrad) Polytechnical Institute and director of the electron phenomenon laboratory of the Petrograd Physical-Technical Institute, serving also as deputy to its director, A. F. Ioffe. In his capacity as deputy director he engaged in an ambitious program of recruiting promising undergraduates from the Petrograd Polytechnical Institute, a policy that was controversial in 1921, when it was instituted, but subsequently became standard practice. Semenov married Natalia Nikolaevna Burtseva in 1924; they would have one son, Yurii, and one daughter, Ludmila. He was appointed professor at the Polytechnical Institute in 1928. In 1929, he was elected a corresponding member of the U.S.S.R. Academy of Sciences; he became an Academician in 1932. The title of Academician has no exact equivalent in the United States. Membership in this small, elite group of senior scientists confers a substantial automatic salary increase, preferential access to funding and publication, and other perquisites, such as the opportunity to travel abroad. Election to the academy is usually a sign of exceptional scientific achievement (this was certainly the case with Semenov), although political considerations can also play a part.

Semenov became associated with the Institute of Chemical Physics of the U.S.S.R. Academy of Sciences in 1931 and became its director in 1939. The institute moved from Leningrad (then being besieged by the Germans) to Moscow in 1943. As director of the Institute, he organized separate sections for the study of the combustion of condensed substances (under the direction of Yuri Khariton), for the study of polymer reactions, and for the study of chemical and biological processes.

Semenov's accomplishments were widely honored both in the Soviet Union and abroad, even before his receipt of the Nobel Prize in 1956. He received the Stalin Prize (the highest recognition for achievement within the Soviet Union, since renamed the Lenin Prize), was seven times awarded the Order of Lenin, and received the Lomonosov Gold Medal. He served as vice president and chairman of the section of chemico-technological and biological sciences of the Presidium of the U.S.S.R. Academy of Sciences. He was also a foreign member of the Royal Society of London and of the American, Indian, German, and Hungarian Academies of Sciences. He held honorary doctorates from the universities of Oxford and Brussels and was chairman of the Soviet Union's All-Union Society for the Propagation of Political and Scientific Knowledge. The testimonial biography published on his seventieth birthday in *Soviet Physics Uspekhi* noted that he was known for his energetic organizational and administrative work and that he devoted much time to the education of young scientists.

Semenov's active career as a research scientist spanned a period of some fifty years, from 1916 (when, as an undergraduate, he published his first paper) to the middle 1960's. He continued to fill administrative roles and act in an advisory capacity to colleagues at the Institute of Chemical Physics for most of the remainder of his life. He died in 1986, at the age of ninety.

Scientific Career

Nikolai Semenov was educated as a physicist, and during the course of his long and fruitful career he investigated a broad spectrum of problems on the borderline between physics and chemistry. He is considered one of the founders of the discipline of chemical physics. Although most noted for his theory of chain reactions and for his work with the chemistry of combustion, he also participated in a number of other noteworthy efforts in the early part of his career; later he served as an adviser to numerous projects, not only in his own field (and laboratory) but also in the application of principles derived from chemical kinetics to biological processes and nuclear physics. The scope of his advisory work is difficult to judge from his publication record, because, as V. N. Kondrat'ev pointed out in his testimonial biography, Semenov (unlike many prominent scientists on both sides of the Iron Curtain) did not claim coauthorship with students or junior colleagues unless he had made a major contribution to the research.

The years between 1920 and 1931, when Semenov was associated with the Petrograd Polytechnical Institute and Petrograd Physical-Technical Institute, were exceptionally productive ones both for the institute and for science in the Soviet Union as a whole. The new Soviet state allotted a disproporationate share of its scanty resources to research and development. Kondrat'ev states that "Semenov made Soviet science famous throughout the world," but Semenov and his institute were not the only laboratory to capture world attention during the decade.

The work for which Semenov won the Nobel Prize in 1956 began in 1924 with experiments by two colleagues, Yuri Khariton and Z. Val'ta, on the oxidation of phosphorus vapor. According to then-prevailing theory, based on Arrhenius' law, this chemical reaction was a single-step process involving a collision between a phosphorus molecule and an oxygen molecule that created sufficient kinetic force to dissolve the molecular bonds and allow the atoms to recombine. Since the reaction is exothermic (heat-producing), and since heat translates into increased kinetic energy of molecules, the reaction is self-propagating and rapidly escalating: It is explosive. As many chemists had observed, however, and as Khariton and Val'ta conclusively demonstrated, the reaction had a number of inexplicable features. A lower concentration limit for reactants—below which combustion will not occur—occurs in this and other reactions and can be predicted from Arrhenius' law, but the combustion of phosphorus also has an upper limit for oxygen concentration. The reaction was also too rapid to be explained by a simple kinetic model, and it was too sensitive to seemingly trivial changes in experimental conditions.

The foremost authority on chemical kinetics at the time, Max Bodenstein, continued to maintain that unspecified perturbation effects must be taking place, but Semenov deduced that a fundamentally different process was involved. In 1928 he published his landmark paper "Towards a Theory of Combustion Processes, Part 1," which outlined the principle of chemical chain reactions. In it he postulated that the initial reaction between phosphorus and oxygen produced, instead of a stable molecule, three free radicals with unpaired outer-shell electrons, which in turn reacted with other molecules to form other free radicals. The rate of reaction thus increases exponentially, which explained one of the anomalies observed—a reaction rate too fast to be governed by Arrhenius' law alone. At high oxygen concentrations, oxygen acts as a chain terminator, explaining the upper limit of concentration above which combustion would not take place. The sensitivity of the reaction to small perturbations could be explained in terms of the relatively high energy needed to initiate a chain. If conditions are such that no free radicals are produced, the mixture remains stable, but it does not take many radicals to initiate an explosion.

The general concept of a chain reaction is now familiar to many educated people in the context of nuclear physics, but the efforts of Semenov and Hinshelwood in the mid-1920's represented the first systematic demonstration of physical processes involving branched chain reactions. Although the chemical model of chain reactions did not directly give rise to research on nuclear chain reactions, as has sometimes been suggested, there are many parallels between the two. Each discipline has influenced the other. Semenov summarized this work and that of others in the Soviet Union and abroad in the classic 1934 textbook *Chemical Kinetics and Chain Reactions*, which has been reprinted many times and translated into many languages. This and *Some Problems in Chemical Kinetics and Reactivity* (1954) are his best-known works.

Semenov and Hinshelwood began their investigations independently, working on different aspects of the same principle. Each, however, was constantly aware of the other's work; they corresponded extensively in a spirit of friendly collaboration. This was possible in the 1920's, when the Soviet government acknowledged the need of its scientists for input from abroad and was less insistent on secrecy than it later became.

Beginning in 1924, Semenov and Kondrat'ev were among the first to use the techniques of mass spectrometry in the Soviet Union; this work was continued by V. L. Tal'roze at the Institute of Chemical Physics. In the early 1920's, Semenov also collaborated with Kapitsa and Khariton in experiments on the behavior of a molecular beam of a paramagnetic gas in an inhomogeneous magnet field, work parallel with similar investigations being undertaken by Stern and Gerlach, who achieved more definitive results and for whom the Stern-Gerlach effect is named.

Chain reaction theory has a place in many of the most essential chemical reactions on which modern industrial development is based. Petroleum cracking, polymer formation, and the combustion of petroleum-derived fuels are but a few notable examples of chain-reaction processes, and the ability of chemists to control the rates and end products of these reactions depends on an understanding of their underlying physical processes. An automobile's catalytic converter functions because its surface properties promote chain initiation in fuel mixtures too dilute to sustain continuous combustion; the "octane" component of gasoline is a chain terminator introduced to prevent explosion. In terms of introducing a new concept into the science of chemistry, the discoveries of Semenov and Hinshelwood were revolutionary; in terms of immediate practical applications affecting the average person, they were profoundly significant—a circumstance of particular pride in Semenov's native country, where both official and popular sentiment support the view of science as a servant of the people.

Bibliography

Primary

CHEMISTRY: "K teorii protsessov goreniyaa, Soobsch. i," *Zhurnal fizicheskoy khimii*, vol. 60, 1928; *Tsepnye reaktsii*, 1934 (*Chemical Kinetics and Chain Reactions*, 1935); "Kinetica slozhnykh reaktsiyakh," *Zhurnal fizicheskoy khimii*, vol. 17, 1943; *O nekotorykh problemakh khimicheskoi kinetiki i reaktsionnoi sposobnosti*, 1954 (*Some Problems in Chemical Kinetics and Reactivity*, 2 vols., 1958); *Heterogeneous Catalysis in the Chemical Industry*, 1955 (with V. V. Voevodskii); *Nauka i obshchestvo*, 1973.

Secondary

Kondrat'ev, V. N. "Nikolai Nikolaevich Semenov, on His Seventieth Birthday." *Soviet Physics Uspekhi* 9 (1966): 304-307. This conventional biographical sketch, written by a colleague of Semenov's, gives an overview of his accomplishments in the field of physics and of the awards and honors that he received from the Soviet government. There is essentially no information on his personal life.
_____. "Present-Day Theory of Chain Reactions." *Soviet Physics Uspekhi* 9 (1966): 308-315. A general review article on the development of chain reaction theory, less technical than a scholarly research paper but requiring some background to understand. Published as a companion piece to the testimonial biography of Semenov in the same journal. Includes a good bibliography of references.
Kondrat'ev, V. N., and E. E. Nikitin. *Gas Phase Reactions: Kinetics and Mechanisms*. New York: Springer-Verlag, 1981. Kondrat'ev was a close colleague of Semenov and continued his research on chemical kinetics. This book discusses the general theory of chemical chain reactions and related topics, including photochemical and radiation-chemical reactions. Too technical to be very accessible to the nonspecialist. An extensive bibliography includes important Russian references, including writings by Semenov.
Parry, Albert. *The Russian Scientist*. New York: Macmillan, 1973. This book is a good, relatively neutral account of science in Russia, beginning in czarist times and continuing to the present. Biographies of representative eminent Russian scientists and mathematicians are given. Semenov is not treated in detail, but this is a useful reference for a perspective on science administration in the Soviet Union and the importance of the U.S.S.R. Academy of Sciences.
Popovsky, Marc. *Manipulated Science: The Crisis of Science and Scientists in the Soviet Union Today*. Garden City, N.Y.: Doubleday, 1979. A Russian specialist in scientific journalism who emigrated to the United States, Popovsky presents a historical overview of the practice of science in the Soviet Union. The emphasis is on failures and weaknesses of the system and the dismal record of the natural

sciences under Stalin. He presents Semenov as an uncritical defender of the Soviet scientific establishment.

Zeldovich, Ya. B., et al. *The Mathematical Theory of Combustion and Explosions*. New York: Consultant's Bureau, 1985. The first chapter of this book is, in the words of the author, a discussion of "the theory of thermal explosions proposed by N. N. Semenov, whose work serves as a starting point in the history of modern combustion theory." The underlying principles of molecular interactions as understood in the first decades of the twentieth century and the contributions of Semenov and colleagues to the theory are presented in clear chronological order, at a technical level appropriate for an undergraduate major in the physical sciences. There is an extensive bibliography, emphasizing Russian contributions.

Martha Sherwood-Pike

1957

Chemistry
Sir Alexander Robertus Todd, Great Britain

Physics
Chen Ning Yang, China and United States
Tsung-Dao Lee, China and United States

Physiology or Medicine
Daniel Bovet, Italy

Literature
Albert Camus, France

Peace
Lester B. Pearson, Canada

SIR ALEXANDER ROBERTUS TODD
1957

Born: Glasgow, Scotland; October 2, 1907

Nationality: British
Areas of concentration: Vitamins, coenzymes, and nucleic acids

Todd's research has centered on natural products such as vitamins B_1, B_{12}, and E and nucleotides (the building blocks of nucleic acids), as well as on such coenzymes related to nucleic-acid systems as the energy-transfer compound adenosine triphosphate (ATP)

The Award

Presentation

Arne Fredga, a Swedish chemist and member of the Nobel Committee for Chemistry, represented the Royal Swedish Academy of Sciences in delivering the address on December 10, 1957, that introduced King Gustav Adolf and the audience to the work of Alexander Todd. Because this audience was composed mostly of nonscientists, Fredga tried to make the term "nucleotide," pivotal to an understanding of Todd's accomplishments, comprehensible. The term refers to this substance's provenance in cell nuclei, where the nucleotides form an important part of chromosomes—the linear material responsible for the transmission of hereditary characteristics. Johann Friedrich Miescher discovered nucleic acids in the nuclei of pus cells and egg yolk in 1869, and although chemists and biologists studied these materials for the next seventy-five years, it was only in the decade following World War II that scientists were able to elucidate their structures and chemistry, largely through the work of Todd and his colleagues.

Nucleic acids are gigantic molecules composed of myriad nucleotide units joined together, and each nucleotide is constructed from three chemical groups: phosphoric acid, a sugar, and a nitrogenous base. Todd showed, both by the degradation of nucleic acids and by synthesizing structures that were the same as or similar to the breakdown products, precisely how the two sugars, ribose and deoxyribose, were connected to the phosphoric-acid groups and to the various nitrogen-bearing bases. One of his important techniques was phosphorylation, a method for introducing phosphoric-acid groups into molecules. Todd was also the first to synthesize such important nucleotides as ATP, a substance consisting of a triphosphate group attached to a sugar (ribose), which in turn is attached to a nitrogenous base (adenine). Todd's work on the nucleotides laid a solid foundation for future breakthroughs in this field, most spectacularly the determination by James Watson and Francis Crick of the double helical structure of DNA (deoxyribonucleic acid), the master molecule of the gene. Todd had recognized the importance of nucleotide chemistry even when others shunned its great complexities. Undaunted, he found ways to overcome the difficulties, and through an illuminating combination of analysis and synthesis, he worked out the structures of some of the most important molecules of life.

Nobel lecture

On December 11, 1957, the day after he received his Nobel Prize, Todd delivered a lecture entitled "Synthesis in the Study of Nucleotides." It summarized his work in the field of nucleotides and nucleotide coenzymes, and in his talk he tried to steer a course "between the Scylla of generalities and the Charybdis of excessive detail." He admitted that this presented problems for him, since it was difficult to describe his work in any other way in the language of chemical structural formulas. Though these formulas may seem alien to the ordinary person, they represent the detailed architecture of molecules vitally important to all living things.

The path leading Todd to the nucleotides began in Glasgow, where he was introduced to natural products, the compounds that chemists isolate from plants and animals. Later, in Germany, he worked on bile acids and, at the University of Oxford, on natural coloring materials. In this early work he came to appreciate the importance of both analysis and synthesis in studying complex organic molecules. At Edinburgh, for example, he learned much about the structure of vitamin B_1, the substance whose absence in the human body results in the disease beriberi, from its breakdown products as well as from constructing it from its component parts. After synthesizing this vitamin, he became interested in the specificity of vitamin function, and since most vitamins are components of coenzymes, he began studying these organic molecules that must be associated with an enzyme for it to play its part. More specifically, he worked on such coenzymes related to the B vitamins as FAD (flavin adenine dinucleotide). These studies convinced him that to understand the action of vitamins in the body, he would have to understand the structure and properties of nucleotides.

Originally, chemists used the term "nucleotide" to describe the phosphate of certain nucleosides obtained by decomposing naturally occurring nucleic acids with water. Chemists found that nucleosides consisted of a nitrogenous base (a purine or pyrimidine) linked to a sugar; the two major purines are adenine and guanine, and the three major pyrimidines are cytosine, thymine, and uracil. Today, the term includes not only the simple nucleotides of the original definition but also the polynucleotides (the nucleic acids) as well as such substances as ATP. Justification for this broader use is the recurrent base-sugar-phosphate structure characteristic of all these compounds. In 1939, when Todd began work in this field, Phoebus Levene and others had established two basic types of nucleic acid, now called ribonucleic acid (RNA) and deoxyribonucleic acid (DNA). Though some aspects of their structures were known—for example, that the bases adenine, guanine, cytosine, and uracil are present in RNA, and that the bases adenine, guanine, cytosine, and thymine are present in DNA—their detailed structures were not known, so Todd decided to clarify this field by starting with the simplest units, the nucleosides. By meticulous synthetic techniques, he was able to establish the structures of individual nucleosides, both ribonucleosides and deoxyribonucleosides.

Since the simple nucleotides are phosphates of the nucleosides, Todd became interested in how the phosphate group was attached to the sugar portion of the molecule. Phosphorylation—the change of an organic substance into an organic phosphate—thus became an essential part of Todd's studies. The synthetic techniques that Todd and his group developed permitted the chemical study of the theoretically possible nucleotides. By the mid-1940's, he believed that the nucleic acids were the genetic material responsible for transmitting hereditary characteristics from mother cell to offspring, and this gave him an added stimulus for figuring out the chemical structure of these polynucleotides. He found that the nucleic acids were linear rather than branched polymers, and he discovered the specific link holding the nucleotide units together.

Todd's work on nucleotides led naturally to his studies of the nucleotide coenzymes, the large group of substances comprising many enzyme systems involved in metabolic processes. The coenzymes generally act in association with specific proteins, and all known members belong to two types: ATP is an example of the first type (a mono-ester), and DPN (the diphosphate of nicotinamide adenine dinucleotide—NAD) is an example of the second (a di-ester). (An ester is an organic acid derivative generally formed by the reaction of an alcohol and an organic acid through the elimination of water.) Todd and his collaborators synthesized many of these coenzymes, and by means of this work they were able to explain many important biological processes. Indeed, by elucidating the structures of these and other molecules, Todd helped biologists to understand more deeply the mysteries of life itself.

Critical reception

Although Watson and Crick would not receive their Nobel Prize for the discovery of the double helical structure of DNA until 1962, their work had, by 1957, already created a revolution in the study of nucleic acids, and the multiplication of significant new discoveries cast a favorable light on the preparatory work of Todd, who had been able to show how the nucleotides are coupled to one another in the nucleic acids. Because Todd's work on nucleotides extended for more than two decades and involved an accumulation of modest discoveries rather than a great breakthrough such as the double helix, he doubted he would ever receive the Nobel Prize and was genuinely surprised when the announcement was made. He received a hint that the award was coming while he was on a lecture tour of the United States. After he had delivered the Hitchcock Lectures at the University of California in Berkeley, he stayed with his friend, the Harvard chemist Robert Woodward, in Massachusetts, where he received a letter from his wife informing him that the Swedish press wanted his picture. The formal announcement of the Nobel Prize arrived about a fortnight later, by which time he was back at the University of Cambridge in

England. He later learned from one of the Nobel Committee members that his name had surfaced early in their considerations, and he had quickly become the principal choice of the majority for the 1957 prize in chemistry.

The British press contrasted the award to Todd in chemistry with the award to Chen Ning Yang and Tsung-Dao Lee in physics. *The Times* of London for November 1, 1957, elaborated upon this contrast. Todd received his prize for work of more than a quarter century on the nucleotides, whereas Yang and Lee received their award for the brilliant suggestion, which had been swiftly developed, that a symmetry property of subatomic particles (called parity) would not be conserved in certain kinds of radioactive disintegrations of atoms. Todd's work on nucleotides led to the double helix of DNA and an explosion of research on the molecular biology of the gene, but no fundamental laws of biology or chemistry were challenged by these discoveries. On the other hand, Yang and Lee's prediction that parity was not always conserved had been experimentally verified, forcing physicists to modify what they had once thought was a fundamental law of nature—that space possessed a quality of symmetry in which every object was balanced by a corresponding mirror image that had to respond to the laws of nature in the same way. Todd's work centered on substances—the nucleic acids—that made their home primarily in the cell nucleus, whereas Yang and Lee showed that the law of parity conservation did not necessarily hold in the world of the atomic nucleus.

One of the British popular magazines compared Todd to a bricklayer working with nature's own bricks: He was a superb molecular architect, synthesizing the complex molecules of nucleotides and nucleotide coenzymes from simple molecular building blocks. *Nature*, England's leading journal of science, viewed the Nobel Prize to Todd as an honor well deserved. His great work had already been recognized by England with his knighthood in 1954, and it was appropriate for the Swedish award to follow. The article in *Nature* for November 9, 1957, praised Todd's "brilliant achievements" in organic chemistry, particularly his synthesis of various vitamins and nucleotides. Todd had dominated the field of synthetic organic chemistry in England for a quarter of a century, as indicated by his presence, often with several scientific papers, in nearly every year of the *Journal of the Chemical Society* through the 1930's, 1940's, and 1950's.

In America, most newspapers gave more attention to Yang and Lee's prize than to the award to Todd, since these Chinese-born scientists had done their prizewinning work in the United States. Nevertheless, American articles also contained praise for Todd's work and analyses of its significance. For example, the account in *The New York Times* for November 1, 1957, emphasized the relationship between Todd's studies of the nucleic acids and the recent understanding through the DNA molecule of how genetic information passes from one generation of life to the next. In this sense, Todd's work was seen as a step on the way to discovering what life itself is. A reporter from *The New York Times* got in touch by telephone with Todd, who said that he felt "slightly ludicrous" when he was told that he had won the award. Though he appreciated the honor, he believed that "it is much more a tribute to a lot of the boys" who had worked with him.

In his autobiography, written more than a quarter of a century after the Nobel Prize, Todd discussed the reception of the award in a general way. He stated that a "lot of nonsense" had been written about it, particularly the popular notion of reporters that scientists strive for this prize in fierce competition with one another. From his own case, as well as from his experience with many other Nobel Prize winners, he felt that he had enough evidence to state that scientists for the most part do not work to win a Nobel Prize but rather to satisfy their curiosity about some puzzle of nature. He also felt that the final selection in his and other cases had elements of a lottery to it, since many more candidates are worthy of the prize than can possibly be chosen.

As a result of the notoriety created about him in the newspapers and magazines, Todd found it more difficult to proceed with his research. He was made into an "unwilling oracle" whose opinion was sought on subjects far removed from organic chemistry, but he believed that the Nobel Prize did not give his or other scientists' opinions on nonscientific questions any more credence than the opinions of conventionally informed citizens. Despite these rather critical ruminations about the effects of the Nobel Prize on a scientist's life, Todd did admit, in the end, that the Nobel Foundation performed an excellent service in honoring scientists for discoveries that had significantly deepened man's knowledge of the natural world.

Biography

Alexander Robertus Todd was born in Cathcart, a southern suburb of Glasgow, Scotland, on October 2, 1907. His father, who had only an elementary education, was then an office clerk of the Glasgow Subway Railway Company. His mother, the former Jane Lowrie, also had only an elementary education, and she had worked in a shoe factory before her marriage. Both parents had a passionate belief in the value of education for their children, who included Todd's older sister Jean and his younger brother Robert. In 1912, Todd entered Holmlea Public School in Cathcart, where he was an excellent student, and in 1918 he went to Allan Glen's School in Glasgow, where he became interested in chemistry. Through the sacrifices of his parents, he was able to attend Glasgow University, and in 1928 he received his B.S. degree with honors. He spent a further year at Glasgow on a Carnegie scholarship before traveling to Germany for graduate studies at the University of Frankfurt. While there, he learned German so well that he was able to write his doctoral thesis on bile acids in German. His thesis was accepted in 1931, when he was awarded his doctorate of natural philosophy.

Upon his return to England, he worked at the University of Oxford from 1931 to 1934 with Robert Robinson, an eminent investigator of plant products. After receiving his second Ph.D. degree, Todd returned to Scotland and joined the staff of Edinburgh University as an assistant in medical chemistry. In 1936, he moved to the Lister Institute of Preventive Medicine in Chelsea; he became reader in biochemistry at the University of London in 1937. At Edinburgh, Todd had met a young woman, Alison Dale, who was doing postdoctoral research in the department of pharmacology, which was next door to medical chemistry. By the time he left Edinburgh, they were engaged, and they married in January, 1937, after he had moved to London. Her father was Sir Henry Dale, the famous physiologist who had won the Nobel Prize in Physiology or Medicine in 1936. The marriage resulted in three children, a son and two daughters.

In 1938, Todd became Sir Samuel Hall Professor of Chemistry and director of the chemical laboratories at the University of Manchester, where he began his important work on the nucleotides. He rejected the chair in biochemistry at Cambridge in 1944, but when he was asked to take the chair in organic chemistry, he accepted. During World War II, he worked on various projects concerning chemical-warfare agents, poisons, and penicillin. After the war, he served the British government in various positions related to science policy. For example, he was chairman of the Advisory Council on Scientific Policy for twelve years, beginning in 1952. For his services to the government and for his scientific achievements, he was knighted in 1954, and in 1962 he received a Life Peerage, becoming Baron Todd of Trumpington, since he lived in Trumpington parish. In 1970, he suffered a severe heart attack, and when he recovered, he cut down on his commitments, although he did accept the presidency of the Royal Society in 1975, a position he held until 1980.

Scientific Career

A fascination with the molecular underpinnings of life formed the foundation of Todd's work in chemistry. He stated many times throughout his career that he preferred thinking of organic chemistry not as the study of carbon compounds, the usual textbook definition, but as the study of substances found in living matter. From very early in his career, he manifested a preference for doing research with natural products. Though these substances are extremely complicated, their complexities animated rather than intimidated him. This interplay between chemistry and biology can be seen in his basic work on the vitamins and nucleotides as well as in his trailblazing researches on the coenzymes. Todd's painstakingly detailed determination of the precise positions of atoms in important biological molecules had great significance in undergirding the revolution in molecular biology that occurred in the 1950's. Indeed, his work on the chemistry of the nucleic acids cleared the way for James Watson, Francis Crick, Rosalind Franklin, Maurice Wilkins, and Linus Pauling to do their crucial studies on the structure of DNA.

Todd's interest in chemistry began early in his life. When he was about eight years old, he received a home chemistry set, which he augmented with equipment and chemicals from a local laboratory supply house. At Allan Glen's School, whose subsidiary title was the Glasgow High School of Science, he entered an institution still following the charge of its founder, a Glasgow carpenter and entrepreneur, that science was an important vehicle of a liberal education. Todd studied chemistry, physics, and mathematics, but a painful experience with a doctor who tried to straighten his elbow dislocated in a tree-climbing accident caused him to abandon his original intention of becoming a doctor. Influenced and inspired by an outstanding chemistry teacher at Allan Glen's School, he settled on chemistry as a profession, and after passing the Scottish Higher Leaving Certificate examination in English, French, mathematics, physics, and chemistry, he went to the University of Glasgow as an honors candidate in chemistry.

At Glasgow in the 1920's, the first-year course in honors chemistry consisted of two terms of general and inorganic chemistry and a single term of organic chemistry. This taste of organic chemistry whetted Todd's appetite for more, and he devoted his second year to advanced lectures and laboratory work in this field. By his fourth and final year, he was already doing original research—a stereochemical study of the reaction of phosphorus pentachloride and ethyl acetate. This led to his first publication in the *Journal of the Chemical Society*, where most of his later work would appear. After graduating first in his class in 1928, Todd was awarded a Carnegie Research Scholarship to continue his studies in organic chemistry, but he quickly realized that to better his understanding of natural products, he would have to leave Glasgow for Germany, where the best chemists were doing the most important work.

In October, 1929, Todd became the research student of Walther Borsche at the University of Frankfurt am Main. Borsche was an organic chemist who had worked with Adolf von Baeyer, Otto Wallach, and Adolf Windaus (Baeyer had won the Nobel Prize in Chemistry in 1905, Wallach in 1910, and Windaus in 1928). Borsche gave Todd a problem in the chemistry of the bile acids. Mammals generate bile as an emulsifying agent which aids the absorption of fats by the body. Cholic acid is one of the most abundant bile acids, and Todd studied a related compound, apocholic acid. Much to Borsche's chagrin, Todd criticized the traditional structure of the bile acids and suggested an alternative, which he published in a German journal of physiological chemistry. The structure that Todd proposed had a seven-membered ring, which other chemists later showed to be wrong, and when Todd completed his doctoral work in 1931 and returned to England, he left the bile-acid field and never returned to it.

Todd was searching for a new way of studying natural products, and he discovered it during his postdoctoral studies with Robert Robinson at Oxford. As organic chemical techniques became more sophisticated, chemists took on more and more complex natural products for structure determination. Robinson had studied the alkaloids, nitrogenous compounds produced by plants, and his great success had been to work out the structure of morphine in 1925. Robinson's work on natural products had a big influence on Todd, in particular his use of analogue synthesis as a tool used in conjunction with classical degradative studies. Robinson, who would win the Nobel Prize ten years before Todd, put him to work in the fall of 1931 on the synthesis of anthocyanins, the red and blue coloring substances of flowers and fruits. These plant pigments often occur in nature as glucosides, organic compounds that produce sugars and related substances on reaction with water. Todd made a breakthrough that opened the way to the synthesis of the major glucosidic anthocyanins. For example, in 1932, he completed the synthesis of cyanin, the pigment of the red rose and blue cornflower.

In 1934, after completing his work on plant pigments, Todd went to the University of Edinburgh, where he became interested in the structure of vitamins. He had learned from Robinson that I. G. Farbenindustrie in Germany and Merck in the United States had begun structural determinations of vitamin B_1, the substance isolated in 1926 that had been shown to cure the deficiency disease beriberi. With the aid of a Medical Research Council grant, Todd separated the vitamin from rice hulls and began analytic and synthetic studies. Though the German and American chemists beat Todd to the synthesis, his method was sufficiently superior to the others that Hoffman La Roche used it to make a major part of the world's supply.

After his synthesis of vitamin B_1, Todd became interested in vitamin E, whose study he began while he was at the Lister Institute in London. With his colleagues, he isolated beta-tocopherol and alpha-tocopherol (two of the E vitamins) from rice-germ oil, established the main features of their structures, and began to work out a total synthesis for each of them. During this period he also began a search for the active principle of hashish (*Cannabis*). The starting material for his first studies came from a distilled extract that had been seized by police in India. In 1938, when he took up his position as Sir Samuel Hall Professor of Chemistry and director of the laboratories at the University of Manchester, he continued his work on vitamins and on *Cannabis* derivatives. Although he failed in his attempt to isolate the active principle of the hemp plant, he was able to investigate the plant's white, crystalline resin sufficiently to discover that this material had promising pharmacological properties.

As interesting as his vitamin and *Cannabis* results were, his most important work at Manchester was on the nucleotides. He was led into these studies through his curiosity about how vitamins function in living things. This activity often involves coenzymes, the biocatalysts that spark certain enzymes to carry out many of the metabolic reactions in cells. For example, Todd knew that vitamin B_1 functions as an active constitutent of a coenzyme that plays a part in the way cells utilize oxygen. Several of the coenzymes, including ATP, contain nucleotides, but Todd was unable to complete the synthesis of ATP before World War II broke out.

During the early part of the war, Todd worked with Robinson on the Group Committee (later renamed the Dyestuffs Division Research Panel) on the synthetic drugs most likely to be needed in wartime. He also spent much of his time investigating potential chemical warfare agents, and he became chairman of the committee responsible for the development and production of these deadly materials. He then took part in the Anglo-American cooperative research project on penicillin. In the late winter of 1943, the University of Cambridge began a search for a successor to Sir Frederick Gowland Hopkins, the expert in vitamins who had won the 1929 Nobel Prize in Physiology or Medicine, in the chair of biochemistry. The electors of the university offered the post to Todd. Todd was not a biochemist, and after investigating the position, he refused it. When he was asked to take the chair in organic chemistry, however, he accepted, after making clear that he was to have complete authority as department head and that the university was to build a new laboratory for him.

Within a year of his taking the Cambridge position, the war came to an end, and Todd's work on the nucleotides expanded, primarily as a result of many chemists from around the world coming to join his group. During the late 1940's, Todd and his colleagues completed the synthesis of ADP (adenosine diphosphate) and ATP, compounds of crucial importance as energy reservoirs in cells. By this time he knew, through the work of others, that DNA was definitely the hereditary material and that DNA and RNA were macromolecules with molecular weights of 500,000 or more. The nucleic acids were therefore polynucleotides, polymers consisting of large numbers of nucleotide units. Todd decided to study how the units were linked together. By the early 1950's, he was able to establish precisely how the sugar ring (ribose or deoxyribose) is joined to the various nitrogenous bases on one side of the nucleotide unit and how this ring is bound to the phosphate group on the other side. He was thus able to put forward the structure of the two types of nucleic acid (DNA and RNA) as unbranched polynucleotides linearly linked through the phosphate groups between the yoked sugar rings and bases (the nucleosides). As an organic chemist, Todd was concerned about how the atoms in these complex molecules were joined together, and he left it to others to determine the three-dimensional arrangement of the atoms.

Todd played only a small role in the actual discovery of the double-helical structure of DNA, but his nucleotide work had a major influence both on Linus Pauling at the California Institute of Technology and on Watson and Crick at Cambridge, the principal investigators of the problem. At the time Watson came to the Cavendish Laboratory (at Cambridge) Todd and his group were finishing their studies on the chemistry of the linkages that bind base, sugar, and phosphate groups together into a polynucleotide chain. Pauling first heard of Todd's work during a meeting of the American Chemical Society in New York in 1949, and he heard about it again in the summer of 1952 through a paper published by Todd. Because Pauling had beaten the Cambridge crystallographers to the alpha-helical structure of proteins in 1950, largely because of their ignorance of the planarity of the peptide link, something any organic chemist could have pointed out to them, Lawrence Bragg, the head of the Cavendish, decided that all future structures proposed by Cambridge physicists would have to be examined by an organic chemist. Therefore, before Watson and Crick released their structure, Todd had to validate it. After careful study, he enthusiastically approved the double helix, believing that Watson and Crick had not only solved the problem of a self-replicating molecule but also opened a new era in molecular biology.

At the time the DNA structure determination was being completed, Todd was engaged in establishing the structure of an adenine-containing coenzyme known as FAD (flavin adenine dinucleotide), a major participant in the oxidation of sugars and starches in nearly every organism needing oxygen for its existence. He was also engaged in structural studies on vitamin B_{12}. This vitamin, found in liver and essential for the growth of red blood corpuscles, was known to be able to cure pernicious anemia and its associated nervous and digestive disorders. It was also one of the most complicated molecules then known, and establishing its structure became a challenge for many chemists. At Cambridge, Todd performed chemical studies of the molecule while Dorothy Hodgkin (who was to win the 1964 Nobel Prize in Chemistry) used X-ray crystallographic techniques to pinpoint atomic positions in the vitamin. Todd's work helped Hodgkin who, in 1955, announced the complete three-dimensional structure of vitamin B_{12}, whose core consists of a central cobalt atom surrounded by five-membered nitrogenous rings.

During the postwar period, Todd had become involved in science policy and international activities, interests that continued throughout his later career. He had assisted in the rehabilitation of German science after the war through several visits to the British zone of occupation. The impressive contributions made by scientists in America, Germany, and Britain during the war led several people in government to believe that a similarly organized effort would be equally profitable in peacetime. Out of discussions between politicians and scientists came the Advisory Council on Scientific Policy (ACSP), and Todd became increasingly active in this and other organizations which provided scientific and technological advice to government officials. Eventually, he succeeded Sir Henry Tizard as chairman of the ACSP.

In 1964, the Labour government modified the political control of science and technology by putting them in separate departments. Todd viewed this change as disastrous, since he believed that scientific and technological concerns were intimately interrelated and separating them administratively harmed both. He also opposed the Labour government's educational policy, a central element of which involved doubling the number of British universities. In Todd's view, this would result in a dilution of money and talent, which would lead in turn to a decline in British science and technology. The policy did lead to an underfunding of basic research and a consequent "brain drain," a loss of talented British scientists to the United States and other countries. Todd believed deeply that excellence breeds excellence and that a scientific elite was not an outmoded idea. As he once put it, in science "the best is infinitely more important than the second best."

In 1975, when Todd became president of the Royal Society, he brought some of these same concerns to this prestigious position. This national scientific academy had traditionally supported outstanding scientific ability, but during the 1960's, according to Todd, politics began to interfere with its mission when some members became too closely affiliated to the party in power. Todd saw his job as above politics. For him, the Royal Society should encourage pure and applied science, advise government officials on scientific and technical matters, and uphold the freedom of the scientific enterprise in England and throughout the world. During his four-year term he proceeded to implement his understanding of the Society's mission by helping to increase support for research, to improve the treatment of scientists in the Soviet Union and other countries, and to bring a scientific viewpoint to bear on the formulation of British policy.

Todd's work as a chemist and an administrator has been characterized by a great love for science and a desire to increase its credibility and prestige. Throughout his career he was fascinated by the molecules of living things, and by elucidating the structures of many natural products, he was responsible, perhaps more than anyone else, for transforming biochemistry from a disparaged discipline into successful modern science. He achieved this through a combination of deep theoretical knowledge and great experimental skill. As a synthetic organic chemist, he was much more than a strategist planning the most logical path to a synthesis; he was also an explorer, strongly inclined to blaze new paths that might reveal deeper knowledge of chemistry and biology. Thus, there was a touch of artistry to his syntheses. Though his primary influence was on organic chemists and biologists, his work has had a direct influence on society through a newly developing field—biotechnology. Against those who fear the chemical manipulation of life, he proposes a faith in biotechnical progress; for him, any problems that arise will come not from the scientists but from the politicians and from the slow rate of social and moral development. He sees the growing antiscience movement as a modern form of anti-intellectualism. Change cannot be stopped, it can only be channeled, and if human society is to survive and prosper, it must so structure itself that its members can not only live with change but also benefit from it.

Bibliography

Primary

CHEMISTRY: "Vitamins of the B Group," *Journal of the Chemical Society*, 1941; "Studies on Phosphorylation, Part I: Dibenzyl Chlorophosphate as a Phosphorylating Agent," *Journal of the Chemical Society*, 1945 (with F. R. Atherton and H. T. Openshaw); "Synthesis in the Study of Nucleotides," *Journal of the Chemical Society*, 1946; "Nucleotides, Part III: Mononucleotides derived from Adenosine, Guanosine, Cytidine, and Uridine" and "Nucleotides, Part IV: A Novel Synthesis of Adenosine Triphosphate," *Journal of the Chemical Society*, 1949 (with A. M. Michelson); "Nucleotides, Part X: Some Observations on the Structure and Chemical Behavior of the Nucleic Acids," *Journal of the Chemical Society*, 1952 (with D. M. Brown); "The Nucleotides: Some Recent Chemical Research and Its Biological Implications," *The Harvey Lectures, 1951-1952*, 1953; "Chemical Structure of the Nucleic Acids," *Proceedings of the National Academy of Sciences (USA)*, vol. 40, 1954; "Evidence on the Nature of the Chemical Bonds in Nucleic Acids," *The Nucleic Acids: Chemistry and Biology*, vol. 1, 1955 (with D. M. Brown); *Perspectives in Organic Chemistry*, 1956.

HISTORY: "A Hundred Years of Organic Chemistry," *Advancement of Science*, vol. 8, 1952.

BIOGRAPHY: "Robert Robinson," *Biographical Memoirs of Fellows of the Royal Society*, vol. 22, 1976 (with J. W. Cornforth).

AUTOBIOGRAPHY: *A Time to Remember: The Autobiography of a Chemist*, 1984.

Secondary

Chargaff, Erwin, and J. N. Davidson, eds. *The Nucleic Acids: Chemistry and Biology*. Vol. 1. New York: Academic Press, 1955. With the rapid growth of knowledge about nucleic acids after World War II, a need developed for a detailed inventory of this progress. Two great biochemists, Chargaff at Columbia in New York and Davidson at Glasgow in Scotland, tried to meet this need by organizing all available information about nucleic acids in a comprehensive treatise. Todd and his colleague D. M. Brown wrote the chapter on the nature of the chemical bonds in nucleic acids. The editors tried to shape their work in such a way that their book reads as a continuous narrative. Todd's work is mentioned often throughout the first volume, which is intended for readers with a good grasp of chemistry.

Davidson, J. N. *The Biochemistry of Nucleic Acids*. 7th ed. New York: Academic Press, 1975. When the first edition of this book appeared in 1950, the nucleic acid field was in its infancy. The rapid appearance of new editions in succeeding years testified to the exponential progress in nucleic acid research and to the great interest in this area shown by chemists and biologists. Davidson's book is an elementary outline of the main features of nucleic acids and nucleoproteins for students of chemistry, biochemistry, and biology. There are excellent lists of references at the ends of the chapters.

Fruton, Joseph S. *Molecules and Life: Historical Essays on the Interplay of Chemistry and Biology*. New York: John Wiley & Sons, 1972. Fruton, a physiological chemist, wrote this book for students of the physical and life sciences. His essays on enzymes, proteins, nucleic acids, and other topics cover the period from 1800 to 1950, and he discusses Todd's work in a chapter called "From Nuclein to the Double Helix." He bases his account on scientific papers and other accounts written shortly after the original work was done, and he treats the work from a personal perspective. The book is successful in revealing how twentieth century interests evolved out of nineteenth century studies.

Judson, Horace Freeland. *The Eighth Day of Creation: Makers of the Revolution in Biology*. New York: Simon & Schuster, 1979. Judson spent several years interviewing more than a hundred scientists for this book. Todd was one of them, though Judson is interested in Todd's work only as it contributed to the evolution of knowledge about the nucleic acids. His main emphasis is on the actual experiences of scientists as they made their revolutionary discoveries. Judson did not intend the book to be a history of biochemistry, and this has led some scholars to question his disproportionate treatment of various topics. Nevertheless, he does an excellent job at capturing the excitement of how twentieth century molecular biologists have transformed the way in which life is viewed.

Todd, Alexander. *A Time to Remember: The Autobiography of a Chemist*. New York: Cambridge University Press, 1984. Todd's own account of his life, which covers the period from his birth to the end of 1980. He wrote his book for a general audience, though some reviewers criticized it for being too technical for the public and not technical enough for the specialist. Todd stresses such broad themes as the state of British chemistry in the twentieth century, his friendship with several of the great modern scientists, and the borderland between science and government. The book contains six appendices, which reprint extracts from Todd's addresses.

Watson, James D. *The Double Helix: A Personal Account of the Discovery of the Structure of DNA*. Edited by Gunther S. Stent. New York: W. W. Norton, 1980. Todd's work on the nucleotides found its culmination in the discovery by Watson and Crick of the double helical structure of DNA. Watson's account of this discovery has sold over a million copies, and it continues to be popular. This Norton Critical Edition, in addition to the complete text of the original edition, contains commentaries, book reviews, and original papers, and it is designed to give students a deeper and more balanced picture of this great discovery.

Robert J. Paradowski

1958

Chemistry
Frederick Sanger, Great Britain

Physics
Pavel Alekseyevich Cherenkov, Soviet Union
Ilya Mikhailovich Frank, Soviet Union
Igor Yevgenyevich Tamm, Soviet Union

Physiology or Medicine
George W. Beadle, United States
Edward L. Tatum, United States
Joshua Lederberg, United States

Literature
Boris Pasternak, Soviet Union

Peace
Dominique Georges Pire, Belgium

FREDERICK SANGER
1958

Born: Rendcombe, Gloucestershire, England; August 13, 1918

Nationality: British
Area of concentration: Structure of proteins

Sanger determined the amino acid sequence of insulin, the first protein molecule whose structure was thus elucidated. His work provided other researchers with the procedure for exploring the order of proteins in general

The Award

Presentation

On December 10, 1958, Professor Arne Tiselius, a separations chemist and a member of the Nobel Committee for Chemistry, presented a synopsis of Frederick Sanger's work. Tiselius first noted the complexity and importance of proteins—the key substances of enzymes, antibodies, and many toxins. He suggested that "the determination of the exact building-plan for these complicated giant molecules appears as one of the greatest problems in today's scientific research."

Proteins are long molecules constructed of combinations of twenty-five smaller units called amino acids. Sanger sought to determine the sequence of these amino acids, that is, the order in which they appear in a protein. For his study, he chose the protein insulin, the hormone involved in the regulation of sugar metabolism. Sanger attached a colored label to the front, or amino, terminal of the protein chain. The protein was then broken into its individual amino acid units: Two were found to be marked with the colored dye. He was thus able to conclude that the insulin molecule was composed of two different chains.

By gentle treatment with weak acid or enzymes, Sanger could break the chains into fragments of three, four, or five amino acids. Each of these segments was then separated and labeled with colored dye. The small fragments were broken into their individual amino acids. By carefully fitting together the complex pieces of this puzzle, Sanger was able to identify the order of the amino acids in each chain. The determination of the structure of insulin was itself a remarkable feat requiring years of persistent and zealous effort. As Tiselius pointed out, however, the development of a sequencing procedure that could be applied to proteins in general greatly broadened the scope of Sanger's achievement.

Nobel lecture

On December 11, 1958, Frederick Sanger delivered his Nobel lecture, entitled "The Chemistry of Insulin." It showed the orderly way in which the complex problem of the relative order of amino acids in proteins was studied and solved. Sanger chose to study the insulin molecule because of its physiological importance and because much was known about its chemistry through the work of Albert C. Chibnall.

The first task undertaken by Sanger was a detailed study of the free amino ends of the insulin chain. A method of labeling them was worked out. A protein chain was permitted to react with a highly colored compound, fluorodinitrobenzene (FDNB). This reagent attached to the terminal amino acid to form a dinitrophenyl-protein. The DNP-protein was then hydrolyzed with acid, creating many free amino acids and a yellow-colored label on the amino terminal unit. These labeled units were separated and identified by comparing them with synthetic DNP-amino acids.

Insulin was found to have two terminal amino acids—a DNP-phenylalanine and a DNP-glycine. This confirmed that insulin had two different protein chains. These chains were separated by breaking the sulfur bonds that linked them and by precipitation methods. Treatment of a protein fraction with concentrated acid caused all the amino acids to become separated from one another. Sanger found that milder conditions, however, could effect a partial hydrolysis, leaving fractions of various sizes. These were separated and the colored label employed to determine their free amino ends. The total composition of each fragment was also determined. Data from overlapping fragments were pieced together. Sanger and Dr. Hans Tuppy first determined the order of the amino acids in the thirty-amino-acid A chain.

The smaller chain of twenty amino acids proved more difficult, because many of the small fragments contained the same type of amino acid. Fortunately, Sanger was able to find another method of more specifically breaking the protein chain. He used proteolytic enzymes such as tryspin and chymotrypsin to hydrolyze the B chain. Separation of the fragments was difficult, but Sanger succeeded by using chromatographic methods that had recently been developed.

Once the amino-acid order of the individual A and B chains had been solved, the task remaining was to show how the two chains were linked. The amino acid cysteine contains a sulfur that can form a disulfide bond with a neighboring cysteine. There are, however, several combinations by which these might be linked. By careful analysis of the residues of the double-chain insulin molecule, Sanger eventually solved this problem.

Toward the end of his lecture, Sanger presented to his audience a diagram of the complete structure of insulin with the bonding between the chains designated. Sanger realized that he had provided others with tools for similar studies on other proteins. He hoped that "studies of proteins may reveal changes that take place in disease and that our efforts may be of more practical use to humanity."

Critical reception

The announcement on October 28, 1958, that Frederick Sanger of the University of Cambridge was to receive the Nobel Prize in Chemistry was received with jubilation in England. *The Times* of London (October 29) compared Sanger's accomplishment in determining the structure of a protein to running a four-minute mile: He had set a new standard for chemists. *Time* (November 10), in announcing the Nobel winners of 1958, gave a brief account of Sanger's work in determining the structure of insulin. The article noted that Dr. Sanger treated insulin gently and was thus able to obtain separate fragments that could be analyzed.

The New York Times (October 29) editorialized about the international and cosmopolitan nature of science. Earlier in the week, the Nobel Prize in Literature had been awarded to controversial Soviet author Boris Pasternak. The article lauded Dr. Sanger's determination of the structure of insulin as one of "the greatest research triumphs of this century." It noted that Sanger's success was attributable in part to his use of chromatography techniques that were the invention of the Russian botanist, Mikhail S. Tsvett. The international nature of scientific accomplishment was also noted by *Scientific American* (December, 1958) as they announced that seven men—three from the United States, three from the Soviet Union, and one from Great Britain—shared the Nobel Prizes in science. Sanger was lauded for his work in sequencing the specific units of insulin.

Science News Letter (November 8) stressed the twelve years that Sanger devoted to the study of insulin and the usefulness of Sanger's work in application to research on other proteins. The journal *Chemistry* (December, 1958) also focused on the great difficulty of Sanger's task, saying that it had taken twelve years and involved 777 atoms. Sanger's patience and skill were praised. In announcing Sanger's selection, *Science* (November 14) quoted the laureate's own assessment of his work, "At the moment, my work is useful mainly in analyzing other proteins. But, since proteins are the most important substance in the human body, understanding them is, in the long run, a step forward in fighting diseases which attack the body."

Chemistry and Engineering News (November 10) provided a bit of insight into Sanger's mode of operation, observing that "Sanger is definitely a research man." It noted that he was the type of person who preferred to work in the laboratory himself with a small group of associates rather than supervise a large organization. The December 22, 1958, edition of *Chemical and Engineering News* had on its cover a picture of Frederick Sanger escorting Princess Margaretha of Sweden to the banquet in Town Hall during the Nobel Festival—an unusual moment in the limelight for a quiet, self-effacing man.

Biography

Frederick Sanger, British molecular biologist and two-time Nobel laureate in chemistry, was born in Rendcombe, Gloucestershire, England, on August 13, 1918. He was the son of Frederick Sanger, a medical doctor, and his wife, Cicely Crewson Sanger. Sanger entered St. John's College, University of Cambridge, in 1936. He earned a first in biochemistry, being graduated with an A.B. in 1939.

In the fall of 1939, Sanger was admitted as a research student to the chemistry department at Cambridge. A year later, he married Margaret Joan Howe; they would have three children—two sons and a daughter. At Cambridge, Sanger investigated the metabolism of lysine and was awarded the Ph.D. in 1943. From 1944 to 1951, he held a Beit Memorial Fellowship at Cambridge and began his prizewinning work on the structure of insulin. This work was finished in 1955 and was the basis of the 1958 Nobel Prize. Sanger continued his scientific work at Cambridge after his award. A quiet man, he preferred laboratory work to teaching or administration. After 1962, he directed the Division of Protein and Nucleic Acid Chemistry at the Medical Research Council Laboratory of Molecular Biology at Cambridge.

Having provided science with the tools for determining the sequence of protein, he turned his attention to nucleic acids, the substances that carry the hereditary information and dictate the proteins to be formed. By 1975, he had plotted the genetic structure of a 5,375-nucleotide virus. He perfected procedures that increased the validity and speed of nucleotide sequencing. Sanger's nucleic acid work was recognized by a second Nobel Prize in Chemistry in 1980. He retired from his research career at the age of sixty-five in 1983.

Scientific Career

Sequencing, or determining the order of units in large molecules, was the central theme of Sanger's scientific work. In the *1988 Annual Review of Biochemistry*, he wrote an overview of his scientific career, which he titled, "Sequences, Sequences, and Sequences." The seemingly repetitive title alludes to a forty-three-year effort that led to major accomplishments in the sequencing of three different types of large molecules—proteins, ribonucleic acids (RNA), and deoxyribonucleic acids (DNA).

An undergraduate course in biochemistry at the University of Cambridge was a major stimulus to Sanger's career. The concept of using chemistry to explain biological phenomena, coupled with the enthusiasm of Dr. Ernest Baldwin for this new discipline, was important in establishing Sanger's direction. He stayed an extra year at Cambridge and earned an A.B. with first class honors in biochemistry in 1939.

He returned to Cambridge as a Ph.D. student and took his degree under the direction of Albert Neuberger. His doctoral thesis was on the metabolism of the amino acid lysine. This work provided him with an introduction to the study of amino acids, facets of which would occupy him for the next fifteen years.

After completion of his Ph.D. in 1943, Sanger had the opportunity to work with Professor Albert C. Chibnall at Cambridge. Chibnall's group was studying insulin, a protein available in pure form for the treatment of diabetes. Chibnall had obtained reasonably accurate data on the amino-acid composition of the protein. Sanger's initial work on insulin was an extension of Chibnall's efforts and was suggested by him. Sanger set out to determine quantitatively the free amino groups in the insulin molecule. He investigated several possible labels for marking the end groups. He finally selected a colored dye, fluorodinitrobenzene (FDNB), as his tool, a reagent that has also provided other researchers with a means of studying proteins. With this dye, Sanger found that insulin had two amino ends and hence had two chains. These were broken apart by an oxidation procedure and two fragments were isolated. In 1947, Sanger visited Arne Tiselius in his laboratory in Uppsala, Sweden; there Sanger learned some of the newer separation procedures that were being developed.

The next phase of his insulin work involved partial hydrolysis (breaking apart) of

the individual insulin chains. By studying the labeled amino ends of short fragments, together with the composition of each fragment, Sanger began to solve the
puzzle of the sequence of each of the chains of insulin. With the aid of enzymes
that can split proteins after specific amino-acid groups, he was able to determine the
order of the amino acids in each of the chains. Purification techniques involving
paper chromatography were also essential to the success of this project.

Once the complete sequence of each chain was determined, the task remained to
find how they were linked together. This problem was complicated, because the
sulfur-to-sulfur bonds tended to rearrange in the acidic solution in which they were
placed. After many efforts, the rearrangement was finally avoided: The structure of
insulin was completed in 1955. This was the first protein to be sequenced; it
contained a total of fifty-one amino acids. Although better methods of labeling and
purification are available to the biochemist today, the importance of Sanger's work
in developing strategy remains.

In his autobiographical account, "Sequences, Sequences, and Sequences,"
Sanger refers to the next phase of his career as "the lean years." He intended to
continue work on insulin but was drawn to other types of problems. Biochemist
Christian B. Anfinsen was on sabbatical leave in Sanger's laboratory in 1954. Together, they labeled a rat with radioactive sulfur in an unsuccessful attempt to
produce radioactive insulin. This effort, however, introduced Sanger to some of the
methods he would later use in nucleic acid sequencing. During the late 1950's,
Sanger and his colleagues also used radioactive phosphorus to identify the active
centers of certain enzymes. He became adept at using radioactive materials, purification techniques such as two-dimensional paper chromatography, and autoradiography. Because radioactive materials give off a signal that can be detected
with photographic film, their location on a piece of filter paper can easily be
identified. These laboratory skills were important in the next phase of Sanger's
research.

Sanger's work had been supported initially by a Beit Fellowship and later by the
Medical Research Council (MRC). In 1962, he moved to the new MRC Laboratory
of Molecular Biology at Cambridge. This move brought Sanger into contact with
Francis Crick, who had revealed the double helical structure of deoxyribonucleic
acid (DNA), and with other scientists who were experienced in nucleic acid chemistry. Sanger realized the importance of sequencing these molecules.

Nucleic acids have only four units, compared to the twenty found in proteins.
This made the task of sequencing them more difficult, since small fragments were
much more likely to contain the same groups. At the time that Sanger began his
work, only one small molecule of transfer RNA had been sequenced. The Cambridge group sought to develop a rapid, simple method for nucleic acid sequencing.
Nucleotides have three parts—a base (which varies), a sugar, and a phosphate link.
Sanger proposed using a radioactive phosphorus as his label with the RNA, much as
he had used the FDNB colored dye to label his proteins. Similar methods of partial
polymer degradation with enzymes were employed.

A strand of RNA was digested with an enzyme, t-ribonuclease. This enzyme broke the molecule after every guanine residue. The problem of purifying the fractions from the enzymatic degradations was solved by using two-dimensional autoradiography on cellulose acetate and ion exchange paper. A plot of the results showed Sanger a definite pattern (graticle) that proved to be a great aid in determining the composition of larger nucleotides. The time for analysis of the results was cut considerably.

Sanger next developed a method for studying the isolated nucleotides from these fractions. These smaller units, or oligonucleotides, were treated with an exonuclease, an enzyme that sequentially removed the first base. The segments were identified by their placement on a chromatographic sheet. Sanger employed the technique to sequence the RNA of a bacteriophage (a bacterial virus) whose protein sequence was known. This work confirmed the "genetic code," the fact that a specific series of nucleic acids dictates the production of a particular amino acid. Sanger had presented the research community with a better method of sequencing RNA.

In the mid-1960's, Sanger began to attack the sequencing of DNA. The methods for RNA were adapted and used successfully for molecules containing up to about fifty nucleotides. A faster approach was needed, however, if molecules of hundreds or thousands of nucleotides were to be studied.

A "copying procedure" began to address this need. DNA polymerase, an enzyme that makes a new strand of DNA from an existing single strand, was used to incorporate radiolabeled ribonucleotides into a DNA segment. The new DNA so formed had a weak link wherever the ribonucleotide was inserted; thus, it could be split, fractionated, and analyzed. This method enabled Sanger to sequence a section of DNA of about eighty nucleotides, but since the smallest DNA genomes (genetic materials) from a bacteriophage consisted of about five thousand nucleotides, better methods were still needed.

In the work with the DNA polymerase, Sanger noticed that the use of small amounts of a particular labeled nucleotide led to the synthesis of DNA fragments of various sizes that all stopped before they got to the nucleotide that was in short supply. This suggested a new approach to sequencing—fractionating the segments according to their size: The relative size would be proportional to their location in the larger DNA. Sanger said, "This new approach to DNA sequencing was I think the best idea I ever had, being original and ultimately successful." With this "plus and minus" technique, Sanger determined almost the total sequence of a bacteriophage of 5,386 nucleotides.

Eventually, modified nucleotides that could be incorporated into a growing DNA segment and then halt its growth were found. Low concentrations of these "dideoxy" nucleotides of each of the DNA bases were mixed, in separate reactions, with the DNA polymerase, nucleotides, and other needed reaction materials. At the end of the reaction, each system contained segments of varying length that stopped with a particular base. The segments were separated according to their size by gel electrophoresis, a process in which electrical current is used to move charged molecules. The locations of the segments could be seen easily on an autoradiograph. As the four gels were aligned parallel to one another, the exact sequence could be read directly.

This new dideoxy method was excellent. Most DNA, however, is not of the single-stranded variety that the DNA polymerase required. This need caused Sanger to move to techniques for cloning the single strands needed by using a bacteriophage vector. Cloning procedures were also used in the purification of the fractions.

One of the most important early applications of the dideoxy method was the sequencing of the DNA of the human mitochondrion. This organelle, nicknamed the "powerhouse" of the cell, is critical in metabolism. Investigation of the DNA sequence of the mitochondrion revealed that the genetic code is not universal, as was previously believed. The three nucleotides that indicate a termination in other systems code for the amino acid tryptophan in mitochondrial DNA. The DNA studied in this work had 16,569 nucleotides.

At the time when Sanger and his Cambridge colleagues were developing fast and reliable methods for nucleic acid sequencing, Walter Gilbert of Harvard University was perfecting an alternate procedure. Both scientists shared the 1980 Nobel Prize in Chemistry (along with a third chemist, Paul Berg) for their contributions to the revolution in methodology. Frederick Sanger retired from his laboratory in 1983 when he reached the age of sixty-five.

Bibliography

Primary
CHEMISTRY: "The Chemistry of Insulin," *Annual Reports of the Progress of Chemistry: Chemical Society*, vol. 45, 1949; "The Amino-Acid Sequence in the Glycol Chain of Insulin: The Identification of Lower Peptides from Partial Hydrolysates," *Biochemical Journal*, vol. 53, 1953 (with E. O. P. Thompson); "A Rapid Method for Determining Sequences in DNA by Primed Synthesis with DNA Polymerase," *Journal of Molecular Biology*, vol. 94, 1975 (with A. R. Coulson); "DNA Sequencing with Chain-Terminating Inhibitors," *Proceedings of the National Academy of Sciences, USA*, vol. 74, 1977 (with S. Nicklen and A. R. Coulson); "Sequencing and Organization of the Human Genome," *Nature*, vol. 290, 1981 (with S. Anderson, A. T. Bankier, B. G. Barrell, and others); "Nucleotide Sequence of Bacteriophage Lambda DNA," *Journal of Molecular Biology*, vol. 162, 1982 (with A. R. Coulson, G. F. Hong, D. F. Hill, and G. B. Petersen).
CAREER AUTOBIOGRAPHY: "Sequences, Sequences, and Sequences," *Annual Reviews of Biochemistry*, vol. 57, 1988.

Secondary
Dickerson, Richard, and Irving Geis. *The Structure and Action of Proteins*. New

York: Benjamin/Cummings, 1969. This small paperback book is probably the best way to grasp the significance and beauty of the work in protein structure that was done by Sanger and other scientists. The drawings demonstrate the concepts in ways no text will permit.

Judson, Horace Freeland. *The Eighth Day of Creation: Makers of the Revolution in Biology.* New York: Simon & Schuster, 1979. This popular account of the beginnings of molecular biology cites Sanger's contributions no fewer than twenty times and presents him as one of the "quiet men, less known to the public," who are deeply respected within the scientific community for their insightful work.

Kolata, Gina Bari. "The 1980 Nobel Prize in Chemistry." *Science* 210 (1980): 887-889. This article provides a concise statement of Sanger's work in nucleic acid chemistry. It contrasts Sanger's sequencing method and his personality with those of Walter Gilbert, with whom he shared his second Nobel Prize.

Tausk, Marius. *Pharmacology of Hormones*. Chicago: Georg Thieme, 1975. This small text on hormones contains an excellent chapter on insulin. It discusses Sanger's work in the larger context of the physiological importance of this pancreatic hormone. It provides the general reader with information on diabetes mellitus and the therapeutic effect of insulin.

Thompson, E. O. P. "The Insulin Molecule." *Scientific American* 192 (May, 1955): 36-41. This article provides the general audience with a lucid account of the steps that Sanger followed to determine the sequence of insulin. It presents clear diagrams of the paper chromatography of the amino acids of insulin, of the complete molecule, and of the peptides that were lined up to determine the amino-acid sequences of the A chain. Thompson was a collaborator of Sanger's.

Helen M. Burke

1959

Chemistry
Jaroslav Heyrovský, Czechoslovakia

Physics
Emilio Gino Segrè, United States
Owen Chamberlain, United States

Physiology or Medicine
Severo Ochoa, United States
Arthur Kornberg, United States

Literature
Salvatore Quasimodo, Italy

Peace
Philip Noel-Baker, Great Britain

JAROSLAV HEYROVSKÝ
1959

Born: Prague, Czechoslovakia; December 20, 1890
Died: Prague, Czechoslovakia; March 27, 1967
Nationality: Czechoslovak
Areas of concentration: Electrochemistry and polarography

Heyrovský discovered and developed polarography, one of the first microanalytical tools available to chemists. It subsequently became a major technique for measuring ion diffusion, equilibrium constants, electron transfer mechanism, and many other chemical and physical parameters

The Award

Presentation

Professor Arne Ölander, a Swedish chemist and a member of the Nobel Committee for Chemistry, delivered the presentation address for awarding the 1959 Nobel Prize in Chemistry to Jaroslav Heyrovský. Ölander stressed the importance of polarography to analytical chemistry and the ability of polarographers to measure accurately small analytical samples and many physico-chemical parameters. He detailed how Heyrovský, early in his career, influenced by Professor Bohumil Kučera of Prague, became interested in the irregularities of the capillarity of mercury, and how this study led to the invention of the polarograph and its use in microanalyses. He also described how Heyrovský tediously made current-voltage measurements that, with the help of his Japanese collaborator Masuzo Shikata, led to the construction of one of the first recording chemical instruments. The apparatus was called a polarograph, and the current-voltage trace it produced was known as a polarogram.

It was nearly a decade before the potential of Heyrovský's discovery was recognized outside his own laboratory, but upon recognition of its merits, it rapidly became widely accepted for its enhancement of microanalyses. Later, Heyrovský and his collaborators were able to solve numerous chemical problems; with a polarograph, almost every element and many organic compounds can be analyzed.

Ölander continued by describing a few special polarographic techniques, but in closing returned to discussing Heyrovský's original instrument; he informed the audience that polarographs were found in most analytical laboratories throughout the world and that they greatly reduced the time and cost of chemical analyses.

Nobel lecture

On Friday, December 11, 1959, Heyrovský delivered his Nobel lecture, entitled "The Trends of Polarography." The laureate opened his lecture with a defense of his lifetime devotion to polarography. He stressed the importance of the dropping mercury electrode in polarography and took time to explain the unique properties of the electrode, which consists of mercury flowing through a capillary from a 0.4 to a 1.0 meter column of mercury. The drop is spherical, reproducible, and of pure metal with a low electrical resistance. It can be polarized—that is, it will assume the voltage of an external voltage source applied to the system. When placed in a conducting solution in tandem with an indifferent or nonpolarizable electrode, the current and voltage can be accurately measured for the electrochemical reaction occurring at the polarizable electrode surface. He alluded to the fact that the voltage of the nonpolarizable electrode is independent of the voltage applied to the system, and its electrochemical reactions do not interfere with the reaction that occurs at the mercury electrode.

By varying the voltage applied to the dropping mercury electrode, Heyrovský was able to make qualitative and quantitative measurements of hundreds of chemical substances. Until 1924, he used a manual galvanometer to measure the current between the electrodes. In 1924, in collaboration with Masuzo Shikata, he developed an automatic instrument for measuring both the applied voltage and current. The resulting graph was called a polarogram. These current-voltage curves, or polarograms, were classified as faradaic currents (current produced by electrolysis) or nonfaradaic currents (the capacitor currents). The nonfaradaic current is very small but significant, Heyrovský said, especially when an oscilloscope is used to follow the reaction or when materials are being studied at very low concentrations.

Since a change in the current flow only occurs at the half-wave voltage for the chemical in the solution, polarography is used for qualitative analysis. (The amount of current is a quantitative measurement of the amount of the chemical in the solution.) Because the dropping mercury electrode is a microelectrode, the current is dependent upon the rate at which the chemical can diffuse to the electrode surface. Heyrovský painstakingly explained this phenomenon and the exactness of the D. Ilkovič and M. Koutecký equations for explaining these physical parameters.

Heyrovský continued his lecture by describing how, in 1943, Wiesner discovered that a chemical change may be necessary before an electrochemical reaction can occur. From this discovery, J. M. Los, L. B. Simpson, and Karel Wiesner determined the chemical properties of glucose. Other investigators showed that catalytic reaction may also produce currents which are much greater than predicted by the Ilkovič equation; Rudolf Brdieka applied this phenomenon to serology for studying individuals with cancer and liver diseases.

Heyrovský gave a short explanation of the properties and basis for electrochemical maxima, the large current that occurs for some substances and distorts the polarograms. Polarography has been studied in nonaqueous solvents, for example, in liquid gases such as sulfur dioxide and ammonia and in fused salts such as sodium chloride and potassium chloride. Heyrovský emphasized that the theory derived for aqueous media also applies to nonaqueous media, and, since polarographic waves are highly reproducible, the application of higher mathematical techniques to polarograms yields more sensitive methods for analyzing substances at low concentrations. He explained some of the later polarographic developments, including square wave polarography, the combination of polarography and radio-chemical techniques to analyze trace quantities of radioisotopes with the same mass number, and the development of amperometric titrations and tensammetric measurements.

Throughout his talk, Heyrovský gave credit to his numerous collaborators and to the scientists who used his discovery for the enhancement of theoretical and practical chemistry.

Critical reception

Jaroslav Heyrovský received the Nobel Prize at a time when East-West political tensions were high. A number of politicians and scientists alike had objected to the closing of the East German border, which led to the building of the Berlin Wall in 1961. Thus some question existed whether it was appropriate to give the distinguished prize to a scientist in a Communist nation. Fortunately, the scientific Nobel Committee was not (and has never been) motivated by politics.

Heyrovský himself tried to remain neutral regarding the political tensions. When informed that he would receive the Nobel Prize in Chemistry, he read a prepared statement to the Czechoslovak news agency, *Ceteka*, which officially reported his response, "My happiness is twofold, since this is the first time in the history of the Nobel Prize that a citizen of the Czechoslovak Republic has received it. [Second,] it is further evidence that new roads for still closer and more fruitful cooperation between scientists of both world systems now are opening up."

Little was reported in the press except that he had received his award for the development of the polarograph. Political tensions prevented direct interviews with the laureate by Western journalists, and most scientists expressed a satisfaction with the committee's selection. Speculation arose, however, about whether Heyrovský would be allowed to travel to Stockholm to receive the prize. If the Czech government ever showed reluctance at granting permission for the laureate to receive his prize in person, it was never evident to Western scientists or newsmen.

Time magazine reported, on November 9, 1959, that the Nobel Prize in Chemistry was being given to J. Heyrovský "as a much-belated recognition for his discovery of polarography, a delicate electrical method of chemical analyses." It described polarography as "measuring of the properties of ions," saying that it "can detect slight traces of metals in a drop or two of a complex solution. Discovered in 1925, polarography is still used all over the world by analytical chemists." *The Wall Street Journal* had reported a few days earlier that the inventor of the polarograph, a fast, accurate analytical tool widely used in metallurgy, had been nominated for the prize. The most common comment in the press was that it was about time that the man was recognized for his outstanding contribution to electrochemistry.

Reporting on the Nobel presentation, *The New York Times* (December 12, 1959) stated simply that the King of Sweden presented the award to Heyrovský for inventing the polarograph. At the Nobel banquet, Heyrovský noted that he was the first Czech to receive the award and hailed the Nobel awards committee for fostering a closer understanding between the two ruling political systems with the aim of strengthening international peace.

Heyrovský was well known for his willingness to collaborate with scientists in other countries. Because of his openness, generosity, modesty, and politeness, there was a general reluctance to criticize the award procedure; even less was said about the political situation until after the scientist's death.

A primary reason for awarding him the Nobel Prize was clearly the fact that polarography had become "one of the most important methods of contemporary analysis," as detailed by Ölander during his presentation speech. Because the scientist had never been a political figure either under the Habsburg rule in the early part of the century, during the Nazi occupation of Czechoslovakia during World War II, or after the Communists came to power in 1948, and because few nonchemists understood what was meant by polarography, many popular news publications failed to mention his selection. The Nobel award was applauded by scientists, especially chemists, but largely ignored by other segments of the society.

Biography

Jaroslav Heyrovský was born in Prague, Czechoslovakia, on December 20, 1890, the fifth of six children of Leopold Heyrovský and Klára Hanlová. Leopold Heyrovský was professor of Roman law at the Czech University of Prague. Jaroslav Heyrovský was educated at the *Gymnasium* in his native city and in 1909 began his science education at the Czech University of Prague (then called Charles-Ferdinand University). He transferred the next year to University College, London, where he studied under William Ramsay, William C. M. Lewis, and Frederick G. Donnan; the latter inspired Heyrovský's lifelong interest in electrochemistry. In 1913, he received a B.S. degree from University College. While a demonstrator in physical chemistry there, he became interested in the electrochemistry of aluminum, a research problem that supplied him with the subject of his doctoral thesis.

World War I broke out while Heyrovský was in Prague on vacation, and he was prevented from returning to London. He served as a dispensing chemist and radiologist in an Austro-Hungarian military hospital during World War I. He continued his studies under Professor Bohumil Kučera during the war and received a Ph.D. from the Charles-Ferdinand University of Prague in the autumn of 1918. After the war, he returned to London, where he earned a science doctorate in 1921.

Heyrovský joined the faculty of Charles-Ferdinand University in 1921 as an assistant to Professor Bohyslav Brauner in the Institute of Analytical Chemistry. He was promoted to associate professor in 1922 and professor of physical chemistry in 1926. On February 22, 1926, he married Marie Koránová. They had two children, a daughter, Judith, and a son, Michael. During the 1920's, he founded the Czechoslovakian School of Polarography and, from 1926 until 1954, was professor of physical chemistry. During the German occupation of Prague (1939-1945), J. Böhm, a highly qualified German scientist, was appointed professor of physical chemistry. Böhm had no sympathies for Nazism and provided Heyrovský with the opportunity to continue his research during this difficult time. In 1950, Heyrovský became director of the newly established Central Polarographic Institute and was inducted into the Czechoslovak Academy of Sciences in 1952, upon its reorganization. In 1964, the Polarographic Institute was renamed the Heyrovský Institute of Polarography and incorporated into the Academy of Sciences. Throughout most of his career, Heyrovský remained in Czechoslovakia; he did visit the United States in 1933 as a Carnegie visiting professor at the University of California and other United States universities. In 1934, he was invited to present one of the addresses at the Dmitry Mendeleyev centenary in Leningrad.

Heyrovský was elected a Fellow of University College, London, in 1927 and received honorary doctorates from the Technical University at Dresden (1955), University of Warsaw (1956), University of Aix-Marseilles, France (1959), and the University of Paris (1960). He was granted honorary membership in the American Academy of Arts and Sciences (1933), the Hungarian Academy of Sciences (1955), the Indian Academy of Sciences (1955), the Polish Academy of Sciences (1962), German Academy of Sciences (1955), and Royal Danish Academy of Sciences (1962). In 1965, he was elected a foreign member of the Royal Society. He was the first president of the Polarographic Society, London. Czechoslovakia awarded him the State Prize, First Class, and the Order of the Czechoslovak Republic; he was the first Czechoslovakian citizen ever to win a Nobel Prize. Heyrovský died in Prague in 1967.

Scientific Career

Jaroslav Heyrovský's interest in polarography and electrochemistry began while he was a student at University College, London, and continued throughout his life. He was a leader in this continuously expanding and changing scientific field, but he paid a high price for his eminent position; for years, he worked eleven-hour days and spent almost every free minute, including weekends, in the laboratory. He sacrificed his personal interests in literature, music, and sports in order to advance the science of polarography. His enthusiasm for the work impressed everyone who met him, however, and many future researchers made electrochemistry their scientific field after listening to him extol the virtues of the dropping mercury electrode.

Frederick G. Donnan became professor of physical chemistry at London University in 1913, the year that Heyrovský began his postgraduate work. The eminent physical chemist suggested that Heyrovský determine the electrode potential for aluminum, which was hampered by the rapid oxidation of the metal, among other problems. Donnan suggested that Heyrovský use a dilute mercury amalgam and allow the amalgam to flow through a capillary. This method gave Heyrovský a fresh metal surface and had a profound effect upon his later investigations.

The outbreak of World War I found Heyrovský in Prague, and in January, 1915, he was conscripted into the Austro-Hungarian army. Fortunately, his weak physical condition prohibited his joining a fighting unit, and he was assigned to a military hospital in Prague, where he continued his studies on the electrochemistry of aluminum under Bohumil Kučera at Charles-Ferdinand University. He passed the final examination for his Ph.D. on September 26, 1918.

On one of Heyrovský's physics exams, Professor Kučera asked a question concerning the electrocapillarity of mercury. Heyrovský attacked the problem with such a profound approach that the senior professor invited the young scientist to visit him and demonstrated a dropping mercury electrode using a glass capillary. Kučera suggested that Heyrovský investigate the problems associated with the capillarity of mercury. For two years, Heyrovský collected mercury drops at various voltages, weighed them, and plotted the weight as a function of voltage.

In 1919, Heyrovský regained his fellowship at University College, London, which had been lost during the war, published three papers on the electroaffinity of aluminum in the *Transactions of the Chemical Society, London,* and submitted his papers as the basis of the thesis for his doctor of science degree, which was conferred upon him in 1921.

Upon returning to Charles-Ferdinand University, Heyrovský continued his studies on the use of the mercury drop as an electrolysis electrode, but he was not satisfied with accurate and reproducible decomposition potentials (potential is a measurement similar to voltage). He expanded his work by measuring both the current and the potential across the dropping mercury electrode using a galvanometer and potentiometer that he borrowed from the physics department. He obtained the first polarograms and described them in *Chemické Listy* in 1922. Being able to obtain both current and voltage measurements excited him, and he put aside the studies on the anomalies associated with the electrocapillarity of mercury.

Heyrovský presented his first paper abroad on November 23, 1923, at the Faraday Society meeting in London. There he met a young Japanese colleague, Masuzo Shikata. Up to this time, both chemists had tediously made point-by-point current-voltage measurements. The two scientists collaborated to construct an apparatus that automatically registered reproducible current-voltage curves; reducing the measurement time from more than an hour to a few minutes. They called their instrument a polarograph and the resulting curves polarograms.

By 1925, Heyrovský had completed the basic development of polarography— electrochemical studies at a mercury microelectrode. Initially he used a large nonpolarizable electrode and a very small polarizable mercury drop electrode. With this arrangement, the current was a measure of the quantity of species (the particular kinds of atoms or molecules) present at the electrode surface, and the potential was a qualitative method for identifying the chemical in a solution. Because of the high hydrogen overvoltage on the mercury electrode, the mercury electrode could be used for a number of species too negative for studying at normal metal surfaces. Attempts to relate the current between solid electrodes and the concentration in the solution had been attempted before Heyrovský's time; however, the changes in electrode surfaces had obscured the results, and few useful data were obtained from the experiments. Using the mercury electrode, Heyrovský was able to overcome these difficulties. The wide fluctuation in current with the change in mercury drop surface area posed a major obstacle, however, which was solved by using a highly damped galvanometer. This decision was subsequently proved to be theoretically sound.

Heyrovský's work was little noticed outside his own laboratory until 1933, when the Carnegie Endowment for International Peace arranged a visit to the United States. His tour, which included lectures at the University of California and Stanford and Princeton universities, was reported in February issues of *The New York Times*, which not only printed a summary of the man's lecture but also included a picture of him and his instrument. The article described the polarograph as an instrument for chemical analyses of liquids and solids by "merely pressing an electric switch, automatically registering on paper in four of five minutes both the kind and amount of chemical substance present." Since the instrument could measure the contents and quality of alcoholic beverages, the article was entitled "Automatic Device Can Test Liquor," a very appropriate title, since prohibition would be repealed in the United States later in the year of the scientist's visit.

In his Carnegie lecture, Heyrovský extolled the polarograph's potential in research laboratories and in industry; he foresaw it as being used to understand fundamental fermentation processes and to determine the composition of ores, alloys, rocks, waters, gases, minerals, and meteorites. He predicted that it would greatly save time and improve the accuracy of the analytical results, a prophecy that was well-fulfilled by the time he was honored by the Nobel committee.

During the late 1920's and early 1930's, Heyrovský attracted a number of brilliant students and colleagues, who developed much of modern electrochemical theory. Although much of the initial work predates Heyrovský's invention, it was never understood until the polarograph became the electrochemical instrument for studying electron transfer and ion migration. Polarographic techniques were expanded by substituting a microrotating platinum electrode for the dropping mercury electrode, developing new cell geometries, and creating new modes of stirring the solutions and methods for the addition of reagents. Heyrovský's invention had become the key to modern electrochemistry.

In 1933, Heyrovský published his first book on polarography; three years later he wrote volume 2 of *Physikalische Methoden der analytischen Chemie* (physical methods of analytical chemistry) on polarography. In 1941, Otto H. Müller began to write a series of articles for the *Journal of Chemical Education* on the inventor's work.

During World War II, Heyrovský's work was interrupted by the closing of Charles-Ferdinand University, but German appointee J. Böhm provided the polarographer with the opportunity to continue his work. Heyrovský used a cathode-ray oscillograph not only to replace the galvanometer in his system but also to extend fundamental studies. Because of the restrictions placed on him during World War II, much of this work was not published until the 1950's.

After the war, Heyrovský actively lectured, presented seminars, and supervised the work of postgraduate students. His devotion to the work pushed Czechoslovak polarography to the foreground of electrochemical research, and, after World War II, the department of physical chemistry at Charles-Ferdinand University became the center of polarographic research.

In 1950, the Central Polarographic Institute was formed, and Heyrovský became its first director. In 1952, he was inducted into the Czechoslovak Academy of Sciences but poor health forced him to reduce his work load, a result of the privation suffered during World War II. In 1962, he became seriously ill and, in 1963, was forced to relinquish the post of director of the institute to his longtime colleague, Rudolf Brdička. In 1964, the institute was renamed the Jaroslav Heyrovský Institute of Polarography, Czechoslovak Academy of Science, and, in 1965, Anton A. Vlček became the director.

Even though he recovered from the illness he suffered in 1962, Heyrovský was no longer able to work full-time; he continued to visit the institute and took an active part in the lectures, seminars, and addresses by his coworkers. His guiding hand was always present, and his continued visits and advice enhanced the institute's operation. His last visit occurred a few days prior to his death.

Heyrovský's prophetic intuition of 1933 came true. By the time the Nobel Committee recognized his work, a polarograph could be found in almost all university and industrial analytical laboratories, and more than twenty thousand papers had been published on techniques and polarographic measurements by the time of the inventor's death. Better electronics continued to produce better polarographs, but other instruments eventually surpassed the polarograph in ease of use and level of determination. The height of polarographic application occurred about the time of the inventor's death.

Early in his career, Heyrovský recognized the need to disseminate scientific information. Even through administration was not his area of expertise, he organized (along with Emil Votěcek) the Collection of Czechoslovak Chemical Communications in 1927, which by the time of Heyrovský's death had become one of the world's prestigious scientific journals. The early issues of the journal contain many excellent papers on the early significance of polarography and serve as an excellent historic source. In 1938, Heyrovský began to produce a bibliography of polarography and was aided by other recognized scientists, although none was as important as his wife Marie, who chose to remain anonymous throughout its fifteen editions.

Heyrovský modeled his work on that of Michael Faraday, but he was also an admirer of Isaac Newton. Both Faraday's famous words, "Work, finish, publish," and Newton's statement, "A man must resolve either to produce nothing new or to become a slave to defend it," were inscribed on his laboratory walls. Heyrovský's interest in the development of polarography did not overshadow his interest in human beings. The interest in the work of his coworkers was deep and genuine. His hospitality was proverbial, and he always welcomed collaboration with other scientists. He worked hard, however, and demanded the same from his colleagues. He often stood on the staircase looking at his watch to note those who arrived after the eight o'clock starting time. He hated to see dust on the instruments or to observe the reading of newspapers in the laboratory, and he usually forced smokers to leave the institute building for a smoke. He took time to feed the squirrels in the institute's garden, however, liked a good joke, and was always present at the institute's annual parties and at the soccer matches.

Although other, earlier Nobel Prize winners were electrochemists, Heyrovský was the first electrochemist to receive the prize in more than forty years. Undoubtedly he, more than any other scientist, made electrochemistry an important midtwentieth century area of research. Unfortunately, his political prophecy that greater cooperation would occur between East and West did not come true within his lifetime.

Bibliography

Primary
CHEMISTRY: "Electrode Reactions and Equilibria," *Chemical News*, vol. 129, 1924; "The Processes at the Dropping Mercury Cathode, I: The Deposition of Metals," *Transactions of the Faraday Society*, vol. 19, 1924; "The Processes at the Dropping Mercury Cathode, II: The Hydrogen Overpotential," *Transactions of the Faraday Society*, vol. 19, 1924; "Researches with the Dropping Mercury Cathode," *Recueil des travaux chimiques des Pays-bas*, vol. 44, 1925; "Maxima on Current-Voltage Curves," *Transactions of the Faraday Society*, vol. 24, 1928 (with N. V. Emelianova); "The Deposition of Radium and Other Alkaline Earth Metals at the Dropping Mercury Cathode," *Collection of Czechoslovak Chemical Communications*, vol. 1, 1929; *Použití polarografické methody v praktické chemii*, 1933; *Polarographisches Praktikum: Anleitungen für die chemische Laboratoriumspraxis*, 1948 (*Guide for Chemical Laboratory Usage of Polarography*, 1968); *Oscilografická polarografie*, 1953 (with J. Forejt); *Základy polarografie*, 1962 (with J. Kůta; *Principles of Polarography*, 1965).

Secondary
Belcher, R. Obituary in *Nature* 214 (1967): 953. A short tribute to the developer of the polarograph by one of the past presidents of the Royal Society of Chemistry.
Butler, J. A.V., and P. Zuman. Obituary in *Biographical Memoirs of Fellows of the Royal Society* 13 (1967): 167-182. A very detailed description of the man and his work presented by a colleague and a former student. The authors use considerable chemical terminology. At the end of the obituary is a list of 193 of Heyrovský's papers from 1932 to 1966. It is one of the most complete bibliographies of his work.
Heyrovská, Marie. "Polarographic Literature." In *Festschrift: Progress in Polarography*, edited by Petr Zuman and I. M. Kolthoff. New York: Interscience, 1962. Historic information on the development of the polarograph and its analytical techniques.
Kolthoff, I. M., and J. J. Lingane. *Polarography*. 2 vols. New York: Interscience, 1952. This is a classic book, but it is severely out of date in regard to the theory

and practice of polarography. It contains much historic information on the early development of polarography, especially on the contribution by the inventor. Requires extensive chemical knowledge for complete comprehension.

Laitinen, Herbert A., and Galen W. Ewing. *A History of Analytical Chemistry.* Washington, D.C.: American Chemical Society, 1977. The authors present a review of the development of analytical chemistry from the end of the nineteenth century to the mid-1970's. The book consists of observations made by prominent analytical chemists. A number of American chemists who met Heyrovský present personal comments on the man and his work.

Ölander, Arne. "Jaroslav Heyrovský, Nobel Prize Winner." *Review of Polarography* 8 (1960). A short review of his Nobel Prize address and presentation.

Teich, Mikulas. "Jaroslav Heyrovský." In *Dictionary of Scientific Biography.* Edited by Charles C. Gillispie. New York: Charles Scribner's Sons, 1972. A detailed biography of Heyrovský that includes a discussion of his work, his Nobel address, and his influence on his coworkers. The article is presented in such a manner that minimal scientific knowledge is required in order to understand the man and his work.

Zuman, P., and P. J. E. Elving. "Jaroslav Heyrovský: Nobel Laureate." *Journal of Chemical Education* 37 (1960): 572. A short tribute to the scientist upon his winning the Nobel Prize by a colleague and a former student.

Larry R. Sherman

1960

Chemistry
Willard Frank Libby, United States

Physics
Donald A. Glaser, United States

Physiology or Medicine
Sir Macfarlane Burnet, Australia
Peter B. Medawar, Great Britain

Literature
Saint-John Perse, France

Peace
Albert Lutuli, South Africa

WILLARD FRANK LIBBY
1960

Born: Grand Valley, Colorado; December 17, 1908
Died: Los Angeles, California; September 8, 1980
Nationality: American
Area of concentration: Nuclear chemistry

Libby's work convinced him that all organic matter has a level of radioactivity that remains constant throughout its lifetime, but that its radioactive carbon 14 begins to decay as soon as life ceases. Libby speculated that by measuring the carbon 14 in nonliving biological material, it should be possible to measure the time since death

The Award

Presentation

Professor Arne F. Westgren, Chair of the Nobel Committee for Chemistry of the Royal Swedish Academy of Sciences, presented Willard Frank Libby for the Nobel Prize in Chemistry on December 10, 1960. In his presentation speech, Westgren noted that in this award the academy recognized work that deepened understanding in a variety of fields rather than work that materially improved living standards.

Westgren explained Libby's initial theory, based on his extensive study of weakly radioactive substances, that as soon as life ends, organisms cease to assimilate the carbon 14 isotope formed in the upper atmosphere and regularly absorbed in small quantities by all living things. When it is formed, this isotope has considerable energy, causing it to oxidize almost immediately to carbon dioxide, which spreads evenly in the atmosphere.

Westgren alluded to (but did not go into detail about) Libby's testing of his hypothesis by devising equipment to measure the small radioactive emissions of material up to seventy thousand years old. Rather, he pointed to the practical outcomes of Libby's research for such fields as archaeology, geology, geophysics, and oceanography. Libby's work enabled researchers to achieve an accuracy in their dating that they could not approach with previous methods.

Noting that more than forty institutions had installed radiocarbon dating laboratories, Westgren indicated the field's growth. He reported that several thousand carbon datings are made every year, all of them published in a general review, giving researchers throughout the world access to the information.

Nobel lecture

Willard Libby's Nobel lecture, "Radiocarbon Dating," delivered in Stockholm on a snowy Monday, December 12, 1960, was a model of lucidity. After he traced the origins of radiocarbon dating theory in earlier research on cosmic rays, Libby identified the four major stages through which the process proceeded from hypothesis to practical application.

Libby noted that when Serge Korff and others discovered in 1939 that cosmic rays produce secondary neutrons in their first collisions in the utmost reaches of the upper atmosphere, it was determined that approximately two neutrons were generated every second for each square centimeter of the earth's surface. Because the primary cosmic rays produced more than a billion volts, it was almost impossible to predict what their nuclei were like. The neutrons, however, being secondary products, were in the million-volt range of energy generation and could be studied. Korff's work indicated that neutrons disappear by forming radiocarbon.

From this beginning, Libby speculated that all living matter absorbs minute quantities of the radioactive carbon 14, whose half-life is 5,730 years. The absorption of carbon 14 ceases at the death of the organism, so the carbon decays slowly and reforms as nitrogen 14. It should follow, then, that if the amount of radioactive carbon 14 in nonliving organisms, which exists in a constant equilibrium, can be measured accurately—given what is known about its half-life—its age should be capable of fairly accurate estimation.

The next stage, Libby explained, was to develop a means of testing the hypothesis by creating a practical radiocarbon dating machine, which he finally did. Once this mechanism existed, Libby had to determine whether the assumptions on which his theory was based held equally for all areas of Earth. Libby and his colleagues tested material from the north and south polar regions as well as from other parts of the world to make sure that the movement of wind and ocean currents did not affect their radiocarbon content per gram of carbon.

This testing revealed that latitude did not affect the radiocarbon content of organic matter; the next step was to test the accuracy of the radiocarbon dating machine by using it to date organic matter whose age was known. Libby tested the inner cores of ancient trees, whose annual circles revealed their age, and such other items as organic materials from Egyptian tombs whose age had been reliably ascertained.

Cautious in presenting his material, qualifying it frequently lest any small error exist in the testing he and his colleagues had done, Libby then proceeded to indicate the applicability of radiocarbon dating techniques to oceanography and other fields, indicating that deep water subjected to his tests also revealed its age and that of the sediment with which it was mixed. He explained how he tested relatively new methane gas from the sewers of Baltimore along with old methane in the form of petroleum, whose organic matter had been dead beyond the limits that his technique could date.

He closed by saying that the group at University of California at Los Angeles with whom he worked hoped to develop an inexpensive portable radiocarbon dating machine for use in the field. He confirmed that thousands of datings done up to 1960 had proved reliable.

Critical reception

Many publications that reported the awarding of the 1960 Nobel Prizes noted that this was the first time that two faculty members of the same institution, working independently, had been awarded prizes concurrently. Donald A. Glaser, of the University of California at Berkeley, received the prize in physics for his invention of the bubble chamber. Willard Libby, also a faculty member of the University of California, was based at the Los Angeles campus. *Newsweek*, reporting the awards in its November 14, 1960, issue, noted that California had produced a dozen Nobel laureates in chemistry and physics.

Shortly before the award was announced, Libby had been under a cloud. He had just ended a term as commissioner of the Atomic Energy Commission (AEC), having been appointed to that post in 1954 by President Dwight D. Eisenhower. In that position, Libby had tried to deemphasize to the public the danger of radioactive fallout from the testing of nuclear weapons, calling the risk small. In a *Saturday Review* editorial (April 4, 1959), Norman Cousins accused Libby and his colleague Edward Teller of putting false facts before the American people to mollify them, because they believed that American security would be compromised if nuclear testing were banned.

In a detailed letter to *The Nation* (May 9, 1959), Walter Schneir accused Libby of denying that he had seen the highly critical report of E. A. Martell on atomic fallout, yet Schneir produced evidence that Libby had referred to findings from that report in a speech some time earlier. Schneir called Libby's theories about fallout "leaky." Libby left the Atomic Energy Commission during this wave of criticism and had been at the University of California for slightly more than a year when his Nobel Prize was announced.

Given this context, it is not surprising that most public notices of the award, including those in *The New York Times* (November 4 and 6, 1960), in *The Times* of London (November 4, 1960), and in such journals as *Physics Today* (January, 1961), *Scientific American* (December, 1960), and *Nucleonics* (December, 1960), confined themselves to explaining the techniques of radiocarbon dating and made no value judgments about Libby's appropriateness for the award. His work on radiocarbon dating was quite different from the work in which he had been involved when he held his political appointment, and his accomplishments were generally discussed with no allusion to his pronouncements as Atomic Energy Commissioner.

All reports in American publications of the Nobel awards dealt with Libby and Glaser together, paying much less attention to an Australian and an Englishman who had also been honored. *The Times* of London report in November paid more attention to Libby's award than to Glaser's, discussing Libby first and at greater length than it did Glaser.

This paper, however, like *The New York Times*, did not report on the acceptance speeches of either American recipient. *The Times* of London confined its December reportage to covering the state banquet held for the laureates on December 11, indicating that the entire royal household attended.

Biography

Willard Frank Libby's father, Ora Edward Libby, was a farmer; his mother, Eva May (née Rivers) Libby, a housewife. Born in Grand Valley, Colorado, on December 17, 1908, Libby began his education in a two-room Colorado schoolhouse. Before he reached high school age, however, his parents moved to the Russian River area of California near Sebastopol, where Libby finished high school, after which he enrolled in the University of California at Berkeley. He received the bachelor of science degree in chemistry in 1931 and the Ph.D. two years later.

Libby became an instructor in chemistry at Berkeley in 1933 and, by 1941, rose to the rank of associate professor. Also in that year, he received a yearlong Guggenheim Memorial Fellowship that enabled him to work at Princeton University. His fellowship year ended abruptly, however, when the United States entered World War II in December, 1941. The University of California granted Libby leave for the duration, and the tall, bespectacled young chemist with the receding hairline soon was at Columbia University working on the Manhattan Project.

At war's end, Libby became professor of chemistry at the University of Chicago, where he was associated with what was later to be dubbed the Enrico Fermi Institute for Nuclear Studies. He remained there until his appointment to the U.S. Atomic Energy Commission in 1954. He left the Atomic Energy Commission on June 30, 1959, to join the chemistry faculty at the University of California at Los Angeles, where he was appointed director of the Institute of Geophysics and Planetary Physics in 1962.

Libby was married to the former Leonor Hickey, a Californian; they had twin daughters, Janet and Susan, born in 1945. Although he retired in 1977, Libby, a member of the National Academy of Sciences, American Academy of Arts and Sciences, and the American Philosophical Society, remained professionally active until his death on September 8, 1980, of a blood clot in his lung following a brief hospitalization for pneumonia.

Scientific Career

Willard Libby was led to his work in radiocarbon dating by his interest, as a graduate student, in weakly radioactive substances. Around 1932, Libby and Georg von Hevesy, working independently, both discovered that the rare-earth metal samarium has slight radioactivity. Radioactive isotopes of samarium are identical to nonradioactive isotopes of the same element, but the radioactive isotopes have unstable nuclei that emit alpha, beta, and gamma rays when they decay. If these radioactive isotopes can be shielded from the cosmic radiation that originates in the upper atmosphere and from other radioactive nuclei, the rays they omit can be measured, and they can be used as tracers of various chemical reactions.

The interest that Libby developed in cosmic rays and weak radioactive substances during the 1930's was ideally suited to his pioneering work in radiocarbon dating. New York University's Serge Korff had discovered in 1939 that when high-energy cosmic rays come into contact with air in the upper atmosphere, showers of neutrons are produced in the environment; these neutrons combine with the plentiful nitrogen isotopes in the atmosphere to form radioactive carbon isotopes (carbon 14) that are distributed through the atmosphere at a ratio of one in one trillion (1:1,000,000,000,000) to the ordinary carbon isotopes.

All living organic matter appeared to Libby to absorb carbon, including small amounts of radioactive carbon, and he speculated that the level of radioactive carbon remains constant during the life of the organism. Once the organism dies, however, it has no way to absorb carbon, and the radioactive carbon it contains begins to decay at a set rate, mixing with nitrogen as the degeneration proceeds.

Martin Kamen discovered in 1940 that carbon has a half-life of 5,730 years; that is, it takes 5,730 years for half the carbon atoms in nonliving organic material to convert into nitrogen, that it takes another 5,730 years for the remaining half to convert to nitrogen, and so forth, to the point where measurement ceases to be practical. Using this information and assuming that cosmic radiation has been constant everywhere on Earth for tens of thousands of years, Libby speculated that it should be possible to measure the weak radiations emitted from the dead material and thereby to determine how much time has elapsed since its death.

Libby could not move beyond this hypothetical stage until he had devised a means of measuring accurately the radioactive emissions from materials to which he sought to ascribe a date. He was convinced that once he had done this, he could date materials that had been dead between five hundred and thirty thousand years. In actuality, as he refined his process, he was able eventually to date materials that had been dead for approximately seventy thousand years.

The measuring device that Libby invented consisted of a Geiger counter inside a housing made of iron eight inches thick. This fortress of iron shielded the Geiger counter from radiation emitted by sources other than the material being tested. Libby used an inner barrier of Geiger tubes connected tangentially to detect cosmic rays that got through the outer shielding. When these tubes registered particles from outside the shielding, the central Geiger counter that was to measure the radioactivity of the sample shut off for one-thousandth of a second.

The inner wall of the detector was lined with pure carbon (lampblack) to assure the highest level of sensitivity. Experimentation revealed to Libby that further sensitivity was achieved when the pure carbon was present as a gas—either acetylene or carbon dioxide—rather than as a solid.

Once his measuring device was operational, Libby tested it by checking the inner cores of old trees whose dates he could ascertain accurately by counting their annual rings. When these experiments substantiated the accuracy of his method, he tested a piece of wood from the funeral boat of the Egyptian pharaoh Sesostris, whose death date was known. The data he gathered coincided almost perfectly with the known dates of the materials he tested.

The next crucial step was to determine whether Libby's assumption that the level of radioactivity in organic matter is the same at every latitude and longitude was really correct. To validate this assumption, Libby tested materials from the Yukon,

Sweden, Chicago, Switzerland, Tennessee, New Mexico (from an altitude of 12,000 feet), North Africa, Palestine, Iran, Japan, Panama, Liberia, Bolivia (from an altitude of 9,000 feet), the Marshall Islands, Ceylon, Tierra del Fuego, New South Wales, and Antarctica. The experiment showed virtually no variation related to an artifact's place of origin, adding one more significant validation to Libby's hypothesis.

Having once made the important determinations that (1) the measuring device accurately dated objects whose actual age was known and (2) the radiocarbon content of objects was essentially the same no matter where on earth they originated, Libby was able to begin to date with some authority objects whose dates either were not known or were highly speculative. He made the important discovery through radiocarbon dating that the last ice age ended some ten thousand years ago rather than the twenty-five thousand years that geologists had presumed.

Libby's discovery of radiocarbon dating held implications for the dating of all organic matter, including ocean waters—particularly the deepest (oldest) waters. His experiments with petroleum suggested the time limits of his research. Petroleum, although it has its origins in decaying organic matter, is processed over such a vast reach of time that carbon 14 dating cannot date it. On the other hand, the methane produced by modern sewage plants can be dated accurately, as Libby proved in his Baltimore experiments.

The work that Libby did on the Manhattan Project during World War II and during his term as a commissioner of the Atomic Energy Commission was closely related to his other work and really did not interfere significantly with it. Probably his service during World War II diverted him somewhat less than the AEC position because it was less public, required less travel, and was not political, as his job with the Atomic Energy Commission was.

As an Atomic Energy Commissioner, Libby had to promote much of the political agenda of the Eisenhower Administration. He appears to have done so without serious personal objections and with few pangs of conscience, because he appeared to believe sincerely that the defense of the nation had to be considered before the possible health consequences of the above-ground nuclear testing being conducted during this period. The Eisenhower presidency had only a year more to run when Libby resigned from the AEC to return to the academic world.

Despite his far-reaching interests in such areas as lunar and space exploration, earthquake prediction and protection, pollution control, planetary atmospheres, and civil defense, Willard Libby's name is associated with radiocarbon dating far more than with any other scientific achievement. The implications of his method are significant in so many areas, from ancient history and archaeology to petrology and geology, that Libby's contribution to society has been among the broadest of recent scientists.

The full impact and implications of his initial work in dating are still not fully known or appreciated. As measuring devices based on his early invention are made increasingly sensitive, it may well be that organic matter much older than seventy thousand years will be susceptible to his method of dating or to one based upon it. Libby's work has already unlocked many secrets of the universe and has altered dramatically scientific perceptions about significant natural phenomena. As means of dating become increasingly sophisticated, methods based on Libby's early ventures into the field will surely help humankind to know much more about the planets to be explored in the decades ahead.

Bibliography

Primary
CHEMISTRY: *Radioactivity of Ordinary Elements*, 1933; *Radiocarbon Dating*, 1952; *Isotopes in Industry and Medicine*, 1957; *Solar Systems in Physics and Chemistry: Papers for the Public*, 1981 (with Leona Marshall Libby); *Tritium and Radiocarbon*, 1981.
EDITED TEXT: *Collected Papers*, 1981 (with others).
MISCELLANEOUS: *Science and Administration*, 1961.

Secondary
Aitken, Martin J. *Thermoluminescence Dating*. New York: Academic Press, 1985. Aitken, whose writing about dating extends to the 1960's, discusses in clear terms the implications for archaeology of thermoluminescent dating, which goes a step beyond the early forms of radiocarbon dating and can date much older materials than Libby could in his initial methodology. Aitken gives full credit to Libby for the sophistication of radiocarbon dating even in its earliest stages.
Berger, R. "Willard Frank Libby, 1908-1980." In *14C and Archaeology*, edited by W. G. Mook and H. T. Waterbolk. Strasbourg: Council of Europe, 1983. Berger, who has written about Libby and his contributions since the 1950's and was his friend, provides a retrospective statement that serves as a memorial to Libby. It details the high points of his life and of his scientific contributions. Despite its brevity, the article is filled with important details and insights, all presented so that nontechnical readers can understand them.
Burleigh, R. "W. F. Libby and the Development of Radiocarbon Dating." *Antiquity* 55 (1981): 96-98. This is essentially an overview article, easily accessible to those with minimal backgrounds in the field. The writer shows how Libby's theory emerged from hypothesis to practical application and emphasizes the extreme meticulousness with which Libby set about testing his hypothesis. He indicates also how the theory grew from one limited to materials no more than thirty thousand years old to include material more than twice that age.
Deevey, E. S., Jr., R. F. Flint, and I. Rouse. *Radiocarbon Measurements: Comprehensive Index, 1950-1965*. New Haven, Conn.: Yale University Press, 1967. This book more than any other indicates the extent of Libby's influence and that of his method of dating. This volume lists thousands of datings that occurred in the first decade and a half of its use. The variety of uses in fields from geology to art history is staggering and gives eloquent testimony to the importance of the

method in fields that affect the lives of practically every human being on earth. This book is to be used as a reference, not to be read from cover to cover.

Renfrew, Colin. *Before Civilization: The Radiocarbon Revolution and Prehistoric Europe*. New York: Alfred A. Knopf, 1973. This book is indisputably one of the most interesting on the radiocarbon process of dating, and it pays careful attention to Libby's contributions in the field. The prose is definitely aimed at general readers rather than specialists, and the comprehensive index makes the volume infinitely usable.

Taylor, Royal Erwin. *Radiocarbon Dating: An Archaeological Perspective*. New York: Academic Press, 1987. This book, stages of which Willard Libby read before his death in 1980, defines Libby's method of radiocarbon dating, then discusses anomalies in it and measurement techniques, after which Taylor evaluates radiocarbon data. The whole of chapter 6 focuses on the history of radiocarbon dating and devotes twenty-three pages to a discussion of Libby and his work. The writing is clear, the research thorough. An extensive index enhances the book's overall usefulness.

Whitehouse, Ruth D., ed. *The Facts on File Dictionary of Archaeology*. New York: Facts on File, 1984. This comprehensive survey devotes three tightly packed pages to Libby's radiocarbon dating. It presents in clear exposition the highlights of the technique, delivered in a style intended for lay people. It contains also a worthwhile chart and illustrations. A reasonable starting point for the novices.

R. Baird Shuman

1961

Chemistry
Melvin Calvin, United States

Physics
Robert Hofstadter, United States
Rudolf Ludwig Mössbauer, West Germany

Physiology or Medicine
Georg von Békésy, United States

Literature
Ivo Andrić, Yugoslavia

Peace
Dag Hammarskjöld, Sweden

MELVIN CALVIN
1961

Born: St. Paul, Minnesota; April 8, 1911

Nationality: American
Area of concentration: Photosynthesis

Calvin's major contribution was in the field of photosynthesis. Using radioactive carbon, he traced the path of the assimilation of carbon dioxide in plants through the complex series of intermediate compounds to the end products

The Award

Presentation

Melvin Calvin was presented for the 1961 Nobel Prize in Chemistry by Professor Karl Myrbäck, member of the Nobel Committee for Chemistry of the Royal Swedish Academy of Sciences. Beginning his address, Professor Myrbäck made a distinction between two types of organisms. Hetcrotophs require energy-rich organic foodstuffs that are made available by the combustion (oxidation) of carbohydrates; such organisms are absolutely dependent on organic material existing outside themselves. Autotrophs, on the other hand, are green plants and certain bacteria that synthesize organic compounds, primarily carbohydrates, from carbon dioxide and water, using light as their energy source, subsequently converting them to chemical energy.

This transformation, the process of photosynthesis, is the prerequisite for all life on earth and is the most fundamental of all biochemical reactions. It has been estimated, Myrbäck said, that plants and microorganisms on earth transform approximately six thousand tons of carbon from carbon dioxide to carbohydrates per second, with at least four-fifths of this amount being contributed by organisms in the oceans.

Research into this important process had gone on for more than a century. Then, as a result of sharp-witted, skillful work using modern technology and many years of chemical experimentation, Calvin succeeded in tracing the carbon atom from the carbon dioxide taken up by the plant to the finished assimilation products. Calvin showed that the primary reaction of the carbon dioxide is a fixation reaction; that is, the light energy first absorbed by chlorophyll (the coloring matter of green plants) and related pigments is converted into chemical potential in the form of high-energy containing compounds. At least ten intermediate products and the reactions between these products are catalyzed by eleven different enzymes. In a brief closing, Professor Myrbäck addressed Melvin Calvin by summarizing his contribution in the field of biochemistry and photosynthesis and congratulated him on his honor.

Nobel lecture

On December 11, 1961, Melvin Calvin delivered his Nobel lecture, entitled "The Path of Carbon in Photosynthesis." In his introduction, he spoke of Emil Fischer, who described his own experiment in the mid-1930's that led to the discovery of the structure of glucose and related sugars. It was now Calvin's task to describe the experiments that led to the understanding of the principal reactions by which those carbohydrate structures are created by photosynthetic organisms from carbon dioxide and water, using the energy of light.

One of the difficulties encountered was determining the process of the reduction of carbon dioxide to carbohydrates. The discovery of the long-lived isotope of carbon, carbon 14, provided Calvin and his associates with the ideal tool to study that part of the energy-converting process of photosynthesis.

The design of the experiment, the plant material used, and the apparatus required, along with the early analytical methods adopted, were elucidated. Paper chromatography fortuitously had been developed at this time, and it was the principal analytical tool that was used. The technique included placing material from an algae plant onto a sheet of filter paper; it was possible with paper chromatography to find the particular radioactive components that were sought without knowing their chemical nature beforehand. The lecture then developed the stages of the path of the carbon 14 and the labeling of the various sugars such as hexose, sucrose, glucose, pentose, and heptose.

Toward the end of his lecture, Calvin described other carbon 14 experiments relating to the contribution of light in the photosynthetic process. Then he arranged all the individual steps separately discussed, in a sequence capsulated by a complicated detailed equation of the photosynthetic carbon cycle. The Nobel lecture ended with a challenge to chemical biodynamics to determine the next stage in the energy conversion process. It will, Calvin stated, involve the fusion of many scientific disciplines.

Critical reception

In its sketch of the Nobel laureates in chemistry and physics for 1961, *The New York Times* (November 24, 1961) acclaimed Melvin Calvin's contribution to the knowledge of the intricacies of photosynthesis as well as his monumental learning in organic and biological chemistry, plant physiology, experimental biology, bacteriology, general systems theory, biophysics, and space science.

When the 1961 Nobel Prize in Chemistry was bestowed on Doctor Calvin, the United States approached a monopoly of laureates in science. Melvin Calvin was the eleventh member of the University of California faculty to merit this distinction and the fourteenth American to win the prize in chemistry.

Doctor Calvin's award was widely acclaimed by his peers, the University of California at Berkeley, his students, and his coworkers. He has been invited to lecture at principal colleges and universities throughout the United States and before scientific bodies.

Biography

Melvin Calvin was born of Russian emigrant parents on April 8, 1911, in St. Paul, Minnesota. At the age of twenty he received the bachelor of science degree in chemistry at the Michigan College of Mining and Technology, and five years later he took his Ph.D. degree in chemistry from the University of Minnesota. The following two academic years were spent at the University of Manchester, England. On his return from England in 1937, Calvin began his academic career at the University of California at Berkeley as an instructor; he has been a full professor since 1947. He served as the director of the bio-organic chemistry group in the Lawrence Radiation Laboratory beginning in 1946; the group became the Laboratory of Chemical Biodynamics in 1960. In 1942, he married Genevieve Jemtegaard.

Calvin has received numerous honorary degrees from universities and colleges throughout the world. He has been elected to the National Academy of Sciences, the American Philosophical Society, the American Academy of Arts and Sciences, the Royal Society of London, the Royal Netherlands Academy of Sciences and Letters, and the German Academy of Scientists, to mention a few. The numerous concurrent positions he has held include: official investigator, National Defense Committee; member of the United States delegation, International Conference on Peaceful Uses of Atomic Energy; member, Joint Committee, International Union of Pure and Applied Chemistry; Armed Forces-Nature Research Bio-Astronaut; member of the President's Science Advisory Committee; and advisory board member of the Department of Energy.

In addition to the Nobel Prize, Calvin has received the Sugar Research Foundation Prize, the Chemical Society's Flintoff Medal & Prize, the Royal Society's Davy Medal, the Priestly Medal, and the American Chemical Society's Oesper Prize. Research disciplines in which Melvin Calvin takes an active part include: physical chemistry, photosynthesis and chemical biodynamics, plant physiology, chemical evolution, molecular biology, chemical and viral carcinogenesis, and solar energy conversion. In 1960, Calvin became an adviser to the National Aeronautics and Space Administration.

His seriousness of purpose and intense dedication to his work is masked by Dr. Calvin's spontaneous and amiable manner. He talks about politics, sports, and science with ease and laughter; he enjoys having lunch with friends on the faculty. He teaches, makes the round of his laboratories on campus, and reads voluminously. He and his wife once devoted some of their leisure time to converting an old chicken ranch into a summer home for themselves and their children, daughters Elin and Karole, and their son Noel.

Scientific Career

As a graduate student at the University of Minnesota, Melvin Calvin was interested in a wide range of subjects, and he did research in various fields of physical and organic chemistry. His doctoral dissertation investigated the halogens iodine and bromine. During his early teaching years at the University of California, he served as assistant to Professor G. N. Lewis, then dean of the college of chemistry. They conducted experiments on the relationship of electronic structure to the color of organic compounds (substances containing carbon). Calvin next worked in physical organic chemistry and wrote a text on this subject that has been credited with exercising a significant influence on modern theory.

Discoveries made by Calvin played a part in United States efforts in World War II. One important contribution to the war effort was made by Calvin's research on oxygen-carrying chelate compounds; these are organic substances that have atoms of metal attached to them. Another result of his research was a simple method of obtaining oxygen from the air for industrial purposes in somewhat the same way as the human body takes oxygen into the blood. This process was used in welding and other industrial operations in the South Pacific during the war when regular supplies of oxygen were not available.

His primary contribution, however, and that for which he received the Nobel Prize, was Dr. Calvin's discovery of the path of the radioactive tracers used to unravel the highly complicated chemical steps in photosynthesis. Photosynthesis literally means putting together with light energy. During photosynthesis in green plants, light energy is used to convert carbon dioxide, water, and minerals into oxygen and energy-rich organic compounds. Without this process, the earth's atmosphere would be deprived of oxygen.

All living cells must convert food into energy and components necessary for life; if plant photosynthesis were to stop, most living things would disappear from the earth in a few years. Even though photosynthesis is one of the fundamental processes of nature, without which no life could exist, its intermediate chemical steps were long considered a complete mystery. There had been no way to learn what happened between the intake of the necessary materials and the formation of the finished product.

Using the green alga *Chlorella pyrenoidosa* in a suspension of water over which a constant light glowed, Calvin introduced carbon dioxide containing a known amount of radioactive carbon 14. He then traced these irradiated carbon atoms from the moment the carbon dioxide entered the plant through its conversion into the different substances the plant produced. He observed the chemical steps by making extracts of the plant at different stages of its growth; he then measured the radioactivity and examined its contents. Dr. Calvin was able to identify eleven intermediate compounds created in the plant, step by step, between the intake of the simple ingredients and the formation of energy compounds. The problem remained, however, as to how the sun's energy is converted to the form required to operate the intermediate chemical cycle.

After further research, Calvin learned that chlorophyll has a phosphorescent quality (the condition of being able to give off a lingering emission of light after exposure to radiant energy). This ability to hold on to energy in the form of light lasts long enough for the energy to be transformed into sugars and other substances. Although the phosphorescence lasts for only about a tenth of a second, this allows enough time for the conversion process and the buildup of an amount of chemical energy so that photosynthesis can be carried out even in the dark.

It was in the late 1950's that Dr. Calvin created methods of tracing the path of oxygen in the photosynthetic process. With his staff, he bombarded the heavy isotopes of oxygen (oxygen atoms having the same number of protons and electrons, but having a different number of neutrons) with protons and neutrons, making the oxygen radioactive and detectable.

Experiments conducted later in Calvin's laboratory proved that chlorophyll, arranged in flat, disclike plates, captures light energy by a layer-to-layer method, operating very much like electronic solar batteries. Calvin has suggested that it may be possible to improve upon the natural processes by which solar energy is converted to chemical energy and thus to duplicate photosynthesis in the laboratory. He has also postulated theories concerning the chemical evolution of life. He supported these theories with studies of organic compounds found in ancient rocks, and of organic compounds formed during the irradiation of gas mixtures under conditions that were thought to simulate the atmosphere of the earth as it existed billions of years ago. Other work of Calvin's suggests that nucleic-acid particles (the essential material found in the nucleus of all living cells) are present in meteors from space, indicating favorable conditions for the development and existence of life on other planets.

Bibliography

Primary

CHEMISTRY: "The Use of Electrons in the Study of Atomic and Molecular Structure," *Journal of Chemical Physics*, vol. 3, 1935; *The Theory of Organic Chemistry: An Advanced Course*, 1941; *The Path of Carbon in Photosynthesis*, 1949; *Isotopic Carbon: Techniques in Its Measurement and Chemical Manipulation*, 1949: *The Photosynthesis of Carbon Compounds*, 1962; *Chemical Evolution: Molecular Evolution Towards the Origin of Living Systems on the Earth and Elsewhere*, 1969; *Organic Chemistry of Life: Compiled Readings from Scientific American*, 1973.

Secondary

Asimov, Isaac. *Asimov's Biographical Encyclopedia of Science and Technology.* Garden City, N.Y.: Doubleday, 1964. This large volume presents the stories of more than one thousand scientists, chronologically arranged from ancient Greece to the Space Age. A sketch of Calvin's accomplishments is given.

Farber, Eduard. *Nobel Prize Winners in Chemistry, 1901-1961.* Rev. ed. New York: Abelard-Schuman, 1963. Farber gives a short biography of Calvin up to his winning of the Nobel Prize, and prints excerpts from his Nobel lecture. There is also a synopsis of the significance of the work.

Moritz, Charles, ed. *Current Biography Yearbook.* New York: H. W. Wilson, 1983. Living notables are honored with current information, beginning with birthdate and titles of recognition. Each biography is followed by a brief account of the work and contribution of the person. Concludes with a list of references.

Wasson, Tyler, ed. *Nobel Prize Winners*. New York: H. W. Wilson, 1987. This reference book arranges the Nobel winners alphabetically and includes essays on their biographies and accomplishments, and a description of their work. Includes a photograph of each laureate. The volume is written for the student and the general reader.

Clarice Lolich

1962

Chemistry
Max Ferdinand Perutz, Great Britain
John Cowdery Kendrew, Great Britain

Physics
Lev Davidovich Landau, Soviet Union

Physiology or Medicine
Francis H. C. Crick, Great Britain
James D. Watson, United States
Maurice Wilkins, Great Britain

Literature
John Steinbeck, United States

Peace
Linus Pauling, United States

MAX FERDINAND PERUTZ
1962

Born: Vienna, Austria; May 19, 1914

Nationality: British
Areas of concentration: Biochemistry and molecular biology

Perutz contributed to the understanding of the processes of life not only by establishing the structure of the hemoglobin molecule but also by helping develop the techniques that made that discovery possible

The Award

Presentation

Swedish King Gustav VI Adolf presented the Nobel Prize in Chemistry to Max Ferdinand Perutz on December 10, 1962, following the presentation speech by Gunnar Hägg, a crystallographer and a member of the Nobel Committee for Chemistry. In his address, Hägg began by quoting nineteenth century Swedish chemist Christian Wilhelm Blomstrand's definition of the chemist's task: to investigate and establish the structure of compounds—that is, the way they are built from atoms. One of the problems the chemist faced in modern times was the difficulty of determining the structure of carbon (organic) compounds. The techniques of pure chemistry were sufficient to establish the general structure of such compounds—which atoms were bonded to which atoms—but insufficient to determine precisely the angles and distances within the atomic bond. To proceed further, it became necessary to make use of the methods of physics.

The most important of the techniques borrowed from physics is X-ray crystallography, which was developed from the fact that diffraction results when X rays meet a crystal. The nature of these diffractions, called reflections, varies according to the type and distribution of the atoms within the crystal. The technique was discovered by Max von Laue in 1912 and applied by William and Lawrence Bragg, a father and son team. It continued to develop through the first half of the twentieth century. The technique worked well on simple compounds, but the calculations were so demanding when it came to such complex structures as organic compounds that progress was briefly stalled.

Supported by Sir Lawrence Bragg, Max Perutz began using X-ray diffraction to study hemoglobin in 1937. Ten years later, he was joined by John Kendrew, who was assigned the study of myoglobin, another globular protein. Their study progressed slowly until 1953, when Perutz successfully introduced heavy atoms of mercury into specific positions in the hemoglobin molecule. With a computer, a vast amount of information was processed, and it became possible to observe the principles on which globular proteins are constructed. Despite Perutz's twenty-five years of effort, there had been "only modest results," but the results opened a door for a greater understanding of the chemistry of life. The two researchers deserve admiration, Hägg concluded, not only for their work "but also for their patience and perseverence, which have overcome the difficulties which initially seemed insuperable."

Nobel lecture

On December 11, 1962, Perutz delivered his Nobel lecture, entitled "X-Ray Analysis of Haemoglobin." The address revealed the continuity of effort involved in modern scientific investigation. Perutz began by noting that forty years earlier, Sir Lawrence Bragg and his father William had received the Nobel Prize in Physics for creating a new branch of physics: X-ray crystallography. He paid tribute to Bragg as his "scientific father." Perutz recalled that he began his work in this area under J. D. Bernal just after Bernal and Dorothy Hodgkin had successfully shown that X-ray diffraction of protein crystals can reveal their atomic structure. Bragg became director of the Cavendish Laboratory in Cambridge shortly thereafter and was so excited by Perutz's work on hemoglobin that he supported the research for many years.

X-ray crystallography is simple in its concept. A protein crystal is suspended in liquid in a glass tube and then subjected to X rays from several perspectives so that a diffracted pattern is printed on film mounted behind the tube holding the crystal. The spots of light on the exposed film represent the molecular arrangement of the component molecules of the crystal. The different "reflections," as they are known, can reveal the precise arrangement of atoms in the molecule. In order to gain a comprehensive picture, the images are reversed to reveal proportional "fringes" which, when superimposed on one another, create a total image. Yet it is not quite that simple. At that point, only the amplitude of the fringes is established; the phase angles are still unknown, so the picture remains incomplete.

The solution to this problem—which was the key to Perutz's technique—is to introduce a heavy atom, such as mercury, to an arbitrarily fixed point in one protein crystal and to a different arbitrary point in a second crystal, while a third crystal is left unchanged. The heavy atoms provide reference points so that the angles can be established. A comparison of the wave crests produced by the three crystals can establish the respective diffraction patterns and thus yield the angles.

The next step is also difficult, because the complexity of proteins demands a three-dimensional image. This is accomplished by superimposing three-dimensional fringes one on top of another to build, bit by bit, the image of the protein. The final problem is that of resolution. To ensure that the image created by the superposition of tens of thousands of fringes is accurate, millions of spots have to be recorded and measured—fifty billion, in fact, in the case of myoglobin. Only the invention of high-speed computers made the necessary calculations possible and allowed Perutz and Kendrew to complete their analysis.

Having presented his method, Perutz turned to the structure and functioning of hemoglobin. In the body, hemoglobin carries oxygen away from the lungs and carbon dioxide back. Its molecule consists of ten thousand atoms, of which four are iron, creating four groups accompanied by four polypeptide chains containing traces of 140 amino acids. The ferrous iron interacts with oxygen to bring it to the lungs, and, when the oxygen is given up, the carbon dioxide is taken away by the red cells because an acid group disappears from each quarter-molecule when its oxygen is released. The hemoglobin molecule can thus be regarded as an enzyme that has two functions. At this point, Perutz stated, the research on both human and the very similar horse hemoglobin shows the structure of the chains and the groups, but not yet the individual amino acids.

Perutz continued with a comparative analysis of horse and human hemoglobin, showing the structural similarities and differences. He concluded by identifying the aspects of hemoglobin function and structure that still need to be established: first, determining the changes in the individual chains, too small to be detected at that time; and second, solving the atomic structure of one of the forms—either horse or human. He noted that such research demands vast amounts of effort, but "not so much, perhaps, as the twenty-two years needed for the initial analysis." A note appended to his lecture in 1963 updated the comparison of reduced human and reduced horse hemoglobin, establishing that a rearrangement in the chains results from an oxygenation reaction.

Critical reception

Max Perutz received the Nobel Prize in Chemistry as part of a dramatic showing by the Cavendish Laboratory at Cambridge. Since he shared his prize with John Kendrew, and was joined at the awards ceremony by colleagues Francis Crick and James Watson, who received the 1962 Physiology or Medicine prize for establishing the double-helical structure of the DNA molecule, much of the attention focused on the group rather than on individuals. Also, the colorful eccentricities of Watson and Crick drew the spotlight away from the much less flamboyant Perutz and Kendrew.

The award aroused no apparent objections and, indeed, was generally praised as honoring a breakthrough into greater understanding of the functioning of the human body. There was general agreement among the commentators in the news media and the scientific journals that this work on the molecular structure of proteins was an exceptionally important scientific step, but it was also made clear that Perutz and Kendrew's research had reached only the threshold of understanding proteins and amino acids and was far from complete.

The New York Times gave the awards nearly a full column on the front page and three column-length biographical sketches later in the first section. Two days later, the newspaper devoted two full columns in the Sunday science section to the physics (won by Lev Landau of the Soviet Union) and chemistry prizes. *Science*, *Scientific American*, and other professional journals noted the awards rather matter-of-factly, perhaps because of the fact that there was more potential than completeness in the research. Almost all of the articles reporting the award used such phrases as "this will make possible . . ." and "may lead to . . . ," showing the incomplete nature of Perutz and Kendrew's work or the lack of immediate applications of it.

If there was anything at all controversial in the reactions to Perutz's winning the prize, it showed up in observations that Kendrew actually made the first breakthrough with myoglobin—though the writers admitted that hemoglobin is much more complex in structure—and that the picture of myoglobin was much more conclusive than that of hemoglobin, where more work needed to be done. Perhaps the retiring natures of both recipients accounted for the lack of drama in the commentary. Only *The New York Times* dealt with personalities, and the only comment was that Perutz is shy and retiring, but "often difficult because of his extreme tenacity." In an obvious attempt to add a touch of human interest, the story mentioned that in his spare time, he had developed an improved varnish for skis— evidence of his love for the mountains. His new celebrity status also led to a report in mid-November of 1962 that a hundred students at Brooklyn Polytechnic Institute were enthralled by his guest lecture while he was visiting Professor Isidor Fankuchen, from whom Perutz had learned X-ray crystallography.

Biography

Max Perutz was born May 19, 1914, in Vienna, the son of Hugo Perutz and Adele Goldschmidt Perutz. Both parents were heirs of prosperous textile manufacturers and hoped that he would enter the family business, but he fell under the spell of chemistry in secondary school and, with his parents' blessing, entered Vienna University. After spending several unfulfilling years studying inorganic chemistry, he learned of the work in organic chemistry being done at the University of Cambridge. With his father's economic support, he matriculated as a doctoral student at the renowned Cavendish Laboratory, where he was to remain for the bulk of his career.

Following the Anschluss in Austria, his family's property was seized by the National Socialists (the Nazis), and Perutz found himself penniless. He was rescued by Nobel laureate Sir Lawrence Bragg, who secured a Rockefeller Foundation grant for the young scholar. In 1940, Perutz was interned in Canada as an enemy alien. Because of his knowledge of glaciers, however, he was assigned to a team led by Lord Louis Mountbatten to study the feasibility of using ice floes as landing strips, rather like natural aircraft carriers. The war ended before this plan could be implemented.

In 1942, Perutz married Gisela Peiser, a medical photographer, with whom he had two children, Vivian and Robin, and in 1945 he was awarded an Imperial Chemical Industries Research Fellowship. In 1947, he was chosen to head the new Medical Research Council Unit for Molecular Biology, with a staff of one: John Kendrew. He continued in the position until 1962, when he became chair of the Medical Research Council Laboratory of Molecular Biology.

In 1962, Perutz and Kendrew were awarded the Nobel Prize in Chemistry. That same year saw the publication of his book *Proteins and Nucleic Acids: Structure and Function*. During the years that followed, Perutz continued his study of protein structures, but he also became more active in civic and professional activities. He retired in 1979 but maintained his laboratory and his research at Cambridge.

Scientific Career

The scientific career of Max Perutz is a dramatic example of the capacity of the human spirit to endure under the most trying circumstances. One of many German-speaking scientists whose lives and homelands were changed by the enormity of Adolf Hitler's ambition, Perutz was in even greater jeopardy because he is Jewish. One of the ironies in his life is that his decision to pursue a scientific career rather than study law and enter the family business may very well have saved his life. It can also be said, quite accurately, that his scientific career began the day he informed his parents of his decision to study chemistry rather than law.

An unswerving dedication to solving the problem he was studying characterized Perutz's career, and the problem that dominated his career was the search for the structure of hemoglobin. From his initial experience using X-ray diffraction in 1937 to (and even after) his formal retirement from administrative duties in 1979 — excepting his curious circumstances during World War II — he tenaciously pursued an ever-growing understanding of proteins, especially hemoglobin. His career was essentially free of the publicity that has surrounded many of his contemporaries, though the quality of his work has been recognized worldwide. No matter what the award, however, Perutz seems always to have been anxious to get back to his laboratory.

In some ways the story of Perutz's scientific career is the story of the Cavendish Laboratory at Cambridge. Seldom in the history of science have so many significant discoveries — or so many Nobel Prize winners — come from a single facility. The story really begins with the award of the 1915 Nobel Prize in Physics to two Englishmen: Sir William Bragg and his son, Sir Lawrence Bragg. They had demonstrated that the diffraction pattern of the spots on a photographic plate when a crystal was bombarded with X rays (a technique discovered by Max von Laue in 1912) was the result of the atoms in the crystal. Moreover, it was possible, through mathematical computation, to establish the atomic structure of the substance being studied.

For the next twenty years, the techniques and applications of X-ray diffraction continued to be studied at the Cavendish Laboratory, particularly by one of Bragg's former students, J. D. Bernal. In 1936, Perutz arrived in Cambridge to study under Bernal. Shortly thereafter, Bragg came as Cavendish professor of physics and soon became director of the laboratory. At various times, the group included Nobel Prize winners Francis Crick, James Watson, Frederick Sanger, John C. Kendrew, and Perutz, as well as such noted scientists as Bernal and Isidor Fankuchen. That four members of the laboratory shared two Nobel Prizes in 1962 testifies not only to their individual achievements but also to the invaluable cross-pollination of ideas that occurs in much modern scientific research.

Perutz's own path to the Nobel Prize really began twenty-five years earlier when, in 1937, he learned the techniques of X-ray crystallography from Bernal and Fan-kuchen. In 1938, the three of them published a joint paper on X-ray diffraction of hemoglobin and chymotrypsin crystals. In 1940, Perutz received his doctorate from Cambridge.

Perutz had just begun to concentrate on hemoglobin when World War II began, with all its attendant problems both for him and for the world in general. He served his internment in Canada working on the possibility of ice floes serving as landing strips for naval aircraft. Such imaginative—some might say far-fetched—ideas were common enough in wartime research: The atomic bomb seemed equally unlikely to many. Perutz was chosen for the ice floe project because of his interest in the crystalline structure and flow of glaciers, an interest he pursued, he said, mainly as an excuse to get into the mountains, his favorite environment. (His knowledge of both skiing and chemistry led him to invent an improved varnish for skis.)

At the conclusion of hostilities, Perutz obtained a two-year grant from the Imperial Chemical Industries and continued his analysis of hemoglobin. His work came to the attention of the Medical Research Council, which was the national clearing-house for research in medicine in England. The council decided to fund a unit for the study of molecular biology at the University of Cambridge, and Perutz was named director; Kendrew, who had arrived in 1946, became his assistant. Although the laboratory building was a wartime temporary structure and was not exactly prepossessing in appearance, the quality of work being done attracted the re-searchers who would make it famous. Kendrew was the first, however, and to him Perutz assigned the related but structurally simpler protein, myoglobin.

Hemoglobin and myoglobin are both globular proteins that function as oxygen carriers in the blood. Hemoglobin carries oxygen from the lungs to the rest of the body; myoglobin's function is to store oxygen in muscle tissue. Though similar, the myoglobin molecule is only one-fourth the size of hemoglobin. Hemoglobin consists of four polypeptide chains and four heme groups, each containing an iron atom. The chains are arranged in tangled, three-dimensional, unfixed patterns. As a result, it proved extremely difficult to establish a clear picture of the molecule, even with X-ray diffraction. This method, which had worked well with simple structures, was nearly useless in studying the complex structure of hemoglobin. If there is one word, however, that describes Perutz as a researcher, it is tenacity. Rather than yield to frustration, he applied himself even more diligently. Finally, in 1953, came the breakthrough—though not the absolute answer, for that was still incomplete in 1962. Perutz succeeded in incorporating heavy atoms (mercury or gold) into definite positions in hemoglobin without disrupting the atomic arrangement of the mole-cule. Drawing upon the work of three Dutch chemists who had discovered how to use heavy-atom positions to create artificial points of reference in crystals without centers, he set to work on the exhausting task of collecting literally thousands of pictures of crystals with heavy atoms in a variety of arrangements. Through the use of a then relatively new tool—the computer—the results were processed with the object of obtaining at least a primitive picture of the molecular structure. Kendrew succeeded first, in 1958, with the simpler structure of myoglobin. As Kendrew struggled to improve the quality of his image, Perutz continued to work with hemoglobin until, in 1960, he was able to achieve results. The resolution of the myoglobin image, however, remained more precise than that of the hemoglobin.

Both Perutz and Kendrew published their findings in the British journal *Nature* on February 13, 1960. Among the more interesting discoveries resulting from Perutz's initial image was that each of the hemoglobin molecule's four subunits is nearly identical to a single myoglobin molecule. Obviously, then, much of what was true of myoglobin might be true of hemoglobin. In addition, in the image obtained, it was possible to see the right-handed twist in the helical structure composed of one type of amino acids. Within a year of Perutz's Nobel lecture, he and his assistant, Hilary Muirhead, had obtained much clearer pictures, and, shortly thereafter, they established the significance of oxygenation in the structural rearrangement of some of the "chains" in the hemoglobin molecule.

In the same year that Perutz was awarded the Nobel Prize, his book *Proteins and Nucleic Acids: Structure and Function* was published. The book, an expanded version of three lectures he delivered at the Weizmann Institute at Rehoboth, in Israel, is a short but comprehensive survey of the work done in the area, with special attention given to the structure of hemoglobin and myoglobin.

Perhaps the most controversial event in Perutz's later life followed the publication in 1968 of James Watson's *The Double Helix*, a memoir of the search for the structure of the DNA molecule. Since much of the action reported took place in the Cavendish unit headed by Perutz, there are fascinating glimpses behind the scenes at the personalities involved in the search for the structures of life. Watson's portrait of Perutz is generally positive, though he takes obvious pleasure in reporting Crick's criticisms of Bragg and Perutz and occasional shortcomings in the hemoglobin research. The reader learns that Perutz bicycled back and forth between laboratories as a kind of liaison between the physicists and the molecular biologists. One passage, however, suggested to some that Perutz had unprofessionally revealed a confidential report of the crystallography being carried on at King's College in London. The publication of Watson's book occasioned three letters to *Science*: one by Perutz, pointing out that the report was in no way confidential but admitting that he should have asked for permission as a matter of professional courtesy; a supporting letter from Maurice Wilkins, one of the crystallographers whose work was in the report; and a letter from Watson apologizing to Perutz for the offending passage.

In the years following 1962, as befits a Nobel laureate, Perutz became more of a public man. He served as an adviser to the Defense Ministry and was chair of the European Molecular Organization from 1963 to 1969. From 1974 to 1979, he was Fullerian Professor of Physiology at the Royal Institution in London. He retired in 1979 but continued his activities at the MRC Laboratory of Molecular Biology.

Perutz is a fellow of the Royal Society and an honorary member of the United States National Academy of Sciences, the French Academy of Sciences, and the

Academie dei Lincei in Rome. He has received honorary degrees from the Universities of Vienna, Aarhus, Edinburgh, and Salzburg. In addition to the Nobel Prize, he was awarded the Royal Society's Royal Medal in 1971 and its Copley Medal in 1979. In 1963, his adopted country honored his Nobel Prize by making him a Commander of the Order of the British Empire.

Throughout his career, Perutz has been more interested in the pursuit of knowledge than in self-aggrandizement. In a time when scientists compete for headlines with "discoveries" that often turn out to be premature, Perutz's careful, single-minded pursuit of the structure of globular proteins seems almost anachronistic. It is also important to remember his administrative leadership in the MRC unit that was to contribute so much to the development of genetic engineering and other biochemical achievements. Once a nearly destitute student without a country, this unpretentious but persistent researcher has played a quiet but vital role in the unraveling of the living universe.

Bibliography

Primary

CHEMISTRY: "Structure of Haemoglobin," *Nature*, vol. 185, 1960 (with M. G. Rossman, Ann Cullis, Hilary Muirhead, Georg Will, and A. C. T. North); *Proteins and Nucleic Acids: Structure and Function*, 1962; "Structure of Haemoglobin," *Nature*, vol. 199, 1963 (with Hilary Muirhead); "The Hemoglobin Molecule," *Scientific American*, vol. 211, 1966; *Atlas of Haemoglobin and Myoglobin*, 1981 (with G. Fermi).

Secondary

Crick, Francis H. C., and John C. Kendrew. "X-Ray Analysis and Protein Structure." In *Advances in Protein Chemistry*, vol. 12, edited by C. B. Anfinsen. New York: Academic Press, 1957. A surprisingly lucid and accessible explanation of the use of X-ray crystallography by two members of the renowned Cavendish Laboratory. Particularly useful are the authors' definitions of the technical vocabulary of X-ray diffraction.

Edelstein, Stuart. *Introductory Biochemistry: Fundamentals of Cellular Metabolism and Molecular Biology*. San Francisco: Holden-Day, 1973. This is an excellent, clearly written introduction, with a significant focus on the structure of hemoglobin, much of which derives from Perutz's work.

Holmes, K. C., and D. M. Blow. *The Use of X-Ray Diffraction in the Study of Protein and Nucleic Acid Structure*. New York: Wiley-Interscience, 1965. This book provides a detailed explanation of the technique that was crucial to Perutz's study of hemoglobin.

Kendrew, John C. "Myoglobin and the Structure of Proteins." *Science* 139 (March 29, 1963): 1259-1266. This article is a reworking of Kendrew's Nobel Prize lecture and as such is a clear nontechnical description of his and Perutz's work from a different angle. Acknowledges that their area of concentration, however specialized, is still in its infancy.

—————————. "The Three-Dimensional Structure of a Protein Molecule." *Scientific American* 205 (December, 1961): 96-110. Kendrew's clearly written account of the work he and Perutz were doing on hemoglobin and myoglobin is the best immediate source for an explanation of the difficulties of protein study and the methods used to study them. Illustrated with some stunning color photography.

Watson, James D. *The Double Helix: A Personal Account of the Discovery of the Structure of DNA*. New York: W. W. Norton, 1980. Watson's controversial 1968 account of the search for the structure of DNA contains a fascinating inside look at the way the scientific establishment functions. In addition to a number of informal sketches of Perutz in Watson's narrative, this Norton Critical Edition includes the letters from Perutz, Wilkins, and Watson regarding the famous "confidential report," and a collection of scholarly and critical commentaries.

Daniel J. Fuller

1962

Chemistry
Max Ferdinand Perutz, Great Britain
John Cowdery Kendrew, Great Britain

Physics
Lev Davidovich Landau, Soviet Union

Physiology or Medicine
Francis H. C. Crick, Great Britain
James D. Watson, United States
Maurice Wilkins, Great Britain

Literature
John Steinbeck, United States

Peace
Linus Pauling, United States

JOHN COWDERY KENDREW
1962

Born: Oxford, England; March 24, 1917

Nationality: British
Areas of concentration: Structural chemistry and molecular biology

Kendrew achieved the first structural determination of a protein, myoglobin, which he solved by X-ray diffraction. He pioneered the use of computers in the calculation of atomic positions and promoted the application of these techniques in the study of biomolecular structures

The Award
Presentation

Gunnar Hägg, a crystallographer and a member of the Nobel Committee for Chemistry, presented John Kendrew and Max Perutz for the Nobel Prize in Chemistry on December 10, 1962. In his introduction, he placed the award in historical perspective by surveying the early development of research on molecular structures. In a reference characteristic of the Royal Swedish Academy of Sciences, the speaker cited a statement from 1869 by the Swedish chemist Christian Wilhelm Blomstrand, who proclaimed the ambitious goal of his discipline: the determination of the spatial distribution of atoms in molecular compounds. Chemists during the nineteenth century, however, were severely limited by their tools, principally synthetic and degradative techniques, which permitted them only to sketch the schematic outlines of molecules. The advent of X-ray diffraction, discovered in 1912 by the German scientist Max von Laue (for which he received the Nobel Prize in Physics in 1914), provided a powerful method for obtaining precise information on atomic positions in crystals. The first researchers to apply X-ray scattering to structure determination were W. Lawrence Bragg and his father, William H. Bragg. The Stockholm committee recognized their accomplishment as well with the Nobel Prize in Physics in 1915.

Early work on crystal structure had been confined to simple materials such as inorganic salts and minerals. By contrast, Perutz and Kendrew tackled the much more difficult subject of proteins. Hägg emphasized the ingenuity and perseverance of the two recipients, who spent many years studying the oxygen-binding molecules hemoglobin and myoglobin. The solution of these structures depended on two innovations: the incorporation of heavy atoms in the proteins and the development of data-processing techniques. Kendrew and Perutz's contributions paved the way for the structural determination of other proteins, which were then being pursued by scientists who had trained in their laboratory at Cambridge. This new knowledge of molecular architecture promised insight into the mechanism of protein function in health and disease.

Nobel lecture

On Tuesday, December 11, 1962, Kendrew delivered his Nobel lecture, entitled "Myoglobin and the Structure of Proteins." Since his colleague Perutz had discussed the principles of X-ray crystallography, he focused on the strategy employed in his study of myoglobin. Kendrew had chosen this molecule because it was relatively small by the standards of proteins (with only 150 amino acids), and it could be obtained in large quantities from the sperm whale. Moreover, being the protein responsible for the storage of oxygen in muscle tissue, myoglobin was closely related to Perutz's subject, hemoglobin, which transports oxygen to and from the lungs.

Kendrew was not shy about describing the difficulties encountered in his work. After choosing myoglobin and locating a convenient source, he laboriously set out to attach heavy metals for reference points within the protein crystal. Several hundred such modifications were studied before he obtained a few with a well-defined structure appropriate for X-ray analysis. The latter process involved the collection and processing of vast quantities of data at a time when automated techniques were virtually unknown in crystallography. Kendrew emphasized the crucial importance of his decision to utilize computers for deciphering the X-ray patterns of myoglobin.

The first outlines of the structure gave Kendrew and his colleagues a surprise: Instead of appearing in a neat, symmetrical array, the protein chain was apparently wrapped in a haphazard fashion around the central iron atom. The polypeptide formed a long, hollow tube that was twisted into an ugly knot. Subsequent examination of the molecule under higher resolution, however, revealed some order in this chaos: The tubes themselves were composed of eight helical sections whose dimensions corresponded exactly with Linus Pauling's model for a protein helix. The shape of the X-ray profile, combined with a chemical analysis by Kendrew's colleague, Allen Edmundson, also provided information on the identity of many amino acid residues. Consistent with their chemical properties, most of the oil-like constituents were located in the interior of the structure, while the amino acids that were known to favor a watery environment were found on the exterior. More highly resolved pictures confirmed and extended these results.

Kendrew stressed that the reasons underlying the peculiar shape of myoglobin were still unknown, but the structural determination of this one protein marked the first step toward the correlation of sequence with structure. Indeed, researchers in other laboratories were already working to solve other structures that would gradually build a library of protein morphology. Progress in this field also stimulated scientists in other specialties, such as peptide chemistry, where physical properties could now be related to molecular structure. Another potential benefit lay in the area of diseases associated with protein defects, especially blood disorders such as sickle-cell anemia, which Perutz and Kendrew had begun to study. Kendrew concluded his lecture by emphasizing that the achievements described in his address marked not a terminus, but the starting point for many new avenues of research.

Critical reception

The Nobel Prizes of 1962 focused particular attention on X-ray crystallography and structural biochemistry. While Perutz and Kendrew shared the chemistry award for their research on proteins, Francis Crick, James Watson, and Maurice Wilkins received the Nobel Prize in Physiology or Medicine for their elucidation of the structure of DNA, the material responsible for the inheritance of genetic traits. Watson and Crick had deduced the double-helical nature of DNA based largely upon X-ray data obtained by Wilkins and his associate, Rosalind Franklin. Although these discoveries were made in different ways, together they demonstrated the power of X-ray crystallography in understanding the two most important classes of biological molecules, proteins and nucleic acids. In characteristic understatement, the British journal *Nature* described the conjunction of these two Nobel Prizes as a "most welcome announcement."

The New York Times called attention to the diverse temperaments of the recipients, contrasting the quiet, mild-mannered Kendrew with the "eccentric" Watson and the "flamboyant" Crick. Perutz and Kendrew had begun research on oxygen-binding proteins years before Crick and Watson (also working in the Cavendish Laboratory at Cambridge) turned their attention to DNA. Whereas the latter structure was grasped through an intuitive leap of scientific reasoning, as described by Watson in *The Double Helix* (1968), the characterizations of myoglobin and hemoglobin were arduous and tedious processes. This feature of Perutz and Kendrew's work was emphasized in popular discussions of their award: *Science News Letter* referred to the "many years of difficult and delicate basic research" that were required to solve the problem, which *Scientific American* succinctly called "formidable." Similarly, *Time* magazine alluded to the "involved experiments using X-rays" that marked "an important early step toward a more complete understanding of proteins." Perutz and Kendrew obviously had earned their award by the sweat of their brows and, as *Newsweek* magazine noted, "the rest of the scientific world agreed wholeheartedly with the Nobel choices."

Not surprisingly, X-ray crystallographers were particularly enthusiastic about the recognition given to their field. David Harker, a biophysicist writing for the journal *Science*, commented that it was "extremely gratifying . . . that this great honor was bestowed on these two outstanding members of our fraternity." The Nobel Prize thus had benefits that reached beyond the recipients of the award, since it called the attention of the scientific world to the particular research specialty thus recognized by the Stockholm committee. Harker pointed to the study of protein structure as a field that had been largely created by Perutz and Kendrew, whose former students and associates had diffused throughout the scientific community.

The announcement of the Nobel Prize fortuitously occurred the week before a prestigious conference on hemoglobin held at Columbia University. The meeting was chaired by Vernon Ingram, who had worked with Perutz and Kendrew before accepting a post at the Massachusetts Institute of Technology. The Nobel designates had already been invited to Columbia prior to the news from Stockholm, and participants at the hemoglobin workshop added their own tributes to the fundamental contributions that Perutz and Kendrew had made. Linus Pauling, who spoke on "Hemoglobin, Evolution and Molecular Disease," cautioned that much work remained to be done, however, before myoglobin and hemoglobin could be properly understood, particularly in terms of the oxygen-binding mechanism.

Biography

John Cowdery Kendrew was born in Oxford, England, on March 24, 1917. His father, the noted climatologist Wilfrid George Kendrew, taught at the University of Oxford, while his mother, Evelyn May Graham (née Sandberg), had a career as an art historian. Within this unusual domestic environment, the young Kendrew developed his scientific vocation while also acquiring an interest in Italian art and classical music.

Kendrew received his early education at the Dragon School in Oxford and at Clifton College in Bristol. In 1936, he entered Trinity College of the University of Cambridge, where he pursued studies in chemistry. Upon graduation in 1939, he spent several months working in the department of physical chemistry at Cambridge until his enlistment with the Air Ministry Research Establishment. As a member of the scientific advisory staff, he held the honorary rank of wing commander in the Royal Air Force, for which he traveled widely in the Middle East and Asia.

Following the war, Kendrew returned to Cambridge to resume his studies. He received his Ph.D. in 1949, working with Max Perutz under the direction of Sir Lawrence Bragg. He continued at Cambridge until 1974, although after winning the Nobel Prize he gradually turned his attention from experimental work to science policy, becoming an adviser to the British government and to professional organizations. In 1981, he was named president of St. John's College in Oxford.

Scientific Career

Kendrew first became interested in the study of biological molecules during his tenure as wing commander during World War II. His travels brought him into contact with two influential scientists: John Desmond Bernal and Linus Pauling. Bernal, whom he met on a trip to Southeast Asia, was a physicist who believed strongly that the most exciting scientific problems lay at the interface between biology and the physical sciences. Indeed, before Bernal's own work was interrupted by the war, he had already begun to apply X-ray diffraction to the study of proteins and nucleic acids. A brilliant scientist with a profound knowledge of many fields, Bernal conveyed to Kendrew his enthusiasm for an interdisciplinary approach to research.

Before the conclusion of Kendrew's military service, he also had the opportunity to visit California, where he encountered Pauling. Like Bernal, Linus Pauling had been trained in X-ray crystallography and foresaw that this technique could be applied to the structural characterization of biological molecules. He was interested in many subjects, including the mechanism of oxygen-binding in hemoglobin and the structure of proteins. Pauling's shift from minerals and salts to the much more complex biological substances reinforced Kendrew's decision to enter the field of structural biochemistry.

Following the war, Kendrew returned to Cambridge to work with Bernal's former student, Max Perutz, at the Cavendish Laboratory, headed by Sir Lawrence Bragg. His choice of universities was shaped in part by financial considerations: At Cambridge, he had a fellowship waiting for him, and he would have had to seek other support if he chose to work with Bernal in London. As Perutz's first graduate student, Kendrew was given a thesis problem closely related to his adviser's work on hemoglobin, the iron-containing protein responsible for the red color of blood. In 1949, Kendrew completed his doctoral research on a comparison between fetal and adult forms of sheep hemoglobin, which exhibit different oxygen-binding properties. Although no general conclusions emerged from this study, it provided Kendrew with a broad training in the techniques of X-ray crystallography.

Upon receipt of his doctorate, he began searching for a new research topic that would be truly his own. As Kendrew later noted in his Nobel lecture, myoglobin proved to be a natural choice both from practical considerations and because it belonged to the same class of molecules as that being studied by Perutz. More important, because myoglobin was only one-quarter the size of hemoglobin, Kendrew was able to determine its structure much more readily. Through a study of heavy atom derivatives, combined with the use of high-speed computers located at Cambridge, he was able to develop successively refined images of the protein structure.

Kendrew's characterization of the first protein by X-ray crystallography has been called "one of the landmarks in the elucidation of the tertiary structure of proteins." This description, written in 1960 by Gertrude Perlmann and Renata Diringer of the Rockefeller Institute, emphasizes the distinction between different levels of detail. The primary structure refers to the way in which the individual constituents are connected. There are twenty common types of components, known as amino acids, and these are connected to one another by linkages known as peptide bonds. Chemical methods for determining the order of these links were developed in the 1950's by Frederick Sanger at Cambridge, where he determined the complete sequence of the protein called insulin—an accomplishment that won for him his first Nobel Prize in 1958. Sanger's methods were modified and extended by other scientists, notably Stanford Moore and William H. Stein of the Rockefeller Institute, to which Kendrew appealed for assistance when he sought information on the sequence of myoglobin.

All but one of the twenty common amino acids may exist in the laboratory as a mixture of right-handed and left-handed pairs, but proteins in nature contain only the latter form. In order to understand the significance of this restriction, it is necessary to consider the secondary structure, or how polypeptide chains are twisted or folded. With a knowledge of the chemistry of amino acids, it is possible to guess the most stable shape of a peptide strand, and this strategy was successfully exploited by Pauling. During a stay at Oxford in 1948, he realized, using a paper model, that a protein chain could be twisted into a helical arrangement that would be held in place by weak attractive forces, known as hydrogen bonds, between neighbors in the helix. In order to form this ordered structure, it is essential that all the components possess the same right-handed or left-handed configuration. Pauling's achievement came at the same time that Kendrew and his colleagues in Cambridge were trying a similar approach, but they failed to develop an accurate helix because their model omitted the rigidity of peptide bonds.

In principle, if all the forces between amino acids could be calculated, it would be possible to predict the overall structure of a protein solely from its primary sequence. Yet even if Kendrew had known the primary sequence of myoglobin when he began his research, it would not have helped him very much. X-ray diffraction was the only technique that could probe the tertiary structure, the orientation of polypeptide chains in space. By examining the interference pattern produced by bombarding a crystal with X rays, the location of individual atoms could be deduced. A bonus of this approach was that it also provided Kendrew with the secondary structure and much of the primary sequence of myoglobin.

Kendrew has remarked that when he began his research with Perutz, he believed that proteins were the most important molecules in living organisms. They make up a very diverse class of compounds, some of which (like the collagen in tendons) provide a strong building material, while others (enzymes such as pepsin in the stomach) serve as catalysts to speed up biochemical reactions. Myoglobin and hemoglobin are examples of proteins that store and transport other molecules. The central role of all these compounds is represented by the name "protein," which was coined in 1838 by the Dutch chemist Gerardus Johannes Mulder to emphasize their "primary" or fundamental nature.

The modern era of protein history began with J. D. Bernal, whose vision exercised such an influence on Kendrew's career. Bernal learned the techniques of X-ray diffraction under Sir William Bragg at the Royal Institution, and then in 1927 moved to Cambridge to establish his own laboratory. His early research focused on individual amino acids and other "small" biological molecules, but in 1932 he was joined by a graduate student named Dorothy Crowfoot (later Hodgkin), who worked on the digestive enzyme pepsin. By 1934, employing a wet form of the crystal, they succeeded in obtaining the first X-ray photographs of this protein. While Bernal was overjoyed at this result, the interpretation of the image appeared too formidable, and hence he did not pursue the structure. His student, however, accepted a post at Oxford, where her structural studies of proteins and other biological molecules eventually earned for her the Nobel Prize two years after Perutz and Kendrew received theirs.

The direction of Bernal's research shifted quite frequently as he searched for new molecules that might be amenable to X-ray analysis. For a time, he focused on cholesterol-like compounds, but later he moved on to viruses. In 1936, he acquired a new graduate student from Vienna named Max Perutz. After some preliminary work with minerals, the Austrian chose for his thesis topic the structural determination of hemoglobin. A year later, Bernal relocated to Birkbeck College in London, leaving Perutz to continue his work under a new boss, Sir Lawrence Bragg. As the physicist who had developed much of the theory of X-ray diffraction, Bragg proved to be an excellent adviser. He lent his full support to Perutz's research, even helping him secure a fellowship from the Rockefeller Foundation.

The collaboration between Perutz and Kendrew benefited from the knowledge and influence of Bragg. Whereas Bernal had often been hampered by his left-wing political views, Sir Lawrence was able to exploit his position as a member of the British establishment to gain support for the Cambridge laboratory. During a lunch at his London club in 1947, for example, he convinced Sir Edward Mellanby, the secretary of the Medical Research Council, that the government should finance the application of X-ray crystallography to biological problems. Thus Kendrew and Perutz became the "MRC Unit for the Study of the Molecular Structure of Biological Systems." By 1962, the unit had been renamed the "Laboratory for Molecular Biology" and had its own new building. Although Bragg left in 1954 to head the Royal Institution, his early efforts helped ensure the stability of Perutz and Kendrew's research and to establish Cambridge as a center for the emerging field of molecular biology.

Kendrew himself played a prominent role in the growth of this new discipline. He served as deputy chairman of the Laboratory for Molecular Biology from 1953 until 1974, a period when the laboratory greatly expanded in size and prestige. In 1959, he founded the *Journal of Molecular Biology*, which published many significant papers during his tenure as editor. He also promoted the study of biological structure and function through various administrative positions—as a member of the British Council for Scientific Policy (1965-1972), for example, and as Secretary General of the European Molecular Biology Conference (1970-1974). He established the European Molecular Biology Laboratory at Heidelberg in 1975 and served as its director until 1982. Kendrew's role as an adviser and administrator contributed much to the growth of the field that he and Perutz established.

Throughout his career, Kendrew emphasized the importance of structural principles in molecular biology. While his characterization of myoglobin demonstrated the power of this approach, the focus of molecular biologists has gradually shifted toward nucleic acids. Nevertheless, the study of the architecture of living systems began with Perutz and Kendrew's research on proteins, and the history of this discipline reflects the influence of their pioneering efforts. The achievements of Kendrew both as a scientist and as an administrator mark him as a primary contributor to the intellectual and institutional vitality of molecular biology.

Bibliography

Primary
CHEMISTRY: "The Three-Dimensional Structure of a Protein Molecule," *Scientific American*, vol. 205, 1961; "Myoglobin and the Structure of Proteins," *Science*, vol. 139, 1963; *The Thread of Life: An Introduction to Molecular Biology*, 1966; "Information and Conformation in Biology," in *Structural Chemistry and Mo-*

lecular Biology: A Volume Dedicated to Linus Pauling by His Students, Colleagues, and Friends, 1986.

Secondary

Bragg, William Lawrence. "First Stages in the X-Ray Analysis of Proteins." *Reports on Progress in Physics* 28 (1965): 1-14. A technical history of the experimental problems that confronted Kendrew and Perutz in their early research.

Crick, Francis. *What Mad Pursuit: A Personal View of Scientific Discovery*. New York: Basic Books, 1988. An autobiographical account of his contributions to molecular biology, this book is intended for the general reader. Several chapters discuss the period spent in Bragg's laboratory with Kendrew and Perutz.

Dickerson, Richard E., and Irving Geis. *The Structure and Function of Proteins*. Menlo Park, Calif.: Benjamin/Cummings, 1969. Written on the level of *Scientific American*, this short book offers an introduction to proteins; contains excellent illustrations, including those of myoglobin and hemoglobin.

Judson, Horace Freeland. *The Eighth Day of Creation: Makers of the Revolution in Biology*. New York: Simon & Schuster, 1979. A lively, well-researched account for the layman, this work includes an excellent account of the early work on hemoglobin and myoglobin, presented in the context of the development of molecular biology.

King, Jonathan. "Deciphering the Rules of Protein Folding." *Chemical and Engineering News* 67 (April 10, 1989): 32-34. Intended for readers with an advanced knowledge of chemistry, this review discusses the progress that has been made in predicting the structure of proteins.

Law, John. "The Development of Specialties in Science: The Case of X-Ray Protein Crystallography." *Science Studies* 3 (July, 1973): 275-303. An excellent portrait of the crystallographers who studied proteins and an analysis of the factors that drew them to this subject.

Olby, Robert C. "The 'Mad Pursuit': X-Ray Crystallographers' Search for the Structure of Hemoglobin." *History and Philosophy of the Life Sciences* 7 (1985): 171-193. Although this article deals only briefly with myoglobin, the author provides a history of previous work on protein structure.

Perutz, Max. "Origins of Molecular Biology." *New Scientist* 85 (January 31, 1980): 326-329. An anecdotal account of the early days of the Laboratory for Molecular Biology, as told by Kendrew's colleague and fellow laureate.

Watson, James D. *The Double Helix: A Personal Account of the Discovery of the Structure of DNA*. New York: Atheneum, 1968. This controversial book deals principally with the events leading to the structure of DNA, but it also provides an informative description of daily life in Perutz and Kendrew's laboratory during the early 1950's. The Norton Critical Edition (New York: W. W. Norton, 1980) is particularly good, including scholarly and critical commentary for a broader point of view.

William J. Hagan, Jr.

1963

Chemistry
Karl Ziegler, West Germany
Giulio Natta, Italy

Physics
Eugene Paul Wigner, Hungary and United States
Maria Goeppert Mayer, Germany and United States
J. Hans D. Jensen, West Germany

Physiology or Medicine
Sir John Eccles, Australia
Alan Lloyd Hodgkin, Great Britain
Andrew Huxley, Great Britain

Literature
George Seferis, Greece

Peace
International Red Cross Committee
League of Red Cross Societies

KARL ZIEGLER
1963

Born: Helsa, Germany; November 26, 1898
Died: Mülheim, West Germany; August 12, 1973
Nationality: German
Areas of concentration: Organometallic and polymer chemistry

Ziegler developed Mülheim catalysts, which fostered the development of new industries and enhanced the life of the public. He made significant contributions both to the theoretical understanding of polymerization processes and to the practical applications of this knowledge

The Award

Presentation

In 1963, the Nobel Prize in Chemistry was shared by Karl Ziegler and Giulio Natta. Professor Arne Fredga, a member of the Nobel Committee for Chemistry of the Royal Swedish Academy of Sciences, made the award presentation on December 10, 1963. Fredga began his address by pointing out the wide variety of synthetic materials in existence, in particular plastics, that have properties making them more versatile than many natural products.

Structurally, plastics can be viewed as large molecules consisting of smaller molecules chemically linked to form long chains. Polymerization is the process of joining these individual links together and usually requires the presence of a special chemical to facilitate reaction. Highly reactive substances called free radicals had been used to induce the polymerization process, but these processes were often difficult to control. Fredga jested that chemical free radicals are similar to their human counterparts.

Ziegler found that compounds containing a metal bonded to organic substances display a very useful property in the vicinity of the metal-carbon bond: Molecules are attracted to this area and inserted between the metal and carbon atoms, thus increasing the chain length. When the chain reaches the desired length, the process is stopped. "Ziegler catalysts" are painstakingly developed organometallic compounds containing aluminum that are now widely used in commercial polymerization processes, Fredga said.

He then outlined the contribution of Natta in the same area, specifically the discovery that certain Ziegler catalysts form polymers that possess few of the structural irregularities found in polymers produced via free radical processes.

In closing, Fredga indicated that Alfred Nobel himself had been interested in synthetic rubber production; Ziegler catalysts enabled that goal to be realized and thus led to the development of important industrial processes.

Nobel lecture

Karl Ziegler presented his Nobel lecture, "Consequences and Development of an

Invention," on December 12, 1963. True to his nature, he pointed out that the award was directly related to explosive growth in macromolecular chemistry brought about by the work of many individuals, all stemming from a few days of dramatic experimentation by Ziegler and his colleagues ten years earlier.

He described the low-pressure ethylene polymerization process and compared the resulting polyethylene to that produced by earlier methods. Ziegler's product possessed greater density, rigidity, and thermal stability. Structurally, it contained long ethylene chains with far less branching than is common in high-pressure polyethylene. Development of the low-pressure process led to a dramatic increase in commercial polyethylene production. At the heart of the process are certain catalysts — compounds having the useful property of facilitating chemical reactions while undergoing no chemical change themselves so that they can be recovered and reused. The class of catalyst developed by Ziegler consisted of organometallic compounds, which contain a metal atom, usually aluminum, bonded to carbon-based groups in contact with a compound of another metal such as titanium or chromium. These catalysts fostered rapid development of the industry. He credited corecipient Giulio Natta with coining the term "Ziegler catalysts"; Ziegler preferred to call them Mülheim catalysts. Rapid progress in the field resulted in simultaneous discoveries being made by several groups, such as the usefulness of the catalysts in the production of various nylons. Ziegler termed this the "third surprising development" resulting from these catalysts.

He then discussed the second surprise, Natta's discovery that the catalysts caused polymerization in a "structurally specific, as well as a stereo-specific manner." Natta's wife coined the term "atactic" to describe this property. Stereospecific processes yield polymers with a regular arrangement of side chains. Synthesis of synthetic rubber is possible because of this property.

In the remainder of his lecture, Ziegler expounded on how his entire scientific career led to the development of Mülheim catalysts. The narrative is an excellent case study of how developments in one area of chemistry impinge on another area that is, by tradition, viewed as a distinct and separate field. Investigations that would culminate in the development of Mülheim catalysts began in 1923, when Ziegler was working on organometallic compounds containing potassium and sodium. These compounds facilitated stepwise formation of long-chained derivatives of styrene and other substances. Another major discovery was that lithium could form substances chemically similar to Grignard's reagent, a magnesium-based compound that is very useful in organic synthesis.

In 1943, this stepwise chain-lengthening technique was applied successfully to ethylene, yielding a variety of product compounds. Lithium was not essential to the process, as the same results were achieved with organoaluminum compounds. A catalytic process was involved in these reactions. Ziegler discovered a way to make these organoaluminum compounds by a direct method, which led to the development of a major industry. While studying systematics of the propagation reactions, it was discovered that a trace of nickel present in a reactor vessel caused displacement of the organic group from the metal. Attempts to exploit this control of chain displacement resulted in the discovery of the catalyst combination that caused ethylene formation at atmospheric pressure.

In his final remarks, Ziegler stressed that his discoveries were made only because he did research with no specific goal in mind. He acknowledged the importance of the Mülheim Institute for Coal Research, and his own demand for unfettered research as a condition of his employment. Appropriately, he closed his talk by thanking his coworkers at the institute who, he said, shared in both his award and his accomplishments.

Critical reception

The awarding of the Nobel Prize to Ziegler and Natta in 1963 was met with enthusiasm in both the popular and scientific press. As most people were familiar with the advantages of materials produced through the use of Ziegler-Natta catalysts, it seemed fitting to reward the scientists who had made these developments possible. *The New York Times* mirrored public sentiment that the award recognized a practical discovery that enhanced the overall quality of life for the general public. This was presented as a sharp contrast to the award in physics of the same year, which dealt with theoretical aspects of atomic structure, a field that was not likely to result in any practical industrial applications. Articles in the popular press at the time conveyed the impression that the development of techniques for the commercial production of polyethylene was both a major objective of the work of Ziegler and Natta and the major impetus for awarding them the Nobel Prize. This is in contrast to the response of the scientific community and the views of Ziegler, who let it be known that he enjoyed the study of chemistry for its own sake and generally had no specific goal in mind when pursuing a line of inquiry in chemical research.

Response in the scientific community differed subtly from that of nonscientific publications. Invariably, commentary in scientific periodicals stressed that the award to Ziegler and Natta recognized basic research that later was found to have widespread industrial importance. Industrial chemists in particular were enthusiastic in their response. In industry, there is often little chance for recognition of the achievements of individuals, as the researchers work in groups. The 1963 chemistry award was only the third prize awarded for work that was later found to be of industrial importance. *New Scientist* cited the award as "the event of the decade" for industrial chemists.

Many contemporary authors expressed the sentiment that Ziegler typified the best of both worlds in science, that of the basic researcher and of the developer of new technology. It was generally noted at the time of the award that Ziegler's breakthrough in polymer chemistry was made possible by work in a totally unrelated area. Scientific periodicals credited him for realizing that his process had tremendous long-term potential. Such insight and observational skill was cited as being typical of the talent, insight, and abilities that made Ziegler particularly worthy of the Nobel Prize.

A few contemporaries were critical of Ziegler's motivations, expressing the sentiment that Ziegler was interested primarily in developments that could be commercially exploited. Such sentiments were definitely in the minority, as most published responses to the award announcement made note of the fact that Ziegler was simply a very good chemist with the gift of insight as well as a sharp mind for business.

Some authors at the time of the award recognized the importance of Ziegler's position as director of the Max Planck Institute for Coal Research in his work. As director, Ziegler was free to pursue any research he wished, regardless of whether it was directly related to coal chemistry. This unrestricted position allowed him to develop the compounds causing the polymerization of ethylene. Moreover, Ziegler had a supply of ethylene readily available from the coal industry in the Ruhr Valley, where the institute was located. An element of luck was reported in the press as well, as the breakthrough leading to low-pressure polyethylene production was made possible by traces of nickel remaining in a reaction vessel from a previous experiment. In general, contemporary writers cited these factors not as fortuitous ones, but as unrelated events that were realized for their significance solely because of Ziegler's perceptiveness and tremendous knowledge as a chemist.

Biography

Karl Ziegler was born on November 26, 1898, to Luise (née Rall) and Karl Ziegler, a Lutheran minister, in Helsa, Germany, near Kassel. Self-study in chemistry enabled young Ziegler to enter the University of Marburg in 1916 and begin an accelerated program, culminating in receipt of a doctorate in organic chemistry from Karl von Auwers in 1920. Next, Ziegler worked to complete his *Habilitation*, or academic certification, which was prerequisite to securing a position at a university.

In 1922, he married Maria Kurz. The marriage would last fifty-one years, until Ziegler's death in 1973. Ziegler remained at Marburg as a lecturer until 1925, when he served briefly as a visiting lecturer at the University of Frankfurt. A ten-year stint at the University of Heidelberg began in 1926, and the following year saw Ziegler's promotion to professor of chemistry. As a chemist with an excellent international reputation, he was appointed professor of chemistry and director of the Chemical Institute at the University of Halle/Saale in 1936. That same year, Ziegler served as a visiting professor at the University of Chicago. In 1943, Ziegler replaced Karl Fischer as head of the Kaiser Wilhelm Institute, later known as the Max Planck Institute for Coal Research. His wife encouraged the move, as it would place them in the British occupation zone after World War II ended. The staff at the institute was pleased as well, as Ziegler's lack of association with Hitlerian politics would make it easier for the institute to work with the Allies after the hostilities.

Ziegler aided the postwar development of German chemistry. In 1949, he helped organize, and served as first president of, the German Chemical Society. His work brought wealth to himself and to the institute. In 1969, Ziegler retired as head of the institute; when he turned seventy, he established the Ziegler Fund with ten million dollars earned as royalties from his polyethylene production licenses. He remained on the staff of the institute as an Honorary Fellow.

On August 12, 1973, Ziegler died after a short illness. He was survived by his wife, his children Marianne (a physician) and Erhart (a physicist), and ten grand-children.

Scientific Career

A study of the accomplishments of Karl Ziegler clearly indicates that he was an exceptionally gifted scientist. Throughout his career, he routinely stepped across the arbitrary boundaries of the traditional disciplines in chemistry, using methods of physical chemistry to study organic reactions and examining the interaction of metal compounds with organic compounds. He also refused to distinguish between basic research and applied research (usually of greater interest in industry), believing that significant discoveries are made in both fields.

While a graduate student, Ziegler became interested in the study of trivalent carbon compounds. As the name implies, these are compounds in which a central carbon atom is bound to three other substances. The particular class of compounds studied by Ziegler was an example of a broader class, the free radicals. These are substances characterized by having a single electron that is neither involved in bonding nor paired with another electron. In general, they are highly unstable and extremely reactive, and thus they decompose or combine easily with other substances. Hexaphenylethane was discovered in 1900. This compound contains two carbon atoms bonded to each other. Each of these atoms is, in turn, bound to three benzene rings. (A ring is a closed chain of atoms within a molecule.) Under certain conditions this compound dissociates into fairly stable free radicals through cleavage of the central carbon-carbon bond.

This intrigued Ziegler, and he began, in 1923, a systematic study of compounds similar to hexaphenylethane that contained various groups in place of the benzene rings. In general, there are two ways that substituting one group of atoms for another (such substituted groups are called substituents) can affect a chemical process. One is called steric effects, caused by the spatial arrangement and size of the group; the other is electronic effects arising from the arrangement of electrons in the substituent. Ziegler was interested in substituent effects both on the initial formation of free radicals and on the subsequent reactivity of these radicals. He applied various physical methods to study the pathway and energetics of the reaction. One important discovery resulting from this work was that aromatic ring compounds such as benzene were not required for radical formation. Other groups would work as well, if not better. Ziegler and his coworkers concluded that in hexaphenylethane and similar compounds, large substituents tended to favor the formation of stable free radicals. His study of substituent effects on free radicals continued for approximately thirty years.

An inroad into another major area of Ziegler's career stemmed from this early work on free radicals. Formation of free radicals could be accomplished by reactions involving compounds in which an alkali metal such as lithium or potassium is bound to an organic molecule fragment by means of a metal-carbon bond. Compounds of this type are commonly called organometallic compounds, and they are important materials in organic chemistry and biochemistry. A key discovery was made in 1928, involving olefins. Olefins are organic compounds possessing a double bond between two carbon atoms. In the presence of organopotassium compounds, reactions take place in which the olefin is effectively inserted between the metal atom and the carbon atom to which it was previously bound. The net effect is to increase the length of the carbon chain bound to the metal atom. These chain-lengthening processes became an important part of the scheme to produce synthetic rubber, and this type of reaction allowed Ziegler to elucidate the mechanism of the reactions involved in rubber production.

In order to understand these mechanisms, Ziegler found it useful to work with organolithium compounds, which tended to react more slowly, facilitating studies of the mechanisms. In 1930, he developed a very simple method for the synthesis of this type of compound. Organolithium compounds are now widely used in organic chemistry, in part because of this development of easy synthetic routes. The use of organolithium reagents in the study of butadiene polymerization reactions yielded the isolation of light polymers and the discovery that the catalyst was itself made part of the polymer structure.

Polymerization involves formation of carbon-carbon bonds. This is the same process that must occur in ring closure, or cyclization, reactions, in which the carbon atoms at the ends of the carbon chain in an organic molecule bond to each other to form a ring structure. The principal difference between cyclization and polymerization is that polymerization involves the interaction of two molecules, whereas cyclization occurs within one molecule. Compounds containing rings with a large number of carbon atoms are particularly important as the base for various perfumes.

Previously described methods of preparation had yielded rings containing up to eighteen carbon atoms, but only in small yields. Ziegler and his collaborators tried a new approach to this problem. In their process, a very dilute solution was used. In other words, the actual amount of reactive material dissolved in the solution was very small. Also, the reaction mixture was homogeneous, meaning that all reactants were in the same phase. With these methods, rings composed of up to thirty-three carbon atoms were isolated, and in much higher yield than had previously been obtained. Development of this technique resulted in the synthesis of a wide variety of compounds, including many substances that until then had existed only in nature, such as muscone, a perfume base. As in the case of free radical chemistry, Ziegler continued his investigation of cyclization processes for many years and developed several useful tools for organic synthesis.

At the time that Ziegler was chosen to head the Kaiser Wilhelm Institute, he was concerned about the loss of freedom to pursue his own ideas, as the institute was primarily involved in research relating to coal. The administrators at the institute, however, assured him of complete research freedom so that he would not be obliged to do work in any way related to coal chemistry. The stage was thus set for the developments that would ultimately win the Nobel Prize for Ziegler.

On his arrival at the Kaiser Wilhelm Institute at Mülheim, he continued his investigations of organolithium compounds. While trying to purify a sample of a particular compound, ethyllithium, Ziegler produced a new compound, lithium hydride. In this compound, lithium is bound to hydrogen in a one-to-one ratio. Along with lithium hydride, various olefins were produced. The lightest of these was ethylene, with only two carbon atoms; other olefins, with longer chain lengths, were formed as well. Ziegler reasoned that reacting lithium hydride with ethylene in the reverse process might generate ethyllithium, in which the carbon chain is two carbons long, which would then undergo insertion reactions with ethylene so that longer-chain organolithium compounds, and ultimately olefins, could be synthesized. It was found that the reaction proceeded too slowly to be of any use, however, which began the search for another metal hydride that might be more reactive. A suitable candidate was found in aluminum hydride. In 1949, it was found that aluminum hydride would react with olefins in a one-to-three ratio to form organoaluminum or, more commonly, aluminum trialkyl compounds. A related compound, lithium aluminum hydride, reacted similarly. Unfortunately, these compounds were relatively expensive. Ziegler utilized the properties of hydrogen and aluminum in the presence of aluminum alkyls to develop a method for the synthesis of aluminum trialkyls directly from aluminum, hydrogen, and olefins.

Study of the reactivity of aluminum hydride and aluminum alkyls with olefins followed. As had been found previously, ethylene could be inserted into the aluminum-carbon bond to produce aluminum alkyls with longer chain lengths. This was a significant achievement in itself, as the resulting long-chain alkyls could be removed by hydrolysis, a reaction with water. Hydrocarbons (compounds containing only hydrogen and carbon) of varying lengths, from light substances such as butane to heavy waxes or paraffins, could be obtained. If the aluminum alkyls were allowed to react with oxygen before the hydrolysis step, long-chain alcohols were produced. The type of alcohol produced by Ziegler's method is known as a primary alcohol; long primary alcohols are useful in the production of detergents, as they aid in biodegradation.

Initially it was thought that the stepwise chain-lengthening process mentioned above would lead to development of an easy method for production of polyethylene, but there was a problem. It was found that after the carbon chain had grown to a certain length, chain displacement occurred, leading to isolation of the hydrocarbon product and initiation of a new chain on the aluminum atom. The net effect, then, is that eventually the ethylene displaces the longer-chained substance from the aluminum. Being able to control when this process took place would thus enable very precise control of the types of products formed. If one of the hydrogen atoms in ethylene is replaced with something else, the reactivity in the presence of the aluminum alkyls is affected. In the case of propylene, in which a methyl group is substituted, the net result was dimerization, or coupling, of two propylene molecules with the aluminum alkyl undergoing no net change. This was true catalytic behavior.

A major discovery of a related reaction was made purely by chance. In a particular chain-growth reaction it was found that, rather than forming long-chain alkyls, the ethylene had merely dimerized—coupled with other molecules. The significance of this observation was that the chain-lengthening reaction had been forced to stop at a precise point, and the question arose as to whether some factor present caused this abrupt displacement. Investigation of the reactor vessel revealed the presence of a very small amount of nickel. As a logical next step, Ziegler and his coinvestigators Heinz Martin, Erhard Holzkamp, and Heinz Breil reasoned that if nickel promoted the displacement reaction, perhaps other metals would also affect the reaction in some fashion. Thus began an intensive period of experimentation as the investigators tested various metal compounds to see what effect they had on the reaction of ethylene and aluminum alkyls. The investigation revealed that cobalt and platinum promoted displacement, while several substances were found that greatly enhanced the rate at which chain-lengthening took place. Continuing investigation indicated several elements that were polymerization enhancers.

Perhaps the most significant finding was that the presence of titanium chloride in the reaction mixture caused extremely rapid deposition of high molecular weight polyethylene at atmospheric pressure. Here was the significant advance over previous industrial polyethylene production methods, as they all had in common the need for fairly high pressures in order for polymerization to occur. Room-temperature polymerization revolutionized the industry and was extremely profitable for both Ziegler and the institute. Within five years of its discovery, it was estimated that the process had earned approximately seven million dollars for Ziegler, while the institute was able to fund major additions to its facilities.

Ziegler's interest in aluminum alkyls led to the discovery of their varied properties. Continuing research with these compounds involved the science of electrolysis. (Electrolysis processes may be best viewed as mirroring the properties of a galvanic cell, or common storage battery. A battery utilizes a chemical reaction to produce electricity, while an electrolytic process utilizes electricity to cause a chemical change.) In mid-1950's, a study of the electrolysis behavior of organoaluminum compounds was begun. In electrolysis processes, it is often possible to plate out metallic substances on one of the electrodes in the cell, and electrolytic methods are often used for metal refining, as in the purification of gold and copper. Ziegler hoped to develop an electrolytic method for refining aluminum from aluminum alkyls. This particular endeavor was not fruitful, but it was found that trialkyl aluminum compounds could be produced, most notably triethyl aluminum. This procedure was then adapted to yield tetraethyl lead, an antiknock additive placed in gasoline and widely used until the 1970's.

Ziegler added much to the body of theoretical knowledge in chemistry, as well as aiding great advances in industrial chemistry. It is rare for one person to be so adept at crossing the artificial boundary between basic research and applied research. He was highly regarded by both his coworkers and the scientific community. Acknowledgment of the importance of his contributions is evidenced by the list of academic awards and honors he received. In addition to the Nobel Prize, he received the Carl Duisberg Award from the German Chemical Society, the Lavoisier Medal, and the Order of Merit for Science and Technology. Perhaps one honor may reflect mostly on his personality, this being his nomination as an honorary chief of the Ponca Indians.

While there is no doubt of his research contributions, his contributions to the resurgence of German chemistry after World War II should not be overlooked. His role in establishing the German Chemical Society was of great importance. In addition, he was the principal author of *Preparative Organic Chemistry*, one of the first chemistry texts to be written in Germany after the war. Ziegler worked well with the Allies and was always quick to express his gratitude for the aid provided. In the July, 1987, issue of *Chemical Week*, Patrick McCurdy recounts a meeting with Ziegler in which signs in laboratories at the Planck Institute prominently indicated materials obtained through the Marshall Plan.

It is difficult to single out any one of Ziegler's accomplishments as the most significant. Because of his own desire to follow no set path in his work, he uncovered a complex tapestry of interrelated properties. His career can even be viewed as a series of dramatic breakthroughs in new areas rather than merely improvements in existing fields. Ziegler, along with other chemists such as Geoffrey Wilkinson in the early 1950's, opened the door into an exciting field, that of organometallic chemistry. The importance of organometallic processes to the petroleum industry and other industries cannot be overstated. His willingness to ignore the traditional boundaries between disciplines in chemistry presaged the modern view that the sciences cannot really be separated from one another. To the layman, perhaps the most telling statement of the importance of Ziegler's contribution may be the widespread use of polyethylene in household items.

Bibliography

Primary
CHEMISTRY: "Polyaryl Substituted Vinyl Carbinols and Their Derivatives," *Berichte der deutschen chemischen Gesellschaft*, vol. 54B, 1922 (with K. Richter and B. Schnell); "Alkali Metals as a Reagent for Weakened Valency Organic Compounds," *Berichte der deutschen chemischen Gesellschaft*, vol. 56B, 1923 (with F. Thielman); "Polymerization by Alkali Metals," *Berichte der deutschen chemischen Gesellschaft*, vol. 61B, 1928 (with K. Bahr); "Polymembered Ring Systems (I). Polymethylene Ketones with More Than 6 Membered Rings," *Justus Liebigs Annalen der Chemie*, vol. 504, 1933 (with H. Eberle and H. Ohlinger); "Radicals with Trivalent Carbon," *Transactions of the Faraday Society*, vol. 30, 1934; "Ring Closure Reactions," *Berichte der deutschen chemischen Gesellschaft*, vol. 67A, 1934; "Importance of Alkali Organic Compounds for Synthesis," *Angewandte Chemie*, vol. 49, 1936; "Polymerization of Butadiene and Preparation of Artificial

Rubber," *Rubber Chemical Technology*, vol. 11, 1938; *Präparative organische Chemie*, 1948; "Aluminum Organic Synthesis in the Field of Olefin Hydrocarbons," *Angewandte Chemie*, vol. 64, 1952; "Aluminum Organic Chemistry," *Experimentia*, 1955; "Low Pressure Polymerization of Ethylene," *Makromolekular Chemie*, vols. 18/19, 1956 (with H. Martin); "New Aspects of Organometallic Complex Compounds," *Chemical Society of London Special Publication*, 1959; "Metallo-Organic Synthesis of Higher Aliphatic Compounds from Lower Olefins in Practice and Theory," *Angewandte Chemie*, vol. 72, 1960; "Trialkylaluminum and Dialkylaluminum Hydride from Isobutylaluminum Compounds," *Justus Liebigs Annalen der Chemie*, vol. 629, 1960.

Secondary

Brown, C. E. H. "Karl Ziegler." *Biographical Memoirs of the Fellows of the Royal Society* 20 (1974): 569-584. Ziegler was elected to membership in 1971 and was memorialized in this annual publication. The article is a comprehensive summary of his professional career. Purely technical aspects of his work are presented, although there are biographical sections included. Includes a completed bibliography of Ziegler's publications.

Chien, James C., ed. *Coordination Polymerization: A Memorial to Karl Ziegler*. New York: Academic Press, 1975. A collection of symposium proceedings, this volume shows the respect for Ziegler held by practicing polymer chemists. A technical work, it presents an excellent cross-section of the field of polymer chemistry shortly after Ziegler's death.

Eisch, John J. "Karl Ziegler: Master Advocate for the Unity of Pure and Applied Research." *Journal of Chemical Education* 60 (December, 1983): 1009-1014. This article was written by one of Ziegler's coworkers and deals with the inseparable nature of fundamental and applied research. A profile of Ziegler and his career is presented in support of this idea. The article is technical in some aspects, but a well-written narrative provides insight into Ziegler's character. A limited bibliography is included.

Kissin, Y. V. *Isospecific Polymerization of Olefins with Heterogenous Ziegler-Natta Catalysts*. New York: Springer-Verlag, 1985. As the name implies, this work is an overview of the field of catalysis processes using Ziegler-Natta catalysts. A background in chemistry is needed to grasp the material, but the book is a testimony to the importance attached to Ziegler's work.

"Meet Karl Ziegler, Mülheim's Man of Many Parts." *Chemical Week*, May 31, 1958: 62-66. A profile of Ziegler written at the peak of his career, this article for a general audience provides readers with a rare profile of Ziegler's professional and personal life. Excellent photographs of both the Mülheim Institute and Ziegler's home are included. This is one of the more enjoyable references about Ziegler to be found.

Craig B. Lagrone

1963

Chemistry
Karl Ziegler, West Germany
Giulio Natta, Italy

Physics
Eugene Paul Wigner, Hungary and United States
Maria Goeppert Mayer, Germany and United States
J. Hans D. Jensen, West Germany

Physiology or Medicine
Sir John Eccles, Australia
Alan Lloyd Hodgkin, Great Britain
Andrew Huxley, Great Britain

Literature
George Seferis, Greece

Peace
International Red Cross Committee
League of Red Cross Societies

GIULIO NATTA
1963

Born: Imperia, Italy; February 26, 1903
Died: Bergamo, Italy; May 2, 1979
Nationality: Italian
Areas of concentration: Polymer chemistry and chemistry education

Natta discovered that macromolecules could be assembled in a specific orienta-
tion that gives the resulting polymer enhanced properties, such as greater durability
and higher heat resistance. He developed methods to control this three-dimensional
orientation, enabling the development of isotactic polypropylene and the prepara-
tion of synthetic rubber from isoprene

The Award

Presentation
Giulio Natta was awarded the Nobel Prize in Chemistry on December 10, 1963. In
his presentation address, Arne Fredga, member of the Nobel Committee for Chemistry of the Royal Swedish Academy of Sciences, noted that plastics were constantly
being used in new ways and were replacing glass, porcelain, wood, and other
common materials in many applications.

Fredga continued with a brief survey of polymer synthesis and made special note
of the improvements made by Karl Ziegler, joint recipient of the Nobel Prize, and
the significance of Natta's research. Previously, the technology of synthesizing polymers, in which thousands of small molecular units are bonded together, was
plagued with irregularities, such as branching of the polymer chain. Ziegler had
discovered that long, unbranched macromolecules were produced by combination of
the organic molecules with organoaluminum derivatives and metal oxides.

The small organic molecules undergoing polymerization often contained a group
of atoms that was not involved in the bonding process. In the resulting macromolecule, these pendant groups could be oriented on the left or right side of the
polymer backbone, giving irregular stereochemistry. Natta discovered certain
Ziegler-type catalysts that gave completely regular stereochemistry. That is, the
relative, three-dimensional orientation of each pendant group along the polymer
chain was the same. As a result of the greater crystallinity of these macromolecules,
new plastics, which were as tough as they were light, had become available.

In closing, Fredga remarked that nature's monopoly on the preparation of stereo-
chemically regular macromolecules had been broken by Giulio Natta.

Nobel lecture
The title of Giulio Natta's Nobel lecture, which was delivered on December 12,
1963, was "From Stereospecific Polymerization to Asymmetric Autocatalytic Synthesis of Macromolecules." Natta credited the fundamental advances in polymer

science to Hermann Staudinger's work from 1920 to 1930 on the elucidation of the structure of macromolecules. After Staudinger's discoveries, relationships between structure and properties were found and some control methods established.

In 1952, Ziegler's work on organometallic catalysts aroused great interest. Natta undertook the study of these processes with a view to explaining the detailed, step-by-step pathway (mechanism). The reason he chose propylene and styrene as the organic molecules, or monomers, for his research was that they were readily available in the petrochemical industry. These organic molecules have unreactive groups of atoms attached to one of the doubly bonded carbons. When Natta first polymerized these alkenes, he obtained materials that were different from those previously prepared from these reactive units (monomers).

Further investigation of his polymer by X-ray analysis led Natta to believe that his product had a significantly higher degree of crystallinity than had been obtained before. He attributed the greater strength of his polymer to this increase in crystallinity. Natta also deduced that the increase in crystallinity was attributable to the relative orientation of the pendant groups along the chain. In previously prepared polymers, these groups were randomly distributed on the left and right sides of the polymer backbone. In Natta's new polymer, the groups were all oriented on the same side of the chain. He named this regular orientation of the atoms along a polymer chain "isotactic," and his new polymer is referred to as isotactic polypropylene.

Natta continued with a description of further advances he had made in controlling the three-dimensional orientation of the atoms relative to one another during the polymerization processes. It was now possible to prepare many different types of polymer with total stereochemical control. In fact, Natta had developed his ideas on the control of polymer structure to the point that he could mimic biological processes, wherein stereochemistry is controlled by the well-known three-dimensional interaction of enzyme and substrate. One example of this was his synthesis of synthetic rubber, which was shown to be virtually identical to natural rubber.

Natta closed with a brief description of his most recent work, in which he was preparing chiral polymers without the advantage of enzyme catalysis, which nature has at its disposal.

Critical reception

The presentation of the 1963 Nobel Prize in Chemistry to Giulio Natta and Karl Ziegler was not a surprise to the chemical community. The award was announced in *The New York Times*, where it was noted that Giulio Natta was often referred to as "the wizard of plastics." Although there is no further mention of Natta's technical achievements, nor of their impact on society, the tone of the article conveys the excitement of the Nobel Prize award. The article is one of the few readily available sources that give any insight into Natta's private life. For example, Natta is quoted as saying that he first became interested in chemistry at the age of twelve, when he could not relinquish his chemistry book but "read it breathlessly, like a mystery magazine. From then on, chemistry was my love." He is also quoted as saying that one of the major advantages that he had in his successful scientific career was that his background gave him a combination of the dedication of a pure chemist with the practical logic of an engineer. Natta's hobbies, such as his habit of going for long walks in the woods in search of mushrooms, were also mentioned. The article stated that Natta's study in Milan was filled with beautiful petrified fish, and that the study of fossils was a favorite pastime.

An article that appeared in *Chemical and Engineering News* was decidedly factual. The same article was published one month later in *Rubber Age*. Although mention was made of the worldwide impact on the plastics industry that the discoveries of Natta had brought about, nothing was said about the impact that such developments were having on the day-to-day existence of people in general. The article, instead, is restricted to a brief biographical sketch of the Nobel laureates, followed by a very short, technical description of their respective discoveries. In discussing the rationale behind the choice of laureates, the article states that the Royal Swedish Academy of Sciences cited Natta and Ziegler for their work in the controlled polymerization of hydrocarbons through the use of organometallic catalysts.

The announcement of the award in *The Times* of London was very brief. An indication of the impact of the laureates' work was given with the statement that the discoveries were said to have opened the way to a whole new range of plastics.

Certainly, there was no controversy regarding the awarding of the Nobel Prize in Chemistry to Natta and Ziegler. Yet there was an apparent lack of appreciation, at least on the part of the journalism industry, for the importance and impact of the discoveries made by the laureates. The comment made by Fredga in his presentation address, which described the modern era as the "Age of Plastics," was not broadly discussed in the announcements and articles relating to the award.

Biography

Giulio Natta was born on February 26, 1903, in Imperia on the Italian Riviera, to Francesco Natta, a prominent attorney and judge, and Elena (Crespi) Natta. The youth was educated in the nearby city of Genoa. His interest in chemistry began at the age of twelve, and he was graduated with honors from Genoa's high school of science, in 1919, at the age of sixteen. Initially, he chose mathematics as his main course of study at the University of Genoa, but he found that it was too abstract. Instead, he was strongly drawn by the idea of putting theories into practice, and this led him to transfer to the Polytechnic Institute of Milan, where he studied chemical engineering. He received his doctorate degree in chemical engineering from the Polytechnic Institute in 1924, five years after his high school graduation.

On April 25, 1935, Giulio Natta married Rosita Beati, a literature teacher at the University of Milan. They had two children, Franca and Giuseppe. He remained close to his wife throughout his life, and it was through her influence and background in literature that the word "isotactic" was coined to describe the structure of the particular form of polypropylene that he prepared, and which marked the beginning of his Nobel Prize-winning research.

In the last twenty years of his life, Natta became increasingly limited in his activities by Parkinson's disease. He could still go for long walks in the woods and hunt for mushrooms with his wife, but his other hobbies, mountain climbing and skiing, were impossible to undertake. Natta died in Bergamo, Italy, on May 2, 1979, following complications from surgery for a broken femur.

Scientific Career

The driving force in Giulio Natta's scientific achievements was the desire to use the theories of chemistry in practical applications. His background in engineering and chemistry provided him with the intellectual tools required to transform ideas into reality. This "wizard of plastics" was one of the foremost personalities in leading the world into the "Age of Plastics." Natta obtained his doctorate degree in chemical engineering in 1924. He remained at the Polytechnic Institute of Milan at the level of instructor after passing the required examinations. His talents as an educator were quickly recognized, as evidenced by his rapid promotions through the academic ranks. In 1925, he was appointed assistant professor of analytical chemistry and was soon promoted to professor of general chemistry, in 1927.

During this period, Natta's research centered on the application of X-ray analysis to investigate the structure and crystallinity of inorganic substances. He also used X-ray analysis to investigate the structural properties of industrial catalysts. In 1932, he visited the University of Freiburg in Germany, and he learned the relatively new technique of electron diffraction analysis. At the first opportunity, he began to make use of this method in his own research. His interaction with Hermann Staudinger at the University of Freiburg stimulated his notion to apply X-ray and electron diffraction analytical techniques to the examination of the structure of polymers. This period marked Natta's transition from inorganic to organic chemistry, which was of great value in the broadening of his chemical background.

After Natta returned to Milan in 1933, he accepted a position as professor and director of the Institute of General Chemistry at the University of Pavia, where he remained for two years. He became professor of physical chemistry at the University of Rome in 1935, professor and director of the Institute of Industrial Chemistry at the Turin Polytechnic Institute in 1937, and then professor and director of the Industrial Chemistry Research Center at the University of Milan in 1938.

At this time, the Italian government (under Benito Mussolini) was stimulating an increasing number of programs aimed at self-sufficiency in as many essential resources as possible. Natta's background in catalyst research and in engineering gave him a significant degree of familiarity with industrial applications of chemistry research, and the Italian government asked him to initiate research and development programs with the goal of producing synthetic rubber. He successfully implemented the industrial production of butadiene-styrene rubbers at Ferrara during World War II. His earlier experience with industrial catalysts was an invaluable aid at this time and also led to his development of catalytic processes for production of buta-diene, methanol, and other alcohols, as well as formaldehyde and butyraldehyde. These were extremely important, because butadiene was used in the synthetic rubber process, and alcohols are well known to be the most versatile organic compounds, which can be transformed readily into a vast number of other organic materials.

After the war, Montecatini, a large Italian chemical company in Milan (whose name was later changed to Montedison), funded much of Natta's research. The low cost and availability of petroleum prompted his work in the use of petroleum as a raw material base for industrial chemicals and as monomers used in plastics production. Natta's ties to Montecatini lasted through the rest of his life, and he remained a consultant for that firm for more than thirty years.

Natta took immediate notice of the results of Ziegler's research. Ziegler had succeeded in preparing high-molecular-weight polyethylene using transition metal compounds as catalysts in 1952. Since Ziegler was working on ethylene polymerization, Natta turned his attention to using transition metal compounds in the polymerization of propylene, which has one more carbon than ethylene.

There were many advantages to using propylene instead of ethylene, and Natta's industrial experience and practical approach to chemistry had already provided him with the knowledge required to make the most of them. The most important of the advantages was that propylene was much cheaper than ethylene, as it was a by-product of the petroleum and propane refining processes, and, up to that time, was considered to be something of a nuisance because there were few known uses for the compound.

In 1954, Natta announced that he had succeeded in preparing a new polypropylene, which was far superior in physical properties, such as durability, heat resistance, and tensile strength, to what previous methods could produce. He used X-ray and electron diffraction techniques to show that the observed enhancement of the physical properties were attributable to a greater degree of crystallinity in his product than could be obtained by using the previously known methods of polymerization.

In fact, all the methyl groups on the original propylene molecules, which are bonded to the backbone of the resulting polypropylene chain, were shown to be oriented so that they were all on the same side of the chain. The new class of polymers, where the stereochemistry (the relative spatial arrangement of atoms and groups) could be controlled, was called stereoregular polymers. Natta continued his research with a wider range of organic molecules containing a polymerizable double bond and a pendant, nonreactive group. By investigating catalyst combinations in the same manner, he developed the process to the point that total control of the three-dimensional arrangement of the atoms in the macromolecule during the polymerization process was practicable.

Isotactic was the name given to polymers wherein all pendant groups were on the same side of the chain, and these macromolecules, as well as syndiotactic ones, with pendant groups alternating from side to side along the polymer backbone, could now be prepared readily and inexpensively.

Natta became a member of the National Academy of Sciences of Italy in 1955. He visited the United States in 1956 and held a press conference, during which he showed several useful articles made from isotactic polypropylene, including a cup, a washing machine agitator, and pipes. The advantages to using such articles were their cost, their strength and durability, and their light weight. By 1957, Montecatini was producing the polymer on an industrial scale, and the patented process was licensed throughout the world.

Natta continued his research in the area of polymer science and made many other significant contributions. These include the total control of the three-dimensional arrangement of atoms during the polymerization of butadiene to give polybutadiene, which was exactly analogous to natural rubber. The copolymerization of ethylene with other monomers gave unusual rubber materials, in that no double bonds were present in the macromolecule. He also developed the asymmetric synthesis of polymers. This describes a process where an optically active macromolecule can be produced from optically inactive monomers. Biological reactions involve a similar process, which is greatly facilitated by the unique nature of enzyme-substrate interactions. To mimic biological processes in this way was therefore a remarkable and insightful achievement. In the 1960's, Natta was continuing his extensive work with the polymerization of nonhydrocarbon monomers, such as benzofuran, and vinyl ether.

Numerous gold medals were awarded to Natta in recognition of his scientific contributions, including the first international gold medal of the synthetic rubber industry (1961), the Society of Plastics Engineers gold medal (New York, 1963), the Perrin medal from the French Chemical Physical Society, and the Lavoisier medal from the French Chemical Society (1963), the Perkin medal (Britain, 1963), the gold medal of the Union of Italian Chemists (1964), and the Lomonosov gold medal of the Soviet Academy of Sciences (1969). He held honorary degrees from the University of Turin (Italy, 1962), the University of Mainz (Germany, 1963), the University of Genoa (Italy, 1964), the Polytechnic Institute of Brooklyn (New York, 1964), and the Catholic University of Louvain (Belgium, 1965).

There are more than seven hundred publications in scientific journals that bear Natta's name, further illustrating the extraordinary contribution he made to the advancement of science. He continued his impact on chemistry education as coeditor of the book *Stereoregular Polymers and Stereospecific Polymerizations* (1967) and was coauthor, with Mario Farina, of *Stereochimica: Molecole in 3D* (1968; *Stereochemistry*, 1972). Natta retired in 1972.

The impact of Natta's contributions cannot be overstated. Plastics are used in household goods, scientific and medical laboratories, microwavable containers, detergents, pipes, and antiknock gasoline additives. The widespread use of plastics in day-to-day applications is a direct result of Natta's work. He laid the foundation for understanding the relationships between polymer structure and the resulting physical properties of polymers. These discoveries profoundly influenced the development of the entire plastics industry. The advancement of technology in many other fields, such as the aerospace industry, computers, and the automotive industry, is directly related to the availability of cheap, lightweight materials that outperform metals, wood, and paper in terms of strength, durability, heat resistance, and other physical properties.

Bibliography

Primary
CHEMISTRY: *Stereoregular Polymers and Stereospecific Polymerizations*, 1967 (with Fernando Danusso); *Stereochimica: Molecole in 3D*, 1968 (with Mario Farina); *Stereochemistry*, 1972.

Secondary
Chemical and Engineering News 57 (1979): 48. A brief article in this issue announces Giulio Natta's death. Lists a few of Natta's most recognized accomplishments without being overly technical.

Daintith, John, et al., eds. *Biographical Encyclopedia of Scientists*. 2 vols. New York: Facts on File, 1981. An excellent, very short entry on Giulio Natta that is easy to read. The article consists of a biographical summary and a brief description of the work for which Natta was awarded the Nobel Prize.

McGraw-Hill Modern Scientists and Engineers. 3 vols. New York: McGraw-Hill, 1980. The one-page entry on Giulio Natta provides an excellent overview of the Nobelist's research. His contributions are discussed with a minimal amount of technical language. A good summary of Natta's career advancements and a biographical sketch are also included. Several cross-references to Staudinger, Ziegler, and various key words, such as "rubber" and "stereochemistry," are supplied.

May, Hal, ed. *Contemporary Authors*. Vol. 113. Detroit, Mich.: Gale Research, 1985. Contains an obituary notice with a brief overview of Natta's contributions to science. References to other obituaries in *The New York Times* and *Time* magazine are listed.

Moritz, Charles, ed. *Current Biography Yearbook*. New York: H. W. Wilson, 1964. Contains much of the biographical material available on Giulio Natta. The article mentions some of his coworkers by name and lists the early trade-names of some of the plastics produced industrially by Montecatini and others. References at the end of the article provide a few other sources.

Nobelstiftelsen. *Nobel Lectures: Chemistry, 1963-1970*. New York: Elsevier, 1972. The chapter on Giulio Natta gives the English translation of the formal presentation speech made by Arne Fredga of the Royal Swedish Academy of Sciences, as well as Natta's Nobel lecture. The lecture is aimed at those with a science background, but the illustrations of Natta's concepts are enlightening, demonstrating the necessity of viewing molecules in three dimensions whenever their structural aspects are under consideration. An extensive list of 107 numbered references is included at the end of the lecture, and these are followed by a condensed biographical sketch that details the awards and honors received by Natta.

Wasson, Tyler, ed. *Nobel Prize Winners*. New York: H. W. Wilson, 1987. The two-page article on Giulio Natta is a fine review of his work and accomplishments, which are described in nontechnical language. There is also a brief description of Natta's character and a summary of awards and honors.

Massimo D. Bezoari

1964

Chemistry
Dorothy Crowfoot Hodgkin, Great Britain

Physics
Charles Hard Townes, United States
Nikolay Gennadiyevich Basov, Soviet Union
Aleksandr Mikhailovich Prokhorov, Soviet Union

Physiology or Medicine
Konrad Bloch, United States
Feodor Lynen, West Germany

Literature
Jean-Paul Sartre, France

Peace
Martin Luther King, Jr., United States

DOROTHY CROWFOOT HODGKIN
1964

Born: Cairo, Egypt; May 12, 1910

Nationality: British
Areas of concentration: X-ray crystallography and biomolecular structure

Hodgkin accomplished structure determinations on many compounds of medical importance, including penicillin, insulin, and vitamin B_{12}, through the use of X-ray diffraction analysis. She also introduced computers into the processing of diffraction patterns

The Award

Presentation
The speech presenting the Nobel award to Dorothy Crowfoot Hodgkin was made on December 10, 1964, by Gunnar Hägg, a member of the Royal Swedish Academy of Sciences. Professor Hägg began by recalling the 1914 Nobel Prize in Physics to Max von Laue for his discovery of the X-ray diffraction phenomenon. That discovery formed the basis of Hodgkin's work being honored fifty years later. He continued noting the historical background of the award work by citing the work of William and Lawrence Bragg, honored with the 1915 Nobel Prize in Physics for their application of the X-ray diffraction phenomenon to structure determination.

Being a crystallographer himself, Hägg commented in detail on the process of structure determination by X-ray analysis, emphasizing the extreme difficulty of the work, which involves "chemical knowledge, imagination, and intuition." It was at this combination that Dr. Hodgkin excelled. Hägg cited two of the many compounds whose structures she had determined as being both typical of the quality of her work and its importance: penicillin and vitamin B_{12}. He summarized the medical importance of penicillin and the need to know its structure. Hodgkin was instrumental in the success of the structure determination project, which involved crystallographers and chemists in the United States as well as England.

He concluded his summary of Hodgkin's work with an assessment of the importance of her determination of the structure of vitamin B_{12} and its relation to pernicious anemia. Hägg stated that Hodgkin played an essential role in that project, with B_{12} being the largest molecule whose structure had been determined at that time. He called this feat a "triumph for X-ray crystallographic techniques" as well as a "triumph for Mrs. Hodgkin."

Nobel lecture
Dorothy Crowfoot Hodgkin delivered her Nobel lecture, entitled "The X-Ray Analysis of Complicated Molecules," on December 11, 1964. She began by recounting her own history in X-ray diffraction work, which began with reading William H.

Bragg's book, *Concerning the Nature of Things*, in which she first encountered the idea of "seeing" molecules. During her professional chemistry education she became even more convinced of the desirability of "seeing" structures rather than relying on structures suggested by experimental techniques alone. She then gave a brief summary of the principles of X-ray diffraction, referring to the explanation of the technique given by Lawrence Bragg on the receipt of his Nobel Prize in 1915. Also referring to the work of Max Perutz and John Kendrew, winners of the 1962 Nobel Prize in Chemistry for X-ray determination of the structure of myoglobin, Hodgkin then discussed the technique of heavy metal substitution in a compound to enhance the X-ray process. That technique allows determination of the position of the heavy atoms, simplifying the possibilities for the structure of the rest of the compound. The proposed structure is determined from the angles of reflection of the X rays by the electron densities of the atoms in the molecule. By mathematically treating these patterns, which are maps of electron density, it becomes possible to determine the structure of the compound.

Dr. Hodgkin considered her early work in the field. She referred to her early determinations of the structures of cholesteryl chloride, bromide, and iodide as "very primitive," in both approach and technique. What took months to accomplish early in her work would have been solved in a matter of hours with the techniques that she and her collaborators developed as they approached the problems of more complicated molecules such as penicillin. Growing a series of isomorphous crystals and comparing the electron density patterns from the series was the technique in use before heavy atom substitution in the compound.

Dr. Hodgkin then recounted the work that led to the determination of the structure of vitamin B_{12}. The first crystals were provided by Dr. Lester Smith after it had been isolated by Dr. Folkers' research group. At the beginning of the work, not even its molecular formula was known with certainty. The analysis of the diffraction patterns for this very large molecule was aided by the use of computers, introducing the tremendous power of the computer into the processing of the diffraction patterns. In explaining the structure of B_{12}, Hodgkin related the different parts of the structure to what was known of its biochemical mode of action. She also included a description of the process and results of the determination of a series of related compounds.

Hodgkin concluded her lecture by discussing the practical results of the structure determinations made by her and her collaborators. The synthesis of pencillin and its coenzyme were made possible, and B_{12} was elegantly synthesized by Robert Burns Woodward. Studies have continued on their roles in metabolism, related to an understanding of their structures. Finally, Dr. Hodgkin warned that not all structure problems can be solved by X-ray analysis and demonstrated the difficulties of X-ray analysis by describing the difficulties encountered in her work on the structure of insulin, a problem that was not solved until several years after the awarding of the Nobel Prize. She ended by recognizing her collaborators, "without whose brains and hands and eyes very little would have been done."

Critical reception

The awarding of the Nobel Prize to Dorothy Crowfoot Hodgkin was announced in Stockholm on October 29, 1964, by the Royal Swedish Academy of Sciences. The work being honored was complex and mathematically technical, so most reports of the award in the popular—as well as scientific—press centered on the human side of the work and the worker. They commented on the importance to mankind of the objects of her work, Dr. Hodgkin's family life, her own unusual activities, her children and grandchildren, and her relation to the previous year's Nobelist in medicine, Alan Hodgkin (a cousin of her husband). As could be expected, mention was made of the fact that Hodgkin was the third woman honored with the Nobel Prize in Chemistry, the others being Marie Curie in 1911 and Irène Joliot-Curie in 1935. Surprisingly, however, no press reports commented on the fact that Hodgkin's award was the second Nobel Prize in three years awarded for X-ray diffraction structure determination of a molecule of biochemical importance—the earlier prize being the 1962 award to Perutz and Kendrew for the structure of myoglobin.

The molecules that Hodgkin investigated were of biochemical and biological importance, and many press reports, such as that in *The New York Times* of October 30, 1964, emphasized that the compounds whose structures were revealed through her work were vital in the treatment of pernicious anemia. In an editorial published at the same time, the editors of *The New York Times* echoed statements in reports from the world press by pointing out that the information supplied by Hodgkin's work was essential in understanding the role and function of these compounds in living organisms. The British journal *Nature*, in a report on the award published on December 5, 1964, assessed her work as a "remarkably coherent and well-planned" study of a "whole field of organic structures of medical and biological importance." Her work was cited as the "high water mark" of X-ray analysis, and she was credited with having "set a new standard," enabling study of even more difficult and important structures.

In a similar vein, the American weekly scientific journal *Science*, on November 6, 1964, also emphasized the dual importance of her work: She had determined the structure of a "very important and complicated molecule—B-12," and in so doing had demonstrated that it is possible to "solve" such complex structures with the techniques of X-ray diffraction and then to think of these complex molecules in "mental stereo." According to *Nature*, her true achievement was in "transcending the limitations of X-ray crystallography," which, prior to her work, was used only to confirm structures that had been determined by traditional chemical analysis. Hodgkin made the "X-ray method one of the major tools for the complete analysis" of structures.

In commenting on the personality of the new Nobelist, *The New York Times* reported that Dr. Hodgkin was in Ghana, Africa, when the prize was announced, which was rather typical for her and her "peripatetic family." She had been reared in Egypt, her husband had directed the Institute of African Studies at the University of Ghana, and their children were involved in education and service in Africa and

India. In an interview in Accra, Ghana, Hodgkin described herself as "very happy" and admitted to "continual partying with her friends since the word had reached her." In a statement typical of the importance she attributed to her collaborators, she regretted that the entire group of crystallographers from her laboratories in Oxford were not with her for the celebration. The article also described her as a "single-minded chemist who is wedded to her work" and a person who "gives the impression of simplicity and directness" but is described by her peers as a "genius" with "an unusual combination of qualities: precision, facility in mathematical analysis, and a special kind of imagination." With a candor rare in such circumstances, a friend of Mrs. Hodgkin's was quoted as saying that she had "hoped for the prize for many years." A year after the prize was awarded, Dr. Hodgkin was named to the Order of Merit by Queen Elizabeth II. This is the highest civilian honor in the British Empire, and Hodgkin was the first woman to be named to the order since Florence Nightingale.

Science stressed that X-ray solutions to structure problems do not come easily. They require the crystallographer to "pit his knowledge, skill, and imagination against the secrets of nature." Dorothy Crowfoot Hodgkin had succeeded where others had failed and was a "wizard at this intellectual unraveling." This evaluation of her abilities was repeated in 1968, when Harvard University awarded her an honorary doctor of science degree, citing her as a "brilliant and persevering lady whose achievements . . . enlarged the horizons of science."

In a report on the awards ceremony itself, *The New York Times* of December 12, 1964, stated that each Nobelist received the award from King Gustav Adolf VI, but that the king had spoken longer to Dorothy Hodgkin than to any of the other Nobelists, commending her on "her useful work for mankind."

Biography

Dorothy Crowfoot Hodgkin was born on May 12, 1910, in Cairo, Egypt. Her father, John Winter Crowfoot, who became a prominent archaeologist, held a position there in the Egyptian Education Service. She was one of four daughters born to J. W. Crowfoot and Grace Mary Hood Crowfoot, who assisted her husband in his work. Her early years were spent in Norfolk, England, where she received her early education at the Sir John Leman School in Beccles, Suffolk. She spent summer holidays visiting her parents in the Sudan, where her father was Director of Education and Antiquities. During one season she participated in an excavation and almost pursued a career in archaeology. A childhood interest in chemistry, however, continued to motivate her when she enrolled in Somerville College at the University of Oxford in 1928. She received her baccalaureate degree in 1932 and began her research in crystallography with John Desmond Bernal at the University of Cambridge that same year. She was awarded her doctorate there in 1937.

Her career at Oxford continued in 1934 with her appointment as tutor in chemistry. Advancement in the academic ranks accompanied her success in research, and eventually she became emeritus professor upon her retirement in 1977. From 1970, she held the position of chancellor of Bristol University and was the first woman appointed to the Wolfson Research Professorship of the Royal Society; she was honored as a medalist of the society in 1957.

In 1937, Dorothy Crowfoot married Thomas L. Hodgkin, an expert in African history and the son of Robin H. Hodgkin, provost of Queen's College, Oxford. They are the parents of three children: Luke, a mathematician teaching on the university level, Tobias, involved in agricultural studies, and Elizabeth, a historian teaching in Africa. Dorothy Hodgkin was elected a Fellow of the Royal Society, a foreign member of the Royal Netherlands Academy of Sciences, and a member of the American Academy of Arts and Sciences.

Scientific Career

Chemistry began to play an important role in the life of Dorothy Crowfoot Hodgkin at a very early age. Encouraged by her parents and a chemist friend of the family, she was performing chemical analyses of minerals by the age of ten during summer holidays spent with her parents on their archaeological digs. One of her first chemical projects upon entering Somerville College at Oxford involved the analysis of glass mosaic tiles from one of the Hodgkins' digs at Jerash. Her entry into crystallography was prompted by advice from her Oxford tutor, F. M. Brewer. After completing a special course in the field and spending a summer in the laboratory of Victor Goldschmidt, a pioneer in the field of geochemistry in Heidelberg, she began work with H. M. Powell. The topic of her work with him was thallium dialkyl halides.

Upon receipt of her baccalaureate degree from Oxford in 1932, and aided by a scholarship from Somerville College, Hodgkin moved to Cambridge to work with John Desmond Bernal. Studying with Bernal established her "scientific lineage" directly to Bragg, one of the founders of the field of X-ray crystallography, since Bernal had studied with him from 1923 to 1927 at the Royal Institution. Her time with Bernal was spent on a wide variety of projects involving the applications of X-ray diffraction analysis. They worked on the crystallography of natural products, including pepsin, a digestive enzyme, as well as inorganic materials such as metal crystals and Rochelle salt. They also considered theoretical problems such as the structure of liquids, particularly water, and tackled improvements to the method of diffraction analysis in studies on isomorphous replacement and phase determination.

Toward the end of her stay at Cambridge, Hodgkin and Bernal (in collaboration with Isidor Fankuchen) conducted a survey of the available crystallographic data on sterols that *Science* has described as "monumental in scope," even by contemporary standards. She particularly focused on two sterols, calciferol and lumisterol, involved in the biological synthesis of vitamin D_2. Besides the sterols, Hodgkin worked on structure determinations of proteins in the Cambridge labs, and through her early work on insulin showed that proteins possess a common structural feature, a rigid molecular framework.

Another project that occupied her efforts while at Cambridge was the determination of the structure of cholesterol iodide; work was done in collaboration with C. H. Carlisle. This was a more ambitious undertaking, since this compound, known to be of biochemical importance even in the early 1930's, was the first complex organic compound whose structure was determined with X-ray diffraction analysis that did not possess an internal molecular symmetry. In most cases, parts of a molecule are mirror images or repeating patterns of other parts of the molecule; this symmetry greatly simplifies the job of interpreting the X-ray diffraction patterns to map the arrangement of the atoms making up the molecule. The success of the determination of cholesterol iodide showed that the techniques of diffraction were sufficiently advanced to be applied to complex molecules whose structures lacked that symmetry.

The early work on the sterols set the pattern for the research that consumed the remainder of Dr. Hodgkin's career. Upon her return to Oxford as a tutor in chemistry in 1934, she continued her researches into the structures of large and complex organic molecules chosen because of their importance in areas of medicine and physiology. The first of these to be successful and win her wide recognition was the determination of the structure of the antibiotic penicillin, which was done in collaboration with Charles Bunn and was completed in 1942, after approximately five years of work. During World War II there was a need for a large amount of this drug. Sufficient amounts could not be supplied from processing of the limited supply of natural material, and there was a need to be able to synthesize the compound. Knowledge of the structure is necessary for any synthesis. The penicillin molecule consists of seventeen atoms and, therefore, represented a significant challenge to the X-ray diffraction techniques in use at that time. The situation was further complicated by the fact that there was little known chemical evidence on the molecule when Hodgkin and Bunn began their study, so there was no information available to aid the crystallographers in their work. The magnitude of the work that Hodgkin performed in this determination was recognized by *Nature* in calling the structure of penicillin "her first triumph."

During these years at Oxford, Dorothy Crowfoot Hodgkin raised sufficient funds through the receipt of research grants from the Rockefeller Foundation and the Nuffield Foundation to equip her own laboratory. She also began to attract a cadre of committed and capable students and assistants to participate in the crystallographic researches she was conducting. The next molecule to occupy the efforts of Dr. Hodgkin's crystallography group was vitamin B_{12}. This compound is the antipernicious anemia factor, and a knowledge of its behavior, nature, and structure was vitally needed in treatment and research. This molecule, which contains more than ninety atoms, was to occupy the group's efforts for more than ten years before Hodgkin began to publish a series of papers announcing their results. The papers were then published over a period of five years as the structure was refined and extended to other forms of the vitamin. This vitamin, the last member of the family of B-complex vitamins to be isolated, was prepared by E. L. Smith at the Glaxo Laboratories in England. Several groups began chemical investigations into its structure, including Todd at Cambridge and Folkers at Merck Company.

The X-ray crystallographic studies of Hodgkin's group at Oxford and the computing efforts of a group led by Kenneth N. Trueblood at the University of California at Los Angeles provided the structure in far less time than it would have taken to produce it by the chemical studies. Hodgkin recognized that the molecule contained a porphyrin-type nucleus, a large, open-ring structure. The X-ray patterns showed that this cagelike ring structure enclosed the cobalt atom. She then built up the structure of the molecule from that foundation until she had placed each of the atoms. *Nature* described her papers on the structure of vitamin B_{12} as a "model of a tactical approach to a formidable problem."

Another characteristic that has marked the career of Dorothy Crowfoot Hodgkin is a concern for the dissemination of the results of the crystallographers' work to those outside that particular research specialty. She realized early that the knowledge that she and her crystallographer colleagues were gaining on the structures of organic compounds would be of vital importance to organic chemists in their synthetic work and to biochemists in their studies of metabolic pathways. To accomplish the goal of sharing this information with them and others she began, in 1935, to write a yearly chapter on organic molecular crystals in the *Annual Reports on the Progress of Chemistry* of the Chemical Society of London. These chapters were considered an extremely lucid and valuable contribution to the advancement of chemistry in general.

In 1969, Dr. Hodgkin published what was her last major contribution to structure determination, the completion of the structure of insulin. The insulin molecule, important in the treatment of diabetes as well as in research efforts aimed at understanding the causes of that disease, consists of 777 atoms. The results of the structure determination study were presented at a meeting of the International Congress of Crystallography held at the State University of New York at Stony Brook. The work from Hodgkin's group showed that the molecule consisted of two chains of amino acids, one chain consisting of twenty-one acid units and the other of thirty. This determination was complicated by the lack of internal symmetry in the molecule, as her earlier work with penicillin had been. In this analysis, however, Hodgkin made significant use of computers to aid in the interpretation of the patterns of reflected X rays from the crystal of insulin. Typically, upon announcing the results, she gave the credit for the final structure determination to "her young colleagues at Oxford who did all the measuring."

As have many other Nobelists, Dr. Hodgkin used her postaward recognition to gain attention for her views on political matters. In 1972, she authored an opinion piece for *The New York Times* on January 7, in which she recounted a recent visit to a village in North Vietnam. She described the destruction of both property and human lives that she had witnessed, saying that it was, to her, "incredible that any civilized nation should drop bombs on the pleasant fields and villages." She used the article to make a plea to nations to turn "from war-making to peace-making—

and soon" to save the world from further destruction. Her activities continued with her being named in 1976 as president of the International Pugwash Conference, a group founded in 1957 by Albert Einstein and Bertrand Russell, concerned with the dangers posed by nuclear weapons. In 1981, Hodgkin wrote in *The Bulletin of the Atomic Scientists*, calling for disarmament and a conversion of efforts from weapons production to pure scientific research that would benefit mankind. She was one of ninety-seven Nobel Prize winners who, in 1982, issued a call for a freeze in nuclear weapons development and deployment through the council of the Pugwash Conference.

In 1977, Dr. Hodgkin retired from active research as Professor Emeritus at Oxford University, completing a career there that began in Somerville College as one of the first classes of women to be awarded degrees from Oxford. That career included recognition within the university and throughout the disciplines of chemistry and garnered for her many honors and prizes. Her career was marked by a logical and systematic approach to crystallographic research on a series of related compounds. The results of her researches have been of great benefit to mankind in the treatment of disease and in the understanding of biochemical processes. She continually recognized and praised the contributions made to that research by her colleagues in her laboratory, as well as by others with whom she has worked. The excitement with which she approached her work is best summarized in her own words. She described her X-ray diffraction research as work in which "our scientific world ceased to know any boundaries."

Bibliography

Primary

CHEMISTRY: "X-Ray Crystallography and the Chemistry of Sterols and Sex Hormones," *Chemisch Weekblad*, vol. 34, 1937 (with J. D. Bernal); "X-Ray Analysis of the Structure of Penicillin," *Advancement of Science*, vol. 6, 1949; "X-Ray Analysis and Protein Structure," *Cold Spring Harbor Symposia on Quantitative Biology*, vol. 14, 1949; "Crystallography of Lumisterol," *Journal of the Chemical Society*, 1952 (with D. Sayre); "The Structure of Vitamin B_{12} I: Outline of the Crystallographic Investigation of Vitamin B_{12}," *Proceedings of the Royal Society of London*, vol. A242, 1957 (with others); "The Structure of Vitamin B_{12} II: Crystal Structure of a Hexacarboxylic Acid Obtained by the Degradation of Vitamin B_{12}," *Proceedings of the Royal Society of London*, vol. A251, 1959 (with others); "The Structure of Vitamin B_{12} III: The Crystal Structure Analysis of the Air-Dried B_{12} Crystals," "The Structure of Vitamin B_{12} IV: X-Ray Analysis of Air-Dried Crystals of B_{12}," "The Structure of Vitamin B_{12} V: Structure of the Air-Dried Crystals of Vitamin B_{12}," *Proceedings of the Royal Society of London*, vol. 266, 1962 (with others); "The Structure of a Calciferol Derivative," *Journal of the Chemical Society*, 1963; "Vitamin B_{12}," *Proceedings of the Royal Institute of Great Britain*, vol. 42, 1969; *Structural Studies on Molecules of Biological Interest*, 1981.

Secondary

Bragg, Sir Lawrence. "X-Ray Crystallography." *Scientific American* July 1968. This review article summarizes both the principles and accomplishments of X-ray diffraction structure studies. It was written by one of the founders of the field and summarizes more than fifty years of research activity in the field. The work of Hodgkin is explained and used as an example of excellence.

Bunn, Charles, ed. *Chemical Crystallography: An Introduction to Optical and X-Ray Methods*. 2d ed. Oxford: Clarendon Press, 1961. Written by Hodgkin's coworker in the structural determination of penicillin, this very technical but well-illustrated work provides a comprehensive treatment of crystals and the means used to determine their structures. The text contains several references to the work on penicillin and praise for Hodgkin's work on vitamin B_{12}, as well as an interesting chapter on examples of structure determination, including vitamin C and rubber. Contains an extensive list of references to the original scientific literature.

Glusker, Jenny Pickworth, and Kenneth N. Trueblood. *Crystal Structure Analysis. A Primer*. New York: Oxford University Press, 1972. This text presents a slightly technical treatment of the area of X-ray crystallography and requires some elementary chemical and mathematical background on the part of the reader. The authors, Hodgkin's collaborators in the work on the structure of vitamin B_{12}, clearly explain the basic nature of crystals and the techniques of the X-ray diffraction process. The book contains an excellent bibliography, with annotated entries on the technical as well as historical aspects of the field, and a glossary of important terms that greatly increases the accessibility of the material covered.

Idhe, Aaron J. *The Development of Modern Chemistry*. New York: Dover, 1964. The development of the understanding of X rays and their use in diffraction studies is included in this comprehensive treatment of the development of chemistry. The work of Dorothy Hodgkin is considered in its chemical aspects as well as in the biochemical applications of the knowledge gained through her structure determinations.

Leonardi, Susan J. *Dangerous by Degrees: Women at Oxford and the Somerville College Novelists*. New Brunswick, N.J.: Rutgers University Press, 1989. This book focuses on the school of novelists to emerge from the first classes at Somerville to receive Oxford degrees. Dorothy Crowfoot Hodgkin is briefly mentioned in relation to this group of women, which includes the well-known mystery writer Dorothy L. Sayers. It provides an interesting view of what Hodgkin's days at Oxford would have been like and shows the foundation for her talent and the enthusiasm for her work that characterized her career.

Pauling, Linus, and Roger Hayward. *The Architecture of Molecules*. San Francisco: W. H. Freeman, 1964. This easily accessible and well-illustrated book by Nobel Prize winner Pauling and his collaborator is intended to serve as an introduction to the general field of molecular structure. It begins with a brief discussion of atomic structure and moves from simple structures such as the hydrogen and water molecules to a consideration of complex organic and biochemical molecules.

Trudy A. Dickneider

1965

Chemistry
Robert Burns Woodward, United States

Physics
Shin'ichirō Tomonaga, Japan
Julian Seymour Schwinger, United States
Richard P. Feynman, United States

Physiology or Medicine
François Jacob, France
André Lwoff, France
Jacques Monod, France

Literature
Mikhail Sholokhov, Soviet Union

Peace
United Nations Children's Fund

ROBERT BURNS WOODWARD
1965

Born: Boston, Massachusetts; April 10, 1917
Died: Cambridge, Massachusetts; July 8, 1979
Nationality: American
Area of concentration: Synthesis of natural materials

Woodward's many achievements in the synthesis of naturally occurring materials had great importance for biology and medicine as well as for chemistry. He achieved the complicated synthesis of chlorophyll; he also synthesized quinine and steroids such as cholesterol and cortisone

The Award

Presentation

Professor Arne Fredga, member of the Royal Swedish Academy of Sciences, presented Robert Burns Woodward for the 1965 Nobel Prize in Chemistry. Professor Fredga began by noting the technical advances that have made it possible to investigate extremely difficult problems regarding the architecture of the molecule. Many scientists involved in this kind of research become intrigued with the problem of synthesis, which is the artificial preparation of chemical substances. At the same time that he is reproducing the substance, the scientist may be able to modify its properties in a desirable way. Professor Fredga asserted that organic synthesis is both an exacting science and a fine art and that Professor Woodward was its finest practitioner.

Woodward's achievements in this field were considered by many skeptics to have been impossible undertakings. During World War II, Woodward synthesized quinine. In later years, he synthesized steroids such as cholesterol and cortisone, strychnine, and reserpine. One of his most outstanding accomplishments was the synthesis of chlorophyll, which has increased science's understanding of the chlorophyll molecule.

Woodward's activities have not been limited to the problems of synthesis, Fredga noted. He has studied the structure of the fish poison tetrodotoxin, the cause of many deaths in Japan. He has also probed the synthetic activities that occur in nature.

Nobel lecture

Woodward delivered his Nobel lecture, entitled "Recent Advances in the Chemistry of Natural Products," on December 11, 1965. He began by discussing one of the most challenging synthetic objectives of the century: the synthesis of penicillin. Beginning with the early work of Alexander Fleming, Woodward traced the history of penicillin research. Although John Sheehan developed methods to synthesize penicillin in 1959, his achievement could not be put to any practical use. Thus, Woodward believed that penicillin still presented challenges to the synthetic chemist.

Woodward attributed the difficulty of synthesizing penicillin to the fact that the beta-lactam ring, which is common to the penicillins and the cephalosporins, is highly susceptible to change. The only successful attempts to synthesize penicillin involved the removal of water from penicilloic acid analogues and closure of the beta-lactam ring. The synthesis of cephalosporin, however, was quite different, because the product of hydrolysis (alteration caused by water) was not known. For the synthesis of cephalosporin, Woodward used L(+)-cysteine as his starting material, which presented in ready-made fashion an important part of the atomic structure of the cephalosporins.

Woodward began the synthesis by modifying the cysteine structure in such a way that the reactivity of the amino, sulfhydryl, and carboxyl groups would be depressed. He converted the cysteine molecule into a molecule whose methylene group was in a much better position in respect to chemical reactivity. Once the methylene grouping was in position, Woodward began attacking the sulfur atom within the methylene group. In addition, the hydrogen atoms had to be transferred from the methylene group to the second nitrogen atom.

After this was achieved, the newly attached grouping exhibited selective reactivity. This new grouping, called the hydrazo diester (XII), was then oxidized in boiling benzene for two hours. After the resulting mixture was treated with excess anhydrous sodium acetate in boiling dry methanol for twenty-four hours, trans hydroxy ester was produced, and this product was transformed further into an acetoxyazo compound. After further chemical reductions and transformations, the entire stereochemical problem presented by the cephalosporins was solved.

Woodward then discussed the second of the key ideas on which his general plan had been based: He attempted the preparation of beta-lactam, because it would contain basic structural elements common to the cephalosporins and the penicillins. Beta-lactam might also serve as the source for a variety of new substances through the fusion of new rings at the reactive nitrogen and sulfur atoms. He tested his hypothesis that beta-lactam was capable of further development through fusion of the atomic groupings. The properties of the resulting synthetic substance were indeed similar to those of material formed from natural cephalosporin.

The final step involved the synthesis of cephalothin itself. First, the group that was to become the final cephalosporin had to be protected during the intermediary stages after the amino aldehyde was condensed. After this crude mixture was esterfied, the two products were mixed and allowed to stand in pyridine at room temperature for three days. The nature of the crystalline barium salt that resulted from these final reactions was found to be identical to the salt of natural cephalosporin: Woodward and his colleagues had successfully synthesized this substance.

Critical reception

The presentation of the Nobel Prize in Chemistry to Robert Burns Woodward was greeted with universal praise, largely because of the scope of his achievements. *The New York Times* of October 12, 1965, observed that Woodward had "long been recognized as one of the world's leading organic chemists on the basis of his dazzling feats in synthesizing a long series of compounds." *Science News Letter* of October 30, 1965, reported that Woodward was granted the award for his "brilliant achievements" in creating organic materials in the laboratory. The article highlighted the "tremendous feat" that Woodward achieved when he synthesized chlorophyll in 1960. It also mentioned his "outstanding work" in the synthesis of other organic substances.

Science of October 29, 1965, acknowledged the importance of Woodward's work by discussing his research in a three-page article, complete with diagrams. The author indicated in the beginning that listing Woodward's achievements "fails to convey the special character of his approach," which is characterized by "bold innovation, as in his elegant synthesis of the naturally occurring alkaloid ellipticine." The article singled out his synthesis of chlorophyll as "the most brilliant of his achievements." Turning his attention to Woodward's personal characteristics, the writer praised his "originality, discernment, and cooperative spirit," which have attracted collaborators from all over the world. The writer concluded with a description of Woodward's very polished laboratory methods, which he attributed to Woodward's "intellectual vitality."

Biography

The son of Arthur Chester and Margaret (née Burns) Woodward, Robert Burns Woodward was born in Boston, Massachusetts, on April 10, 1917. His interest in chemistry was so stimulated by the gift of a chemistry set that he set up a laboratory in the basement of the family home. When Woodward was graduated from high school, his knowledge of chemistry is reported to have exceeded that of most science majors in college. At the age of sixteen, he entered the Massachusetts Institute of Technology (MIT). Because of his refusal to attend gym class, however, and his failing grade in economics, Woodward was on the verge of flunking out at the age of seventeen. The faculty fortunately recognized Woodward's aptitude for science, and they organized a special program for him, with the requirement that he take the examinations. He received his doctorate from MIT at the age of twenty, at the same time that other members of his class were graduating with bachelor's degrees.

At the age of twenty-one, Woodward began his lifelong association with Harvard University. He accepted a position as a postdoctoral fellow at Harvard immediately after his graduation from MIT and became a faculty member in 1938. That same year, he married Irji Pullman. In 1940, he was named instructor in chemistry. During World War II, he was consultant to the committee on medical research of the Office of Scientific Research and Development, and to the War Production Board. During his stay at Harvard, he was also employed in June, 1942, as a consultant for the Polaroid Corporation. While searching for a substitute for quinine crystals, which were needed for Polaroid lenses, Woodward began work on the total synthesis of quinine on February 1, 1943, and completed his work fourteen months later at Harvard's Converse Memorial Laboratory. He was appointed assistant professor in 1944 and associate professor in 1946. During 1946, he was married again, this time to Eudoxia M. M. Muller.

Woodward continued to perform feats of synthesis in the decades that followed. With C. H. Scramm of Harvard, Woodward completed the synthesis of protein analogues, substances that resemble natural proteins. In 1947, he also improved the polymerization process, which resulted in a plastic film that brought about a number of new products. Harvard named him Dupont Research Professor in 1949-1950 in order to free him from his teaching duties.

At the April, 1951, meeting of the Chemical Society in London, Woodward announced that he had achieved the first synthesis of a steroid, which is the group of chemicals that includes cortisone, digitalis, vitamin D, and the sex hormones. In 1960, Woodward synthesized chlorophyll, the plant pigment. Two years later, he headed a group that spent three years synthesizing tetracycline. After his receipt of the Nobel Prize in 1966, he continued to lecture at Harvard and to conduct research into the synthesis of compounds such as vitamin B_{12}. He died on July 8, 1979, in Cambridge, Massachusetts.

Scientific Career

Woodward's career as a chemical synthesist began while he was acting as a consultant for the Polaroid Corporation. Because of the wartime shortage of quinine, Woodward was assigned the task of seeking a substitute for quinine crystals, which were needed for optical lenses. Not satisfied with simply seeking a substitute for quinine, Woodward began exploring the possibilities of synthesizing quinine in 1943 at Harvard's Converse Memorial Laboratory. He and his associate, Dr. William E. Doering, began with benzaldehyde, an inexpensive coal-tar derivative which contained all of the essential materials. Using research conducted by Rabe and Koenigs in 1908, Woodward and Doering converted the benzaldyhyde into a substance known as 7-hydroxy-isoquinoline. Then, through a series of sixteen additional conversions, they finally derived a product in 1944 whose molecular structure closely resembled that of quinine. This was essentially a total synthesis in that the compounds that they started with could be synthesized from nitrogen, oxygen, carbon, and hydrogen. Woodward and Doering did not find it necessary during any stage of the synthesis to use organic materials.

One year after his synthesis of quinine, Woodward attempted to synthesize penicillin. Although penicillin had been partially synthesized in 1959, the process lacked practicality. Woodward chose as his starting material L(+)-cysteine, a readily available substance that already possessed a large portion of the crucial substituted beta-lactam ring of penicillin. After a series of fifty-six conversions, Woodward obtained a synthetic crystalline barium salt whose properties were identical to those of penicillin.

In 1947, Woodward once again used his considerable talents to produce materials that had vast implications for industry. Employing a technique known as polymerization, which is the joining of small molecules to form large ones, Woodward attempted to synthesize protein by joining amino acids. This linking was accomplished through the formation of peptide links, in which a carbon atom at the end of one amino-acid molecule would attach to a nitrogen atom in the next. He found a combination of amino acids in which every additional molecule that joined the chain reacted to form at its unattached end a new active center for another linkage. Using this method, he was able to link as many as ten thousand amino-acid units. One of the products of this synthesis was a substance that had the chemical nature of silk and, therefore, offered industrial prospects for real silk without silkworms.

In 1950, Woodward and his team of six researchers explored the possibility of synthesizing cortisone at the Converse Chemical Laboratory, Harvard. His starting material was a simple coal-tar derivative known as orthotoluidine. Beginning with a single ring of carbon atoms with one methyl group attached, he began adding four more atoms, then five atoms, then three, and finally two. These atoms eventually arranged themselves into a configuration of two methyl groups and four carbon rings of the basic steroid pattern. Even though Woodward's process, completed in 1951, involved twenty steps, it was much simpler and less expensive than the standard thirty-seven-step method of converting ox bile to cortisone.

Woodward continued to perform feats of synthesis during the 1950's. In 1954, he synthesized strychnine, an extremely complicated and poisonous alkaloid consisting of seven intricately related rings of atoms. That same year, he synthesized lysergic acid, a hallucinogenic drug of some consequence. Two years later, he synthesized reserpine, a tranquilizing drug that had been widely used since its discovery by R. W. Wilkins a few years before. During this decade, he synthesized another alkaloid, ellipticine, by condensing an indole with a 3-acetylpyridine, which gave a bisindolyl derivative. This derivative was converted to a diacetyldihydropyrine, which yielded ellipticine after pyrolysis.

The most brilliant of Woodward's scientific achievements was his synthesis of the tremendously complex green plant pigment chlorophyll in 1960. Chlorophyll resists oxidation because the formation of the related porphyrin is sterically inhibited. His synthesis was based on the theory that the steric crowding could serve as the driving force to bring about the conversion of a properly substituted porphyrin. Although porphyrin had been synthesized in the past, the resulting compound was complicated and low in yield. Woodward began with a new porphyrin synthesis, which was used for the creation of the vitally important intermediate compound. Starting with the extremely sensitive dipyrrylmethane, Woodward created a sixteen-step process that depended on favorable steric factors. The synthesis of chlorophyll opened the doors for a better understanding of what occurs in photosynthesis and the complex life process of plants.

Woodward's later work was primarily concerned with establishing the structure of many important compounds. In 1962, he headed a group that spent three years attempting to synthesize a tetracycline antibiotic. Toward the end of the decade, he examined the structure of the fish poison tetrodotoxin in an effort to find an antitoxin. In 1971, his interest in the synthetic activities in nature led him to develop an original and promising approach to the synthesis of polypeptides such as vitamin B_{12}.

Woodward's scientific accomplishments represent a climax to a long series of organic syntheses that had begun 150 years before with the work of Friedrich Wöhler. The syntheses achieved by Woodward are not only of tremendous importance to both industry and medicine but also invaluable from a scientific viewpoint to the extent that they increased man's knowledge of the structure of some of the most complex compounds known to science. Because of Woodward's work, few nonpolymeric molecules still present a challenge to the chemical synthesist.

Bibliography

Primary
CHEMISTRY: "Total Synthesis of Quinine," *Journal of the American Chemical Society*, vol. 66, 1944 (with W. E. Doering); "Total Synthesis of a Steroid," *Journal of the American Chemical Society*, vol. 73, 1951 (with others); "The Total Synthesis of Cholesterol," *Journal of the American Chemical Society*, vol. 73, 1951 (with F. Sondheimer and D. Taub); "The Total Synthesis of Cortisone," *Journal of the American Chemical Society*, vol. 73, 1951 (with F. Sondheimer and D. Taub); "The Total Synthesis of Reserpine," *Journal of the American Chemical Society*, vol. 78, 1956 (with others); "Total Synthesis of Vitamin B_{12}," *Pure and Applied Chemistry*, vol. 33, 1973.

Secondary
Asimov, Isaac. "Robert Burns Woodward." In *Asimov's Biographical Encyclopedia of Science and Technology*. 2d ed. Garden City, N.Y.: Doubleday, 1982. This short entry is primarily a chronological record of his most important scientific achievements, culminating in his receipt of the Nobel Prize. It is written for the general reader.
Bartlett, P. D., and F. H. Westheimer. "Robert Burns Woodward, Nobel Prize in Chemistry for 1965." *Science* 150 (October 29, 1965): 585-587. This article is an in-depth explanation of Woodward's most significant scientific accomplishments. It includes a detailed diagram of his synthesis of chlorophyll. Profiles his personality and teaching method. The intended audience is definitely readers with a scientific background.
"The Protein Makers." *Newsweek* 29 (June 23, 1947): 57-58. This early announcement of Woodward's synthesis of protein emphasizes its practical application.
"Robert Burns Woodward." In *Current Biography, 1952*. Edited by Anna Rothe and Evelyn Lohr. New York: H. W. Wilson, 1952. This article is the most extensive biography of Woodward that is easily obtainable. Although it does include his most important feats of synthesis, it is primarily a history of his career. It includes a short bibliography.
Schlessinger, Bernard S., and June Schlessinger, eds. *Who's Who of Nobel Prize*

Winners. Phoenix, Ariz.: Oryx Press, 1986. This reference book contains a very brief description of Woodward's life and publications. The entry is valuable for its bibliography. The "commentary" section explains the nature of his research and shows why he won the Nobel Prize.

"Tailor-Made Steroids." *Newsweek* 37 (May 7, 1951): 93-95. An early account of his synthesis of cortisone. Includes a detailed but simplified description of the experimental method used.

Alan Brown

1966

Chemistry
Robert S. Mulliken, United States

Physics
Alfred Kastler, France

Physiology or Medicine
Charles B. Huggins, United States
Francis Peyton Rous, United States

Literature
Shmuel Yosef Agnon, Israel
Nelly Sachs, Sweden

Peace
no award

ROBERT S. MULLIKEN
1966

Born: Newburyport, Massachusetts; June 7, 1896
Died: Arlington, Virginia; October 31, 1986
Nationality: American
Area of concentration: Structural chemistry

Through the application of quantum mechanics, Mulliken developed the theory of molecular orbitals, which provided new insight into the structure of the chemical bond. He also studied molecular spectra and isotope separation

The Award

Presentation

Professor Inga Fischer-Hjalmars from the University of Stockholm presented the Nobel Prize in Chemistry to Robert S. Mulliken on December 10, 1966. She began by explaining how the natural sciences had begun as separate domains but slowly began to converge as man's knowledge deepened. This convergence has been especially true of physics and chemistry.

Professor Fischer-Hjalmars then recounted the history of research on the chemical bond, beginning with Jöns Jakob Berzelius' assertion in 1812 of the importance of positive and negative electrical charges of the atoms, continuing with Gilbert Newton Lewis' 1916 hypothesis that the chemical bond is caused by two electrons which remain between the bonded atoms, and ending with Walter Heitler's investigation of Lewis' pair theory by means of quantum mechanics. It was, however, Niels Bohr's theory in 1922—that electrons can be assigned different shells at varying distances from the nucleus—that provided the point of departure for Mulliken's research.

In 1925, Mulliken applied Bohr's principle for atoms to the molecular problem. Using a theoretical concept called the electronic orbital, Mulliken described the electronic motion as extending over the entire molecule. His new view, which started from the quantum mechanical interaction between all atomic nuclei and all the electrons of the molecule, has explained many molecular properties and reactions.

Since theoretical results provided by experiments could not provide Mulliken with enough precise data regarding the properties of molecules, he adapted the molecular orbital method to computer language. This method enabled him to derive important information regarding the atomic bond and to investigate molecules that had been inaccessible to experiments before.

Nobel lecture

Mulliken delivered his Nobel lecture on December 12, 1966. He began his discussion of molecular orbitals, entitled "Spectroscopy, Molecular Orbitals, and

Chemical Bonding," by reviewing the atomic theories of Arnold Sommerfeld and Niels Bohr. These two scientists believed that electrons moved in orbits around the nucleus in the same way that planets moved around the sun. They also assumed that the sizes and shapes of the orbits were determined by quantum rules. Then, in 1925-1926, the Newtonian mechanics that they had been using were replaced by quantum mechanics, and later scientists were forced by these radical new concepts for small-scale particles to view molecular orbits in a far different way.

An orbital is something like an orbit. It refers to "one-electron orbital wavefunction," also known as an eigenfunction. Each orbital favors some particular regions of space and disfavors another. All orbitals extend throughout all regions of the atom or molecule. Unlike Bohr's theory, the molecular orbital theory does not assume that electrons travel in specific paths. Each orbital possesses its own energy. Orbital energy is the force required to take the electron out of its orbital and into free space. In the "normal" or "ground" state, the electrons are settled into the lowest-energy orbitals available. There are also vacant orbitals available which any electron can occupy if "excited," or given a burst of energy.

Orbitals can be described as either valence-bound orbitals, to which Mulliken refers as atomic orbitals (AO), or molecular orbitals (MO). In the atomic orbital method, the electronic structure is composed of atoms and atomic orbitals of these atoms. The molecular orbital method, on the other hand, regards each molecule as a self-sufficient unit. The MO method is more useful for a detailed understanding of molecules, and the AO method is more appropriate in cases where atoms have only one electron, as with the hydrogen atom. Mulliken considered both methods to be viable alternatives to each other because both are only approximate solutions to the complete equation which governs the behavior of molecules.

Mulliken developed his theory of molecular orbitals soon after the development of quantum mechanics. Atomic electronic orbits were replaced by atomic orbitals, although they were not given that name until 1932. Between 1925 and 1927, Mulliken and his friend Friedrich Hund applied quantum mechanics to a detailed study of atoms.

A true AO or MO for an electron is an orbital which corresponds to a self-consistent field. Each orbital possesses its own energy. Orbital energy is the force required to take the electron out of its orbital and into free space. In the "normal" or "ground" state, the electrons are settled into the lowest-energy orbitals available. There are also vacant orbitals available which any electron can occupy if "excited," or given a burst of energy. The purest and most accurate MOs are the "delocalized" ones that spread over the entire molecule. Mulliken referred to these as spectroscopic MOs. These are especially important for understanding electronic spectra in molecules.

Mulliken supplemented his discussion of MOs with a slide show that illustrated the essential difference between his theory and Gilbert Newton Lewis' theory. Lewis' theory of molecular orbits did not explain how electrons moved or why they paused long enough between atoms to form bonds. Mulliken then showed how the intervention of quantum mechanics in 1926 had enabled him to develop MO theories that would more clearly demonstrate electron correlation.

Mulliken's later work was characterized by an interest in intramolecular charge-transfer spectra. He began his explanation of this phase of his career by showing how "localized" MOs become "delocalized." Delocalization results from a small decrease in the calculated energy. In a completely delocalized description, the localized MOs are completely replaced by the spectroscopic MOs.

Mulliken then shifted the focus of his lecture from his work to the work of others. He began with the research performed by his associates in his group in Chicago. Large-scale computer calculation constituted most of the work that was done at Chicago. Under the direction of Mulliken's colleague C. C. J. Roothaan, the group produced machine calculations that included all the electrons in the atom or molecule instead of only a few electrons, as had been done in the semi-empirical studies. The group was also able to compute the values of several molecular properties, some of which had been hitherto unknown, using the computer and the MO method. Mulliken also mentioned the research done by Clementi in 1966 with the assistance of computers at the Yorktown laboratory of International Business Machines (IBM). Through a technique called population analysis, he was able to calculate how the total population of electrons is distributed among the atoms in a molecule.

Mulliken concluded his lecture by predicting that in the future, thousands of chemists would go to the computer instead of to the laboratory to do their research.

Critical reception

The presentation of the Nobel Prize in Chemistry to Robert S. Mulliken was received with almost unanimous acclaim by the media. Because Mulliken had spent almost forty years developing the molecular orbital theory, his fame had been well established by the time he was given the award. *Time* magazine of November 11, 1966, said that Mulliken's award was for an achievement that was "so esoteric that few laymen could even begin to understand." The writer added that the award was "well-deserved" but "belated," because most of the important work that had been done over the previous three decades was based on Mulliken's theory. Citing his reputation as "Mr. Molecule," *Science News* of November 12 said that Mulliken had "paved the way" for much of the knowledge that scientists have of the behavior of chemical compounds. The article also praised Mulliken for destroying the "stereotyped concept" that atoms form molecules as bricks do walls, with the identity of each brick preserved. *Newsweek* of November 14 pointed out that modern chemists owe a great debt to Mulliken, because he did the "onerous" theoretical work that made their research possible. The article also quoted a former student of Mulliken, Arnold C. Wahl of the Argonne National Laboratory, who went so far as to say that without Mulliken's theories, "chemists could not even think about chemistry." *The New York Times* of November 4, 1966, also took note of the fact that Mulliken had devoted his life to the study of electrons. In another article in the same issue, *The*

New York Times quoted the spokesman for the Academy, Erik Rudberg, who predicted that Mulliken's work might lead to the synthesis of new molecules through the use of computers.

Science of November 11, 1966, devoted the most space to Mulliken's achievement. The writer noted at the beginning of the article that the award was unusual because it had been given to a man who had spent his entire life as a member of the physics department, not the chemistry department. The award was also distinctive because it was given "not for any experimental results" but for the development of a "purely theoretical method of description, analysis, and computation." The writer stated his belief that most chemists would approve of the award because it helps "restore the balance of recognition between the two rival descriptive theories of chemistry," the atomic orbital method and the molecular orbital method. Although many scientists, such as Friedrich Hund, Erich Hückel, and Julius Robert von Mayer, had contributed to this approach, it was Mulliken who put it into a "rigorous mathematical form." The writer also praised Mulliken for his immense output of papers. Averaging four papers per year, Mulliken had set a record that had been exceeded by only one man in the American Physical Society. The article concluded by praising Mulliken for his habit of revising his manuscripts until they were perfect.

Biography

Robert Sanderson Mulliken was born in Newburyport, Massachusetts, on June 7, 1896. The son of Samuel Parsons Mulliken, a professor of organic chemistry at the Massachusetts Institute of Technology (MIT), young Mulliken decided at an early age to follow in his father's footsteps. His interest in molecular theories dates back to high school, where he delivered an oration entitled "The Electron: What It Is and What It Does." In 1917, Mulliken was graduated from MIT and went on to earn his Ph.D. in physical chemistry under W. D. Harkins at the University of Chicago in 1921. After receiving a National Research Council fellowship, he pursued further study at Harvard University.

Mulliken developed the basic for his revolutionary molecular theory during the 1920's. Between 1923 and 1925, he studied molecular spectra at the Jefferson Physical Laboratory of Harvard University. In 1925, he went to Europe, where he collaborated with Friedrich Hund. Between 1925 and 1927, Mulliken and Hund applied the newly developed quantum mechanics to molecular structure. In 1928, he returned to the University of Chicago, where he was appointed associate professor of physics. (He would remain at the University of Chicago for the next thirty-seven years.) The next year, 1929, he married Mary Helen von Noè, whose father was a professor of geology at the University of Chicago.

In the years just before World War II, Mulliken lectured and published his theoretical papers in the *Journal of Chemical Physics*. In 1941, Mulliken was on one of the committees for the National Academy of Sciences, which advised President Franklin D. Roosevelt on the feasibility of building an atom bomb. Between 1942 and 1945, Mulliken acted as director of editorial work and information on the plutonium project. He also participated in the drafting of the project's "Prospectus Nucleonics," released in 1944, which proposed future uses for nuclear energy.

After the war, Mulliken helped rebuild the spectroscopic laboratories. In 1965, he left Chicago to become Distinguished Research Professor of Chemical Physics at Florida State University. He received the Nobel Prize in Chemistry in 1966.

Scientific Career

Robert S. Mulliken's career as a research scientist actually began in 1922, when he suggested a method of isotope separation by evaporative centrifuging. At the Jefferson Physical Laboratory of Harvard University, Mulliken investigated, between 1923 and 1925, the visible and ultraviolet spectrum. Because basic spectroscopy was considered to lie within the domain of physics, Mulliken began his long affiliation with physics departments. While at Harvard, he benefited greatly from the instruction in experimental spectroscopy provided by F. A. Saunders and the instruction in quantum theory provided by E. C. Kemble.

In the course of his study of band spectra, Mulliken noticed that these spectra fell into several distinct types which pointed to the existence of several types of molecular electronic states. He also observed that these types seemed to differ in respect to angular momentum properties. Because no alternative method existed, Mulliken was forced to use the same symbols for atomic states to describe these states, even though he realized that they were inappropriate. It became clear to him that the structure of the molecule could not be adequately studied by classical chemical methods.

The advent of quantum mechanics in 1925-1926 exposed the shortcomings of the old quantum theory of atoms and provided Mulliken with the means for constructing his theories. In 1927, his friend Friedrich Hund impressed Mulliken with his attempt to clarify scientists' understanding of spectra and atoms. It soon became clear to Mulliken that molecular orbitals could provide suitable homes for electrons in molecules in the same way as atomic orbitals for electrons in atoms. Thus, Mulliken discarded the earlier notion that electrons circled nuclei in orbits just as planets circle the sun. He favored Erwin Schrödinger's view of the electron as a wave that spread out in orbitals over the atoms in a chemical bond. This theory held tremendous promise for the researcher, because he could now investigate molecular properties that are dependent upon these electrons, such as spatial structure, chemical binding energies, ionization potentials, and spectra.

In the 1930's, Mulliken tried to deduce all that he could about MOs from qualitative considerations of energy and symmetry combined with empirical evidence from molecular spectra. At his laboratory in Chicago, he and a succession of distinguished colleagues and students conducted research in experimental spectroscopy and extended his molecular-orbital ideas to complicated diatomic spectra. Mulliken's approach to finding molecular orbitals was through the linear combination of atomic orbitals, or LCAO method. Not only did he and his students explain the weak absorption spectra of the ketones during this decade, but also he wrote several papers on the spectra of organic compounds. While attempting to explain the spectra of iodine in benzene, he became interested in the interaction of molecules with one another, to which he referred as intermolecular charge transfer spectra.

In the absence of computers, Mulliken resorted during the 1940's to semiempirical methods to determine the structure of molecular properties. He realized that before his new theory could be used to determine molecular structure in detail, massive calculations would have to be made. The simple structure of the nitrogen molecule, for example, occupied the time of five chemists working constantly for ten years. Anticipating the invention of massive computers, Mulliken began developing new formulas that could be utilized when the computer age finally arrived in the 1950's.

After World War II, Mulliken tried to build the spectroscopic laboratories back up again. To accomplish this task, he organized a "laboratory of molecular spectra and structure," in which he gathered a group of brilliant quantum chemists. For twenty years, this group produced an annual red-bound technical report. Most of Mulliken's work during the 1950's dealt with the "charge-transfer" interpretation of the binding and spectra of molecular complexes. Through quantum mechanics, he showed how observations of weak, intermolecular forces might be explained. He illustrated electronegativity, which is the ability of a particular atom in a molecule to draw electrons to itself, in a formula: $\frac{1}{2}$ (I + E), where I is the ionization potential of the atom and E is its electron affinity.

Mulliken is unique among Nobel Prize-winning scientists in that his award was not given for any experimental results. Yet, his influence has been so far-reaching that chemistry itself has been revolutionized as a result of his molecular orbital theory. This new theory made it much easier to understand the complex interactions between molecules that, prior to his theory, had been inaccessible to scientists. Thus, most of the important work that has been done on molecular structure in the second half of the twentieth century owes a great debt to Robert Sanderson Mulliken.

Bibliography

Primary

CHEMISTRY: "The Assignment of Quantum Numbers for Electrons in Molecules," *Physics Review*, vol. 32, 1928; "The Assignment of Quantum Numbers for Electrons in Molecules. II. Correlation of Molecular and Atomic Electron States," *Physics Review*, vol. 32, 1928; "Electronic States of Diatomic Carbon and the C-C Bond," *Physics Review*, vol. 56, 1939; "Quantum-Mechanical Methods and the Electronic Spectra and Structure of Molecules," *Chemical Reviews*, vol. 41, 1947.

Secondary

Asimov, Isaac. "Robert Sanderson Mulliken." In *Asimov's Biographical Encyclopedia of Science and Technology.* 2d ed. Garden City, N.Y.: Doubleday, 1982. A short biography of Mulliken, this entry briefly explains Mulliken's molecular orbital theory. Suitable as an introduction to Mulliken.

Daintith, John, et al., eds. *A Biographical Encyclopedia of Scientists*. 2 vols. New York: Facts on File, 1981. Composed mostly of highlights from his scientific career, the entry on Mulliken is intended for the general audience. Offers simplified explanations of Mulliken's complex theories.

Ferguson, Lloyd N. *The Modern Structural Theory of Organic Chemistry*. Englewood Cliffs, N.J.: Prentice-Hall, 1963. Although this book is not solely devoted to Mulliken, it does go into great technical detail on the theories that Mulliken pioneered. Includes many references to Mulliken. Intended for college students and scientists.

Offenhatz, Peter. *Atomic and Molecular Theory*. New York: McGraw-Hill, 1970. Although Mulliken the man is not discussed, his theories are. For college students and scientists.

Platt, John R. "1966 Nobel Laureate in Chemistry: Robert S. Mulliken." *Science* 154 (November 11, 1966): 745-747. Although this article contains a brief biography and personality profile of the man, it is primarily concerned with his molecular orbital theory, which it explains in detail. Some science background is useful.

"Practical Theorists." *Newsweek* 68 (November 14, 1966): 73. This announcement of Mulliken's award contains a fairly lengthy explanation of his molecular orbital theory in terms that can be understood easily by the layperson.

Schlessinger, Bernard S., and June Schlessinger, eds. *Who's Who of Nobel Prize Winners*. Phoenix, Ariz.: Oryx Press, 1986. A brief entry on Mulliken's life and publications, including a secondary bibliography. The "Commentary" section explains the nature of Mulliken's research and shows why he won the Nobel Prize.

Alan Brown

1967

Chemistry
Manfred Eigen, West Germany
Ronald G. W. Norrish, Great Britain
George Porter, Great Britain

Physics
Hans Albrecht Bethe, United States

Physiology or Medicine
Halden Keffer Hartline, United States
George Wald, United States
Ragnar A. Granit, Sweden

Literature
Miguel Ángel Asturias, Guatemala

Peace
no award

MANFRED EIGEN
1967

Born: Bochum, Germany; May 9, 1927

Nationality: German
Areas of concentration: Electrolyte theory and fast reactions

Eigen pioneered the development of methods for measuring the rates of chemical reactions that had previously been considered instantaneous. Starting with systems in equilibrium, he shocked the molecules with electrical or sonic pulses, then studied the kinetics involved in establishing a new equilibrium

The Award

Presentation

Arne Ölander of the Royal Swedish Academy of Sciences and a member of the Nobel Committee for Chemistry, presented Manfred Eigen for the Nobel Prize in Chemistry on December 10, 1967. In his address, Ölander undertook a review of the history of chemical investigations of rates of chemical reactions, beginning with some of the classical work of Jacobus Henricus van't Hoff, winner of the first Nobel Prize in Chemistry in 1901. The research of van't Hoff and Svante August Arrhenius (Nobel Prize winner in 1903) indicated the temperature dependence of rates of reaction and also showed that only a small number of molecular collisions resulted in reaction. Reactions at the turn of the century could only have their rates measured if a physical property change could be measured and the time could be measured on a clock of that day. Reactions that proceeded more rapidly could not be studied. In 1923, H. Hartridge and F. J. W. Roughton studied reaction rates involving two solutions flowing through separate tubes before mixing; reaction times involving milliseconds could then be measured. Investigations of molecular energy states, however, showed that atomic oscillations were in the order of nano seconds. Eigen developed a variety of methods to measure these ultra-fast reactions. For example, he used an electric pulse to dissociate a surplus of acetic acid molecules in solution and then measured the rate at which equilibrium could be re-achieved. The methods developed by Eigen have been adapted by others to study a wide variety of problems involving fast reactions such as acid-base neutralization reactions.

Nobel lecture

On Monday, December 11, 1967, Eigen delivered his Nobel lecture, entitled "Immeasurably Fast Reactions." His exceptional address was delivered in a style more literary than the usual lecture in chemistry, revealing Eigen's breadth of interests. He started his lecture with the revelation that his interest in the topic went back at least as far as the days in which he was preparing for his doctorate examinations.

Considering the ultimate in fast reactions, he pondered the reaction of the hydrogen ion and the hydroxide ion to form water; others, including Albert Einstein, Lars Onsager, and Peter Debye, had all independently studied the reaction and had derived equations for the frequency of ionic collisions. Eigen worked the problem of diffusion-controlled reaction for himself and found the reaction time to be in the order of 10^{-10} to 10^{-11} seconds. The time did indeed appear to be immeasurable. Using the flow methods developed by Hartridge and Roughton, it was possible to mix reactants within a millisecond and study the reaction sequence. The gap of 7-8 orders of magnitude served to illustrate the difficulty of the problem.

Eigen showed that a signal rapidly disturbing the chemical equilibrium would briefly produce reaction in the forward direction which would give a measurable signal in response. The disturbing signal could be either mechanical or electrical. Resolution times for mechanical signals were in the order of a microsecond, and for electrical ones about 10^{-10} seconds. All that was needed was the methodology to generate appropriate mechanical/electrical signals and to measure the response times.

Eigen's first attempts involved the use of sound signals to affect the particular chemical equilibrium under study. Sound absorption techniques proved to have limited value, however, because of the high background absorption of the solvent. Eigen's attention soon turned to an examination of the possible use of changes of the electrical properties of solutions. This method proved to be useful in the study of the kinetics of hydrogen bond formation. Recent improvements in the methodology originated by Eigen and his coworkers utilize step-type disturbances that enable the study of return to equilibrium conditions in a stepwise manner. Fast reactions in gas kinetics can be studied with pressure waves in a shock tube (reaction chamber), giving comparable results. Utilization of these methods has brought the measurement of chemical reaction times down to the span of fractions of a nanosecond— within the desired reaction period.

Applications of these techniques have proliferated in inorganic, organic, and biological chemistry. Examples include measurement of changes of the solvent layer surrounding metallic complex ions, keto-enol transformation kinetics, and, most spectacularly, kinetics of enzyme-catalyzed processes.

Critical reception

The reaction to Eigen's Nobel Prize was generally one of approval and a lack of surprise. His career was well known to the scientific community, and his contributions to many fields of chemistry guaranteed that his name would be familiar to chemists throughout the world. The fact that he and his corecipients of the 1967 prize had made very similar contributions may have hidden the fact that Eigen's then-current concerns were very far removed from the developments that led to the award.

Henry and Edward Eyring, in *Science* (November 10), noted that "Eigen has authored or co-authored almost a hundred scientific papers. His students and postdoctoral associates have produced many more which, though they do not bear his name, owe a great deal to his inspiration and incisive criticism. Most of Eigen's own papers are milestones in the sense that they break open completely new fields." The Eyrings continued, "Those who have worked with Eigen find some of his most striking characteristics to be his cheerfulness, his flair for the dramatic in presenting his research (in impeccable English), his generosity with his time and his almost inexhaustible energy. When he is not on one of his frequent speaking trips he usually reaches his laboratory by midmorning and frequently works until 2 A.M. at his home after a late supper."

The New York Times for October 31, 1967, announced the Nobel awards and noted Eigen's ties to the United States scientific community. It stated that Eigen often traveled to the United States and was a member of the National Academy of Sciences [actually a foreign honorary affiliate] and was a visiting lecturer at Cornell. Impressed by Eigen's breadth of concerns, *Newsweek* noted that "Eigen, early in his life, wanted to be a musician like his father. 'But . . . I really wasn't good enough to be a musician, just good enough to be a chemist.' Eigen . . . still plays the piano and harpsichord—and does great chemistry." *Newsweek* also recognized the importance of Eigen's new ventures: " 'By discovering how basic substances form delicate balances . . . one gets into the fascinating subject of how inorganic matter acquired life.' "

Science News (November 11) was more cognizant of the importance of Eigen's early work on fast reactions, which more directly led to his receipt of the Nobel award. *Science News* did point out the important applications to which Eigen's efforts already had led and described future possibilities in "increased knowledge of body chemistry . . . development of new plastics . . . and more practical light-weight batteries for auto propulsion." *Science News* appropriately provided a lengthy list of Eigen honors and pointed out that Eigen, a few days before the Nobel ceremonies, would accept the second annual Pauling Award of the Northwest sections of the American Chemical Society—the first award having gone to two-time Nobel laureate Linus Pauling himself.

Biography

Manfred Eigen was born on May 9, 1927, in Bochum, Germany. His parents were Ernst Eigen, a chamber music player, and his wife Hedwig (née Feld). His secondary education was obtained at the *Gymnasium* in Bochum. In the final months of World War II, Eigen was drafted for military service and served at an antiaircraft installation. Immediately following the war, Eigen was a student of physics and chemistry at the Georg-August University in Göttingen; he received his doctorate in natural sciences there in 1951. His dissertation was written on the specific heat of deuterium oxide and aqueous solutions of electrolytes; his major professor was Arnold Eucken. He spent two more years at Göttingen as an assistant lecturer in physical chemistry with Professor Ewald Wicke before joining the Max Planck Institute for Physical Chemistry, which had just moved to Göttingen. The Max

Planck Gesellschaft (society) appointed Eigen as a Scientific Member in 1957, and he was named its head in 1964. From 1967 to 1970 Eigen served as managing director of the institute and became a member of West Germany's Scientific Council. Later, Eigen became director of the Max Planck Institute for Biophysical Chemical Research and a major contributor to speculation about the chemical origin of life.

Eigen married Elfriede (née Müller) in 1952; their children, Gerald and Angela, were born in 1952 and 1960 respectively. He is an accomplished musician, playing the piano and harpsichord, and has been at various times a hiker, mountaineer, and gatherer of wild mushrooms. He has also been an avid promoter of far-reaching reforms in the German higher education system.

Scientific Career

Much of Manfred Eigen's career has been spent in the search for new and better methods of measuring the rates of ultra-fast reactions. His field of interest, however, has shifted from his early studies in acid-base neutralization and concern with the behavior of electrolytes to physical organic chemistry and the identification of various reaction mechanisms and later to biochemical concerns with nucleic acids, enzymes, lipids, membranes, and biological control and regulation.

While preparing for his doctoral examination at Göttingen, Eigen became fascinated with the notion that the rates of some chemical reactions, such as neutralization, were said to be immeasurably fast. The challenge of immeasurability was too much to resist, and he endeavored to find methods to pick up the gauntlet. After completing his doctorate, Eigen spent two years at Göttingen as an assistant lecturer in physical chemistry. His colleagues, Konrad Tamm and Walter Kurtze, had become expert in the measurement of absorption of ultrasound waves; Eigen soon found a way to adapt their expertise to his problem, studying neutralization and other fast ionic reactions in solution. A series of papers by the three appeared in 1953-1954.

Simultaneously and fortuitously, the Max Planck Institute for Physical Chemistry moved its operations to Göttingen; its offer of employment to Eigen was accepted, and his lifelong association with the institute followed. Its incredible facilities and team of outstanding associates were of immeasurable assistance to Eigen and his research. Eigen soon began his long collaboration with Leo DeMaeyer at the institute. DeMaeyer, a Belgian physical chemist with considerable electronics expertise, shared many of Eigen's interests, and they have had a lengthy and productive history as a team. Together they investigated the association of hydrogen and hydroxide ions to form water as well as its reverse reaction process, water ionization.

Throughout the time when Eigen and his colleagues were developing and applying new techniques for the measurement of very fast reactions, Eigen's fertile mind was exploring future applications of the techniques to organic and biological chemistry. He and his growing group of researchers also began to explore new fields: theory of electrolytes and the measurement of thermodynamic properties of water and aqueous solutions. Some of the approximately one hundred papers published by Eigen and his coworkers prior to the Nobel award included reports of the unusual conduction characteristics of protons in crystalline ice and the hydrogen atoms connecting nucleic acid molecules, as well as some early papers on biological control, regulation processes, and information storage processes of the brain and nervous network. Although Eigen's award was based primarily on the development of improved techniques for measuring the ultra-fast rates of various important chemical reactions, it was increasingly the end-use of those methods that attracted Eigen's attention.

Fascination with the usefulness of the periodic table and periodic behavior of the elements has been characteristic of chemists for more than a century. Eigen was no exception. He became interested in the behavior of various positive metallic ions and their ability to combine with negative ions (in aqueous solution). The negative ion had to penetrate the sphere of neighboring water molecules, and, since the innermost molecules of water are held most tightly, the rates for their displacement are the slowest and could be easily measured by the Eigen techniques. The rates of reaction were found to be essentially independent of the nature of the negative ion and apparently dependent primarily on the electronic structure of the metallic ion—thus leading to relatively standard periodic behavior. The rates of even the slowest of these reactions would have been too fast to measure without the Eigen technology.

Organic chemistry turned out to be an even more fruitful field for the Eigen fast reaction team. Their first studies dealt with neutralization reactions of organic acids and bases. From these experiments, Eigen perceived the opportunity to study the mechanism of a number of reactions involving acidic or basic catalysis. Hydrogen transfer from oxygen to carbon atoms in enol-keto transformations was another obvious concern to the Eigen research group. Even though the concentration of enol was exceedingly small, Eigen's methods proved successful in measuring the exceptionally fast rate of enol conversion to the keto form.

Eigen then turned his attention to biophysical chemistry, and has spent most of his post-Nobel years in that vital field. He was struck by the fact that biological molecules undergo extremely complex reaction processes, and, in fact, even appear to "learn" and change their interactions. Eigen investigated the reaction of hemoglobin with oxygen and found different types of reaction, dependent upon the partial pressure of oxygen. He and his colleague, Kasper Kirschner, were able to elucidate some of the steps in the reaction mechanism by use of the Eigen relaxation spectrum techniques. Prior to his Nobel award, Eigen had begun to unravel the code sequence for nucleic acids, and in the following twenty years much more progress was made.

Eigen and his coworkers published a large number of review articles during the 1970's and 1980's. These publications tended to reflect the thoughts of the group with respect to the application of the Eigen principles to fundamental biochemistry, and, increasingly, to the origin of life itself. Some of the topics for both the original and review publications have included: the molecular mechanism of biological recognition; RNA sequencing (with Ruthild Winkler-Oswatitsch and Andreas Dress); models of RNA replication in viruses (with Christof Biebricher); macromolecular evolution; biological selection and the chemical processes that govern it, described by Eigen and Winkler-Oswatitsch in *Das Spiel* (1975; *Laws of the Game*, 1981) and demonstrated in Eigen's board game of *Life*; and "hypercycles"—the self-organization of nucleic acids into complex products, followed by interaction with proteins to given basic genetic material.

Bibliography

Primary

CHEMISTRY: *Investigations of Rates and Mechanisms of Reactions*, 1963 (with Leo DeMaeyer); "Dynamic Aspects of Information Transfer and Reaction Control in Biomolecular Systems," in G. C. Quarton et al., eds., *The Neurosciences*, 1967; "Kinetics of Reaction Control and Information Transfer," in *Fast Reactions and Primary Processes in Chemical Kinetics*, 1967; "New Looks and Outlooks on Physical Enzymology," *Quarterly Review of Biophysics*, vol. 1, 1968; "Molecular Self-Organization and the Early Stages of Evolution," *Quarterly Review of Biophysics*, vol. 4, 1971; *The Hypercycle: A Principle of Natural Self-Organization*, 1979 (with Peter Schuster); *Das Spiel*, 1975 (with Ruthild Winkler-Oswatitsch; *Laws of the Game*, 1981); "The Origin of Genetic Information," *Scientific American*, vol. 244, 1981 (with William Gardiner et al.); *Structure, Dynamics, and Interactions of Evolutionary Biological Macromolecules Colloquium*, 1983 (with Ruthild Winkler-Oswatitsch); "New Concepts for Dealing with the Evolution of Nucleic Acids," *Cold Spring Harbor Symposium on Quantitative Biology*, vol. 52, 1987.

Secondary

Abbott, David, ed. *The Biographical Dictionary of Scientists: Chemists*. New York: Peter Bedrick Books, 1984. A summation of the important research carried out by Eigen before and after the Nobel Prize.

Asimov, Isaac. *Asimov's Biographical Encyclopedia of Science and Technology*. 2d ed. Garden City, N.Y.: Doubleday, 1982. Contains a brief description of Eigen's career and the importance of the scientific research that led to his being awarded the Nobel Prize.

Eyring, Henry, and Edward M. Eyring. "Nobel Prizes: Chemistry." *Science* 158 (November 10, 1967): 746-748. This article presents a reasonably detailed account of the background for the 1967 Nobel chemistry awards to Eigen, Ronald Norrish, and George Porter.

"Fast Chemical Reactions." In *McGraw-Hill Encyclopedia of Science and Technology*. 5th ed. New York: McGraw-Hill, 1982. Presents a description of Eigen's prizewinning work that gets slightly more technical than some articles.

Greene, Jay E., ed. *McGraw-Hill Modern Men of Science*. 2 vols. New York:

McGraw-Hill, 1966-1968. This includes a survey of Eigen's background and his major research efforts prior to winning the Nobel Prize.

Haglund, Herman. "Life-Game, with Glass Beads and Molecules, on the Principles of the Origin of Life." *Journal of Chemical Education* 53 (1976): 468-470. This is a summary of Eigen's lecture to the LKB Produkter in Stockholm on December 10, 1975. The topic was Eigen's observations on the status of knowledge about the chemical origins of life.

Science News 92 (1967): 464-465. This issue contains a simplified account of the work of Eigen, Norrish, and Porter that led to their sharing of the Nobel Prize.

Wasson, Tyler, ed. *Nobel Prize Winners.* New York: H. W. Wilson, 1987. Wasson presents a brief examination of Eigen's life and recounts his major scientific contributions.

William J. Wasserman

1967

Chemistry
Manfred Eigen, West Germany
Ronald G. W. Norrish, Great Britain
George Porter, Great Britain

Physics
Hans Albrecht Bethe, United States

Physiology or Medicine
Halden Keffer Hartline, United States
George Wald, United States
Ragnar A. Granit, Sweden

Literature
Miguel Ángel Asturias, Guatemala

Peace
no award

RONALD G. W. NORRISH
1967

Born: Cambridge, England; November 9, 1897
Died: Cambridge, England; June 7, 1978
Nationality: British
Areas of concentration: Photochemistry and reaction kinetics

Norrish contributed much to the maturation of the field of photochemistry and to the study of the kinetics of very fast chemical reactions. In the development of the technique of flash photolysis, he added immeasurably to the understanding of processes as diverse as polymerization and combustion

The Award

Presentation

In a chemical reaction, reactants are mixed and then converted into products as the reaction progresses. Among the most fundamental concerns when studying a given reaction is the determination of its "rate," that is, how quickly the starting materials are converted into products as the reaction proceeds. Additionally, one would like to know explicitly how factors such as reactant concentration and temperature influence the rate of reaction. Such studies constitute the field of chemical kinetics.

When a reaction takes place at a "convenient" rate—that is, when half of the reaction is completed within a few minutes or hours or days—the job of gathering kinetic data is relatively simple: One only needs to mix the reactants and then to measure the time-dependent change in the concentration of the various chemical species involved. Even in cases where the reaction is very slow, the task can be accomplished if one is patient. What can be done, however, when the reaction is very fast? How can the rate be measured when the reaction occurs more quickly than the reactants could possibly be mixed? Prior to the work of Manfred Eigen, Ronald George Wreyford Norrish, and George Porter, no one had a general or workable solution to this problem. The 1967 Nobel Prize in Chemistry was awarded to these three men, whose research was instrumental in making possible the study of the kinetics of very fast reactions.

On December 10, 1967, Professor Arne Ölander of the University of Stockholm, a member of the Nobel Committee for Chemistry, made the presentation of the Nobel Prize to Eigen, Norrish, and Porter. Norrish and Porter were credited with developing "flash photolysis," which allowed for the momentary production of high concentrations of very reactive atomic or molecular species. These species could be studied spectroscopically, that is, by seeing what sorts of light they absorbed over the course of their very short lifetimes. Eigen was cited for his work in the development of various techniques of relaxation kinetics, in which a chemical system in equilibrium is disturbed—for example, by subjecting a solution to a high-tension electric pulse—and is then observed spectroscopically as it returns, or "relaxes," to its former equilibrium state.

Ölander stated that the methods developed by Eigen, Norrish, and Porter were being applied to such a wide variety of chemical problems that he was reluctant to pick any one of these problems as representative of the whole. The rapid adoption and use of these techniques by researchers in laboratories all over the world, however, attested their significance.

Nobel lecture

Norrish's Nobel lecture, entitled "Some Fast Reactions in Gases Studied by Flash Photolysis and Kinetic Spectroscopy," was given on December 11, 1967. He began by outlining some of the principal early developments in the study of photochemistry, and in particular, the notion of the participation of "free radicals" in some photochemical reactions. (A free radical is an atom or molecule possessing one or more unpaired electrons. Most commonly, this implies that the species in question has an odd number of electrons.) In a photochemical reaction, energy from light is absorbed by at least one of the reactants. Thus energized, this species can react with other materials, or can fragment into smaller pieces. Additionally, it is possible for an atom or molecule to absorb light without this leading to a chemical reaction. The energy absorbed can simply be reemitted as light of the same or of lower energy than the original light. This phenomenon is the basis of spectroscopy, in which chemicals are studied by observing what specific sorts of light they absorb.

Since free radicals are frequently produced in photochemical reactions, photochemists had long sought to study them by direct observation; however, because free radicals are ordinarily very reactive and hence very short-lived, few efforts along these lines had been successful. In fact, in 1946 Norrish and his coworkers had attempted to observe certain free radicals spectroscopically, but even using the most powerful continuous light source available, they could not generate these species in high enough concentration for their spectra to be obtained.

Shortly thereafter, Norrish and his student, George Porter, hit upon the idea that led to the development of flash photolysis. Because the free radicals they wished to study were not going to persist for very long anyway, it was not necessary for the light that produced them to last very long. Gas discharge lamps, which had only recently been developed and which had found applications in high-speed photography, produced light flashes of very short duration but very high intensity—much higher than that available from any lamp that was on continuously. When the light from the flash of such a lamp, termed the "photoflash," was allowed to pass through a sample of a photoreactive gaseous substance, very high levels of dissociation were observed. If a second light pulse of much lower intensity, the "specflash," were timed to go off only milliseconds or microseconds after the photoflash, then light from the specflash could be absorbed by the high-energy free radicals before they had a chance either to recombine (to give back the original reactant) or to go on to other products. The absorbance of light from the specflash can be measured;

if several specflashes are timed to go off sequentially after the photoflash, then the lifetime of the free radical can be determined by noting how long it takes for its absorbance spectrum to fade away.

After explaining something of the history of development of the technique, Norrish turned his attention to quite a few specific applications of flash photolysis, which fell into two categories: studies using either the "adiabatic" or the "isothermal" method. In the adiabatic method, no attempt is made to neutralize the heating effect caused by absorption of light from the photoflash, which can easily raise the temperature of the reaction mixture by several thousand degrees Celsius. Although many of the reactions that occur in these sorts of experiments are attributable to the heat rather than the light flash per se, the technique is nevertheless useful when studying reactions such as combustion and explosions, which ordinarily occur at very high temperatures anyway. In the isothermal method, the reactant gas is diluted with a large excess of a nonphotoreactive, inert gas, which serves to absorb most of the heat generated and prevents the temperature from rising very much. As such, the chemical processes occurring in the isothermal experiments are almost purely photochemical, as opposed to thermal.

An example of each of these methods will suffice to illustrate the myriad reactions that Norrish discussed during the remainder of his lecture. Among the reactions best suited to investigation by means of flash photolysis are those of combustion. Free radicals are intermediates in combustion processes and in fact are responsible for propagating the "chain" in chain reactions such as combustion and explosions. For example, the reaction between hydrogen and oxygen produces, among other things, hydroxyl (OH) radicals whose concentration buildup and decline can be monitored spectroscopically throughout the course of the (very short) reaction. Since two hydroxyl radicals can be produced from one oxygen molecule, the rate of hydrodxyl radical formation can actually exceed the rate of its disappearance, through other reactions, and the combustion reaction can develop into an explosion. This general scheme for the explosive reaction between hydrogen and oxygen had been proposed earlier, but prior to the technique of flash photolysis it was not possible to observe the reactive intermediates directly.

The combustion of hydrocarbons, such as the principal constituents of gasoline, also produces hydroxyl radicals. Norrish and his coworkers were able to establish that tetraethyllead, the additive in "leaded" gasolines, acted as an antiknock agent by removing (that is, reacting with) some of the hydroxyl radicals that otherwise would lead to an explosive reaction (the "knock"), instead allowing for smooth, controlled combustion.

Energy transfer in molecular collisions is another area studied extensively by Norrish. Using the isothermal method, the flash photolysis of chlorine dioxide produces chlorine monoxide and oxygen atoms. The highly reactive oxygen atoms can react with undissociated chlorine dioxide to produce more chlorine monoxide and diatomic molecular oxygen in a highly excited vibrational state, that is, a state having much more vibrational energy than oxygen has in its lowest-energy state. As such, flash photolysis allowed for the production and study of "ordinary" molecules—and not merely free radicals—in energy states far different from those in which they would ordinarily be found.

In closing, Norrish described some of the most recently published work to come from his research group and discussed prospects for the future of flash photolysis. Among his predictions was that the then-recent development of gas lasers would make possible the production of exceedingly short flashes of high-intensity light that would permit chemists to study reactions that occurred even more quickly than those he and his colleagues had examined. Exactly how true this prediction proved to be may have surprised even Norrish himself. Chemists using very brief pulses of laser light can now study reactions whose rates are measured in billionths and even trillionths of a second.

Critical reception

"It is probably fair to say that Nobel Prizes are of two kinds," it was stated in the November 4, 1967, issue of *Nature*, "those awarded for discoveries of an immediate character, and those awarded for the opening up of a new field of investigation." The development of the technique of flash photolysis, for which George Porter and R. G. W. Norrish each earned a quarter-share of the 1967 Nobel Prize in Chemistry, was an award of the second variety, for this discovery opened for study the field of kinetics of very fast reactions. Along with its sister techniques, the methods of "chemical relaxation" developed by Manfred Eigen (who received the other half of the 1967 prize), flash photolysis presented chemists with the opportunity to study reactions that previously had been impossible to observe directly.

Because of the exceedingly broad applicability of these techniques, chemists who were asked were reluctant to cite any one problem best suited for study using flash photolysis or chemical relaxation. Scientists from around the world, however, were quick to visit the laboratories of Norrish and Porter to acquire "hands on" instruction in the use of flash photolysis, and quick also to adopt the technique for use in their own research studies. Among the diverse applications of flash photolysis are its use in free radical spectroscopy, excited state spectroscopy, gas phase reaction kinetics, and even solution phase photobiology and enzyme kinetics.

Whereas the use of chemical relaxation by Eigen (age forty in 1967) and flash photolysis by Porter (age forty-seven in 1967) represented what was essentially the life's work of these men, Norrish's part in the development of flash photolysis was generally recognized as the crowning achievement of a long and illustrious scientific career. In an essay addressing the contributions Norrish made to photochemistry, William Albert Noyes, Jr., of the University of Texas remarked that "few people live to see a field grow from infancy to maturity in their lifetimes and have a right to feel that without their own contributions this growth could not have occurred so well and so rapidly."

There is a pleasing symmetry to Norrish's research career in this regard. Many of the chemical phenomena he had investigated prior to the development of flash photolysis were amenable to reexamination and further clarification afterward, among these being the mechanism of combustion reactions, gaseous photochlorinations, and liquid phase photochemistry.

Norrish received high praise from his colleagues not only for his role in the invention of flash photolysis but also for his ingenuity and thoroughness as an experimentalist and his skill as an educator. F. S. Dainton, then vice-chancellor of the University of Nottingham, referred to Norrish as an "obsessive experimentalist, for whom a sufficient reward is that the description . . . of an observed phenomenon will stand the test of time." This view was echoed by John H. Knox of the University of Edinburgh, who commented that "it remains a remarkable feature of the work of Norrish that so much of his original insight into the nature of chemical reactions has proved to be correct in principle if not always in detail." As far as his role as the leader of an academic research group was concerned, John C. Bevington of the University of Lancaster described Norrish as having the ability to "strike the very delicate balance" between training students in the methods of research and advancing knowledge, two functions of university research that are frequently in conflict with each other.

Biography

Ronald George Wreyford Norrish was born on November 9, 1897, in Cambridge, England. He obtained his early education at a local school, and in 1910 he received a scholarship to the Perse Grammar School, where he was given individual attention and encouragement by several teachers who recognized his scholarly talents. Having earned an entrance scholarship to Emmanuel College of the University of Cambridge, Norrish began his studies in natural sciences in 1915, but these were brought to a temporary halt in 1916 when he became a lieutenant in the Royal Field Artillery, serving in France. He was captured in March, 1918, and remained a prisoner of war for nearly a year.

After his repatriation in 1919, Norrish finished undergraduate school and in 1921 began his graduate work under the aegis of Professor Eric Rideal—later to become Sir Eric Rideal—in the area of photochemistry. In 1924, Norrish received his Ph.D., becoming a member of the Cambridge chemistry faculty in 1925. He was appointed Humphrey Owen Jones Lecturer in Physical Chemistry in 1930 and was made professor and chair of the department in 1937 after the death of Thomas Martin Lowry. Norrish continued as professor and chair of physical chemistry at Cambridge until his retirement in 1965, and as emeritus professor after that until his death in 1978. Except for the interruption occasioned by World War II, when it became important to redirect the research efforts of the department toward matters of a more defense-oriented nature, Norrish had a full and active academic career. In addition to his considerable research efforts and his teaching, Norrish served on the Councils of the Chemical Society, the Faraday Society (president, 1953-1955), and the Royal Institute of Chemistry (vice president, 1957-1959). He received honorary doctorates from the Sorbonne in Paris (1958), from the University of Leeds and the

University of Sheffield (1965), and from the University of Liverpool and the University of Lancaster (1968). Norrish was presented with the Meldola Medal of the Royal Institute of Chemistry in 1926, The Davy Medal of the Royal Society in 1958, and the Lewis Medal of the Combustion Institute in 1964.

In 1926, Norrish was married to Annie Smith, a member of the faculty of education at the University of Wales in Cardiff. The couple had two daughters. After his retirement in 1965, the Norrishes spent much of their spare time traveling, partly in response to the many invitations he was given to speak after winning the Nobel Prize. Norrish died in his native Cambridge on June 7, 1978.

Scientific Career

Norrish's scientific career spanned more than forty years, during which time he made many important contributions to various fields within the domain of physical chemistry. Foremost among these, and certainly most visible, were his efforts in the area of photochemistry. In 1965, a colleague stated of Norrish that the modern science of photochemistry had been "largely shaped in his image."

Photochemistry is the study of chemical reactions that are energetically driven, or at least initiated, by the absorption of light. An example of a photochemical reaction is photosynthesis, which, in a biological context, refers to the process by which green plants use energy from sunlight, along with their own biochemical machinery, to convert carbon dioxide and water into glucose and oxygen. Other important photoreactions occur in the earth's upper atmosphere. These "photoionization" and "photodissociation" processes absorb most of the high-energy ultraviolet radiation—which would be harmful to life—before it can reach the ground.

Norrish began his graduate school research with Eric Rideal in 1921, shortly after the birth of classical photochemistry. Although at this time photoreactions had been studied for nearly two hundred years, the distinction between primary and secondary photochemical processes had only recently been made. (Primary reactions are a direct consequence of the absorption of light by a molecule, whereas secondary reactions, the so-called dark reactions of photochemistry, are initiated by the products of primary photochemical reactions.) His first papers in the area of photochemistry were published with Rideal in 1923 and dealt with certain aspects of the photochemical behavior of aqueous solutions of potassium permanganate. These were followed by several others, both with and without Rideal as coauthor, during the period 1923-1926. Topics addressed in these papers included photochemical reactions between hydrogen and chlorine to form hydrogen chloride (hydrochloric acid) and the chlorine-catalyzed reaction between hydrogen and oxygen to form water.

After obtaining his Ph.D. in 1924 and beginning to direct his own academic research group at Cambridge in 1925, Norrish's interest in photochemistry remained high. He clarified the nature of the retarding effect that certain nitrogen compounds, called amines, had on the photoreaction between hydrogen and chlorine, a process he was to reinvestigate later using flash photolysis. He also determined sharply defined explosion limits in the chlorine-catalyzed reaction between hydrogen and oxygen. At a given temperature, the reactions were slow and controlled in the presence of a limited amount of chlorine, but uncontrolled and explosive above the limit. This, and many similar observations in these sorts of chemical systems, played a large role in the development of theories of adiabatic explosions based on branching chain mechanisms.

In 1928, Norrish published his first work on the photochemistry of carbonyl compounds—those containing a carbon-to-oxygen covalent double bond. (A covalent bond is a pair of electrons shared between two atoms. This shared pair provides the "glue" that holds atoms within molecules together. A double bond is two shared pairs of electrons.) These compounds are especially well suited for study, given their favorable light-absorbing characteristics. During the next ten years, Norrish demonstrated two distinct pathways by which certain carbonyl compounds known as ketones decompose under the influence of light. These processes were later referred to, aptly enough, as "Norrish Type I" and "Norrish Type II" cleavage reactions. In the Type I process, direct cleavage of the bond adjacent to the carbonyl group yields two free radical species. After its discovery and characterization by Norrish, the Type I reaction was put to good use by many other chemists as a source of free radicals, such as in the production of methyl radicals from dimethyl ketone, or acetone. A more elaborate mechanism occurs in the Type II reaction and produces a diradical species as the key intermediate. This diradical subsequently fragments to give a new ketone, smaller than the original one, and another molecule containing a new covalent double bond. In this fashion it has been possible to produce all sorts of compounds containing double bonds, some of which are relatively exotic or not easily accessible by other means.

The prewar years also saw other lines of research open up for Norrish. In addition to expanding his work in the area of the kinetics of combustion and explosion processes, he became interested in polymerization reactions, the means by which all plastics are formed. Aside from the great commercial significance—or at that time, perhaps more correctly, the great commercial potential—of the products of polymerization reactions, Norrish already had a reason to be interested in their study. Many polymerizations can be initiated by free radicals, and so research on the kinetics of polymerization reactions related to the ongoing work in Norrish's group.

The onset of British involvement in World War II had its inevitable effect on the academic research efforts of Norrish, and he published no papers between 1943 and 1946. During the war years, Norrish, by that time chair of the physical chemistry department of the University of Cambridge, redirected the research activity of the faculty toward more pressing problems, such as flame hazards, the use of liquid fuels, and defense against incendiary projectiles.

After the war, Norrish began his collaboration with graduate student George Porter, with whom he developed the technique of flash photolysis. At the heart of the photolysis apparatus was a powerful gas discharge lamp, capable of dissipating large amounts of electrical current as a very brief yet very intense pulse of light. This flash had the ability to dissociate certain gaseous molecules into free radicals or other high-energy species. When a spectrograph was coupled to the device, triggered electronically to record the spectrum of the products at brief intervals after the initial light pulse, flash photolysis as an analytical technique was born.

It is worth noting that the electronic components of the flash photolysis apparatus were relatively new devices in 1947, when work on the development of this technique commenced. Although spectroscopy as such was not new, the photoelectric method utilized by Norrish and Porter to time the specflashes at short intervals after the photoflash was only about fifteen years old. Additionally, much work had been done during the war to increase the power of gas discharge lamps; in fact, the bank of capacitors that Norrish and Porter used to store the electrical charge that was released through their own photolysis lamp had been obtained from military surplus stores. It might be argued that the time had made the men, since flash photolysis was simply the marriage of two preexisting, although recently developed, techniques. This sort of argument is invalid, however, because it misses one of the central elements of creative genius, scientific or otherwise. Entirely novel or unconventional thinking is rare and, very often, unproductive. Far more practical is the ability to combine ideas, new or old, in novel ways and thus to create new and useful theories or techniques. The people who make the breakthroughs in science quite often are the first to recognize how several other ideas can be blended to give something new and valuable.

Prior to the work of Norrish and Porter, chemists were limited, as far as chemical kinetics is concerned, to the study of reactions that take place relatively slowly. They had tried to examine and characterize the short-lived free radical species they knew must be involved in a great number of diverse reactions, but with virtually no success. Flash photolysis allows for the momentary production of relatively high concentrations of these reactive species, which can, if one "works quickly," be examined spectroscopically. Two important sorts of information come out of these spectroscopic studies. First, analysis of the spectrum of a free radical itself gives structural and energetic data on that species. Second, a sequence of spectra recorded at short intervals after the photoflash provides information about the lifetime and fate of a particular substance, as its characteristic spectral absorbance lines— its "fingerprint"—grow into and fade from successive spectra.

The first experiments in flash photolysis, reported in 1949, did not involve any spectroscopy; they simply demonstrated the altered course certain photochemical reactions took when the light was delivered in one big wallop, instead of gradually over a period of minutes or hours. For example, in the "ordinary" photolysis of acetone, hydrocarbons and carbon monoxide are produced via a Norrish Type I process. In the flash photolysis, however, a complex mixture was produced, including hydrogen gas and elemental carbon, strung like a cobweb across the interior of the reaction vessel. (It should be noted that a large measure of the altered reactivity in these adiabatic experiments may have been attributable to the heating effects, and not simply to a change in the photochemical processes taking place.)

When a spectrometer was incorporated into the apparatus in subsequent experiments, the course of the reactions could be followed and the study of the kinetics of very fast reactions became possible. At this point Norrish turned a large portion of his attention to the reexamination of certain reactions that he had previously studied. These included gaseous photochlorinations, solution phase photochemical reactions, and various combustion processes. In many of these reactions, Norrish and his coworkers were able to identify and characterize free radical intermediates spectroscopically. In a way, Norrish's research career came full circle in 1963, when he published a paper on the photovoltaic effects observed in aqueous solutions of potassium permanganate, as studied via flash photolysis. It was this same system, examined without the aid of the flash photolytic technique, that Norrish and Rideal had described in 1923.

As a result of flash photolysis, new lines of research opened for Norrish. The technique made it possible, for example, to observe the intimate details of energy transfer processes occurring in molecular collisions. Such studies are of central importance to scientists' understanding of chemical reactivity, since most reactions involve collisions betwen the reacting partners.

Norrish's scientific career seemed to be coming to a close quietly enough in 1965 when he announced his retirement and stepped down from his position as chair of the physical chemistry department at Cambridge. Friends and colleagues collaborated on a festschrift for Norrish, *Photochemistry and Reaction Kinetics*, in which they reviewed his contributions to various branches of chemistry—seemingly a fitting final tribute to a man who had covered so much new scientific ground in his life.

When the announcement of the Nobel Prize to Eigen, Norrish, and Porter was made in October, 1967, it came as a complete shock to Norrish himself, who described it as a "delightful surprise out of the blue." A surprise, perhaps, because it had been twenty years since the work on flash photolysis had begun and two years since his formal retirement, but a well-deserved honor nevertheless. In the first chapter of *Photochemistry and Reaction Kinetics*, William Albert Noyes, Jr., states of Norrish's research in photochemistry that "work must be judged to be of real value if it stimulates further good work." In view of the number of people now involved in the study of fast reactions, and the developments that have been made since 1965 that now allow for picosecond rate studies to be made, it is not at all difficult to judge the work of R. G. W. Norrish as truly valuable.

Bibliography

Primary

CHEMISTRY: "Transition Elements and the Octet Theory," *Chemistry News*, vol. 124, 1922; "The Conditions of Reaction of Hydrogen with Sulphur. Part 1. Direct Union," *Journal of the Chemical Society*, vol. 123, 1923 (with Eric K. Rideal); "The Photosensitive Formation of Water from Its Elements in the Presence of

Chlorine," *Journal of the Chemical Society,* vol. 127, 1925 (with Rideal); "Photochemical Equilibrium in Nitrogen Peroxide. Part II. The Dependence of Quantum Efficiency on Wave-length," *Journal of the Chemical Society,* 1929; "Photodecomposition of Aldehydes and Ketones," *Nature,* vol. 138, 1936 (with C. H. Bamford); "Catalyzed Polymerization of Methyl Methacrylate in the Liquid Phase," *Nature,* vol. 150, 1942 (with R. R. Smith); "Chemical Reactions Produced by Very High Light Intensities," *Nature,* vol. 164, 1949 (with George Porter); "The Application of Flash Techniques to the Study of Fast Reactions," *Discussions of the Faraday Society,* vol. 17, 1954 (with Porter); "The Behaviour of Additives in Explosions and the Mechanism of Antiknock," *Proceedings of the Royal Society of London,* vol. A259, 1961 (with A. B. Callear); "Kinetic Spectroscopy and Flash Photolysis," *American Scientist,* vol. 50, 1962; "The Kinetics and Analysis of Very Fast Chemical Reactions," *Chemistry in Britain,* vol. 1, 1965; "Rate of H-Abstraction by OH from Hydrocarbons," *Nature,* vol. 215, 1967 (with D. G. Horne); "The Progress of Photochemistry Exemplified by Reactions of the Halogens," *Proceedings of the Royal Society of London,* vol. A301, 1967; "Fifty Years of Physical Chemistry in Great Britain," *Annual Review of Physical Chemistry,* vol. 20, 1969; "Some Reactions of Organic Photo-chemistry as Revealed by Flash Photolysis and Kinetic Spectroscopy," *Mémoires de la Société royale des sciences de Liège, sixième série,* vol. 1, 1971; "Some Fast Reactions in Gases Studied by Flash Photolysis and Kinetic Spectroscopy," in *Spectroscopy of the Excited State,* 1975, edited by the NATO Advanced Study Institute on the Spectroscopy of the Excited State.

Secondary

Ashmore, P. G., F. S. Dainton, and T. M. Sugden, eds. *Photochemistry and Reaction Kinetics,* Cambridge, England: Cambridge University Press, 1967. The definitive work on the contributions that Norrish made to chemistry. Fifteen friends and colleagues from around the world collaborated on this festschrift, dedicated to Norrish shortly after his retirement. Each of twelve chapters covers a different aspect of Norrish's prolific research career. Subject and author indexes are provided.

Bamford, C. H., and C. F. H. Tipper, eds. *Comprehensive Chemical Kinetics.* Amsterdam: Elsevier, 1969. The reason chemists study kinetics is that the proper interpretation of the results of such studies provides a means by which they can determine reaction mechanisms—detailed descriptions of the bond-forming and bond-breaking processes that occur as reactant molecules are converted into products. Volume 1 of what, as of 1989, is a twenty-seven-volume series (and still growing) includes a chapter on the study of fast reactions, which covers such topics as flash photolysis and pulse radiolysis, chemical relaxation methods, and the use of molecular beams in kinetic studies.

Calvert, Jack G., and James N. Pitts, Jr. *Photochemistry.* New York: John Wiley & Sons, 1966. A comprehensive book on the mechanisms and applications of photochemistry. While it is directed toward scientifically sophisticated readers, much of the introductory material is well within the grasp of the interested nonscientist. Fully indexed.

Dainton, F. S. *Chain Reactions: An Introduction*. 2d ed. London: Methuen, 1966. In a chain reaction, the products of a "propagation" step include at least one new reactive species that can carry on the "chain." Quite often these intermediates are free radicals. If more than one reactive center is formed in a propagation step, the reaction can develop into an explosion via a "branching chain" mechanism. This book spells out these and other aspects of chain reactions. An index is included.

Dorfman, Leon M., and Max S. Matheson. *Pulse Radiolysis*. Cambridge, Mass.: MIT Press, 1969. Pulse radiolysis is a technique similar to flash photolysis, except that it uses a brief pulse of high-energy electrons instead of light to produce the chemical changes. (Pulsed X-rays are sometimes used instead of electrons, but this is still called "pulse radiolysis.") Aspects of the technique covered include theory, hardware, applications, and interpretation of typical data collected in these sorts of experiments. Indexed.

Knoche, Wilhelm, and Hans Strehlow. *Fundamentals of Chemical Relaxation*. Weinheim, Germany: Verlag Chemie, 1977. This book begins with a brief survey of various physical methods used to study chemical kinetics, and the range of reaction rates over which each of these techniques is useful. After describing the principles behind chemical relaxation and some of the specific methods used in relaxation studies, many of which were developed by Manfred Eigen, specific applications of the techniques and the information available from such studies are discussed. Various appendices; author and subject indexes are included.

Lewis, Bernard, and Guenther von Elbe. *Combustion, Flames, and Explosions of Gases*. 3d ed., Orlando, Fla.: Academic Press, 1987. An advanced treatise, covering the topics listed in the title. The authors' primary aim is to provide chemists, physicists, and engineers with a scientific basis for understanding combustion phenomena, a field in which Norrish was heavily involved. It is interesting to note that Norrish's preceptor, Sir Eric Rideal, was general editor to the first edition. Author and subject indexes are provided.

National Research Council. *Opportunities in Chemistry*. Washington, D.C.: National Academy Press, 1985. Chemists and nonchemists alike will enjoy browsing through the "Pimentel Report," so-called because the late George C. Pimentel— formerly professor of chemistry at the University of California, Berkeley— chaired the NRC committee that prepared the report. The book describes the current state of chemistry and speculates about opportunities for the future. Recent advances in the area of the kinetics of very fast reactions are covered, as are many other topics. Index and appendices are given. Highly recommended as a general reference.

Porter, George. "Flash Photolysis and Some of Its Applications." *Nature* 160 (1968). A reprint of Porter's Nobel lecture. While not specifically aimed at the "lay" reader, even those whose primary interest is not chemistry will find much of the article digestible. The paper reviews the technique of flash photolysis, the history of its development, some specific applications, and prospects for the future.

Zurer, Pamela S. "Complex Mission Set to Probe Origins of Antarctic Ozone Hole." *Chemical and Engineering News*, August 17, 1987. the evolving story of stratospheric ozone depletion by chlorofluorocarbons (also called CFCs or Freons) is described in this article. These substances are widely used in industry as refrigerants, solvents, and blowing agents, among other uses. Their use and production is being phased out on a worldwide scale, however, as evidence accumulates that they can cause the catalytic destruction of the earth's ozone layer, which is vital to our survival. The key intermediates in this process are the free radical species, chlorine monoxide and free chlorine atoms. See subsequent issues of *Chemical and Engineering News* for updates, as well as the May, 1989, issue of *Consumer Reports* ("Can We Repair the Sky?") for a somewhat different slant on this very important problem.

Thomas H. Eberlein

1967

Chemistry
Manfred Eigen, West Germany
Ronald G. W. Norrish, Great Britain
George Porter, Great Britain

Physics
Hans Albrecht Bethe, United States

Physiology or Medicine
Halden Keffer Hartline, United States
George Wald, United States
Ragnar A. Granit, Sweden

Literature
Miguel Ángel Asturias, Guatemala

Peace
no award

GEORGE PORTER
1967

Born: Stainforth, Yorkshire, England; December 6, 1920

Nationality: British
Areas of concentration: Photochemistry and reaction kinetics

Porter developed and refined flash photolysis, which offers a means of measuring extremely fast chemical reactions. This technique has proved valuable in studying a wide variety of important reactions throughout chemistry

The Award

Presentation
Arne Ölander, professor of physical chemistry at the University of Stockholm, Sweden, and secretary of the Nobel Committee for Chemistry, presented the Nobel Prize in Chemistry to George Porter on December 10, 1967. Professor Porter shared the 1967 prize with professors Manfred Eigen of the Max Planck Institute and Ronald George Wreyford Norrish of the University of Cambridge for the development of a pair of techniques enabling the study of reactions so fast that they occur on the time scale of a millionth of a second (in microseconds). Ölander traced the development of experimental chemical kinetics from the first measurements of reaction velocities in the late nineteenth century to the time of the presentation. The beginnings of the theoretical basis of chemical kinetics extend to Jacobus van't Hoff and Svante Arrhenius in the early twentieth century.

A major need in the study of faster reactions involved the mixing of the reactant solutions. One way to solve this need is to design the experimental apparatus so that the solutions flow rapidly down a tube. Unfortunately, methods of this type do not allow the study of reactions on a time scale of less than one-thousandth of a second. In order to start a reaction more quickly than one-thousandth of a second, Ölander noted, it is necessary to mix all the reactants together prior to the start of the reaction and then initiate the reaction. Each of the 1967 laureates developed a method that does exactly that.

Nobel lecture
On December 11, 1967, George Porter delivered his Nobel lecture, entitled "Flash Photolysis and Some of Its Applications." His stated purpose was to reveal the potential of the flash photolysis technique by stressing the wide range of its applications. He first noted the amazing growth in the field of fast-reaction kinetics, from essentially nothing in 1947 to complete symposia on that topic at professional meetings only a few years later. This growth was stimulated in part by the development of the methods used by the three Nobel Prize winners for 1967.

The lecture itself was organized historically, from the first "thrill of discovery" experiments to later investigations that cleared up fundamental and applied questions of an extremely important nature. Experimentally, the first apparatus was extremely simple, photographically measuring the absorption of molecules as a function of time following a flash of light. While studying known molecules, Porter frequently found that new unstable molecules were formed in his flash photolysis experiments. For example, the first discovery of the chlorine monoxide (ClO) molecule, which is so important in the decomposition of ozone in the stratosphere, was made in a flash photolysis experiment by Porter.

The structure and rates of processes involving triplet states, with two unpaired electrons, are easily measured using flash photolysis. Gilbert Norton Lewis originally observed the triplet state of organic molecules in 1944 in a rigid medium. The triplet state (with the electron spins in the molecule unpaired) and the free radial (with one unpaired electron) mechanisms are the most important ones in organic chemistry, because a great majority of reactions proceed via one of these two mechanisms. Porter found that flash photolysis provided a ready tool for the examination of either triplet state or free radical mechanisms. Among the many photochemical reaction mechanisms that he examined are those for photosynthesis, the aging of colored fabric dyes by light, and electron or proton transport among molecules following the absorption of light.

Critical reception

Time magazine pointed out that the Nobel Prize is usually awarded for scientific contributions and developments made years, perhaps even decades, before the actual awarding of the prize, rather than for discoveries made within the past few years. Such was the case with the award in 1967 to Eigen, Norrish, and Porter for experiments performed in the late 1940's and early 1950's. All three, while using different detection techniques, had developed similar methodologies for measurements of species within chemically reactive mixtures. The methodology employed was recognized as being important and continues to be so, particularly as the technique of flash photolysis spreads to the different subdisciplines of chemistry.

Henry and Edward Eyring, both professors of chemistry at the University of Utah, wrote in *Science* (volume 158, 1967) that the Nobel Prize was given to all three laureates in "recognition of important new developments in the study of very fast chemical reactions." The Eyrings, in their article, gave several examples to illustrate the variety of processes that can be studied using flash photolysis, including the formation of oxygen from ozone using light, the explosive combustion and burning of hydrogen and a number of other gases, and the rates of energy distribution in molecules following vibrational excitation. They also found that the "impact the men [the laureates] have had on the field of chemical kinetics is attributable in no small measure to their gifts of exposition . . . as well as their unusual talents for scientific invention."

Scientists looking at the development of the field of chemical kinetics since the 1970's recognize flash photolysis, first performed by George Porter, as one of the most significant advances in experimental techniques. Later development of this technique has been spurred on by the advent of commercial high-power short-pulse lasers with a variety of wavelengths in the visible and ultraviolet. This technique and a variety of similar techniques based on flash photolysis remain the principal experimental methods for investigating the rates and dynamics of collisions in both the gas and liquid phases.

Biography

George Porter was born in Stainforth, Yorkshire, England, on December 6, 1920, to John Smith Porter and the former Alice Ann Roebuck. His early education was all in local primary and secondary schools. In 1938, he won an Ackroyd Scholarship to Leeds University. He was graduated from Leeds in 1941, during the height of World War II, with an interest in chemical kinetics, but specially training in radio physics. He was commissioned as a reserve officer in the Royal Navy Special Branch, concerned with the use of radar.

Immediately following the war, he entered graduate school in Emmanuel College of the University of Cambridge, where he worked with Professor Norrish, investigating fast reactions using flowing gas techniques. He received his master's degree from Cambridge in 1947. Early in that year, he thought of using light pulses to initiate chemical reactions and constructed an apparatus to do that experimentally. He received his Ph.D. for that project in 1949. Also during 1949, he married Stella Jean Brooke.

Following receipt of his Ph.D., he was appointed demonstrator for chemistry at Cambridge, and later, assistant director of research, positions that allowed him to continue his collaboration with Norrish. After a short period at the British Rayon Research Association, he returned to academe as professor of physical chemistry at Sheffield University. In 1963, he was named head of the chemistry department. Since 1966, he has been director and Fullerian Professor of Chemistry at the Royal Institution, as well as director of the Davy Faraday Research Laboratory. His experiments in the understanding of elementary photoprocesses have continued, and he has been instrumental in educating nonscientists about the excitement of scientific research. For these efforts, he was knighted in 1972.

Scientific Career

A man known and respected by fellow scientists and the general public of England as well, George Porter has a diversity of interests based upon three main themes: the science of studying fast reactions, the effort to spread knowledge gained in scientific endeavors to the society of man, and the creation of a value system for science that respects ethical issues facing the society of scientists, and of humanity in general.

The scientific innovations pioneered by George Porter occurred early in his career, but refinements on them continue to this day. The flash photolysis method for the measurement of fast reaction rates was developed in the late 1940's while Porter was still a graduate student at Cambridge. In this method, a chemical reaction is initiated by a short burst of light. The scientist can follow changes in the amount of each reactant or product in the microseconds that follow by looking at the absorption caused by each molecule. Typical modern instruments for doing this type of experiment are based on Porter's original apparatus. They employ at least two light paths, which cross at right angles. One is used by the initiating flash of light. The initiating light pulse is usually created by an electrical discharge in a gas. Such a discharge results in a broadband ultraviolet light pulse of 0.1-10.0 microseconds in width. Similar light pulses are used in electronic flash units for cameras or in the stop-motion pictures of a milk drop splash or a bullet breaking a balloon. The light pulse travels into a cell containing a gas or liquid mixture and initiates the desired reaction. The second light beam crossing the first interrogates the concentrations of reactants or products by measuring their absorption or emission and the subsequent mathematical relation of their absorption to the concentration.

Several elements of the experimental design make the method extremely versatile. These include the wide variation that is allowable in the cell design, the unique absorption or emissions band of every molecule and atom for its detection, or for its use as the photoinitiator in a particular process. Unrelated developments in the production of short-pulse-length lasers have contributed to the success of Porter's methodology by allowing faster and faster processes to be observed—for example, the movement of electrons at the beginning of photosynthetic processes in plants, which occur in about a millionth of a millionth of a second.

George Porter's early research using flash photolysis concentrated on the use of small molecules as both initiators and as products of reactions resulting from the simpler spectra of small molecules (those with fewer than roughly ten atoms). Other scientists built on Porter's work by using the technique of flash photolysis to describe the spectra of the molecules themselves as well as the rates of their reactions. Observation of molecular spectra is important to understand the bonding in molecules and in the measurements of the distances and angles between the atoms in a molecule. Flash photolysis also brought to molecular spectroscopy an increased ability to study unstable or reactive species that were present in too low a concentration or that did not live long enough to be observed by previous methods.

After studying small molecules for a period of time, Porter began a series of investigations into the photochemistry of larger organic molecules, those containing principally carbon and hydrogen atoms. His interest in organic photochemistry was piqued by the widely differing properties of organic molecules before and after they absorb a photon (light). These differing properties are most easily illustrated by noting that a small bit of molecule can insert into a chemical bond in another molecule when a photon has been absorbed, but that the same bit of molecule will pull a hydrogen atom off the same molecule into whose bond it would have inserted if the photon had not been absorbed. Porter was also interested in looking at the way in which the energy of the photon moves around within the molecule once it is deposited in the molecule. This aspect has intrigued many scientists because it hints at how energy deposited by photon absorption in one bond in a gas phase molecule redistributes itself into other parts of the molecule. Experiments of this type allow comparison of the experiment with various theories of how this photon energy should redistribute.

By extending his research into liquids in the late 1950's, Porter opened up a range of questions about the interactions in liquids, which are much more complex than those among relatively isolated gaseous molecules. The technology required for the study of liquids had slowly developed during the period of Porter's investigations and was in part developed by Porter and members of his research group. The key problem in studying liquids is that a tremendous increase in the speed of measurement is required over gaseous systems in order to examine the results of only a few collisions. One must observe events within a few picoseconds (millionths of a microsecond) to examine the rate of energy redistribution in liquids. While Porter's studies of interactions in liquids may have been initiated as a natural extension of his gas phase experiments, they have also been useful for their explanation of large molecule intramolecular energy redistribution and for their examination of the effects of collisions on molecular shapes and energies.

Porter's research moved beyond purely chemical systems, and, by the late 1980's, it focused on illuminating the mechanism of photosynthesis in plants. His experimental technique for these studies is a modification of the flash photolysis method for very fast reactions. It uses a picosecond-long pulse of light to begin the photosynthetic process, and a second picosecond-long photon pulse to examine the shapes of the chlorophyll molecule at times following the first pulse. These studies are important to biologists who want to understand the beginnings of, and the elementary steps involved in, photosynthetic activity. The particular observations are of the beginnings of the electron transport away from the chlorophyll molecule, which provides the energy necessary to decompose carbon dioxide to cellulose and oxygen.

Porter, as director of the Davy Faraday Laboratory of the Royal Institution, has followed in the tradition of previous directors in his efforts to make chemistry accessible to nonscientists. In particular, he has written several books on chemistry for nongraduate students and numerous articles on famous chemists and their work for the general public. As an esteemed member of the Royal Institution, he is regularly called upon to give public lectures on new developments in chemistry or on general scientific topics. He spends much of his time educating nonscientists about the importance and excitement of scientific study, not only through books, articles, and lectures, but also by his participation in the development and production of several films and television programs, most notably the BBC television series *Young Scientist of the Year.*

Porter has sought to enhance the standing of chemists within world society. In addition to his efforts to educate the general public about the role of the scientist, he has also worked to stimulate philosophical discussion of various ethical questions raised by current trends in scientific investigation. That he has been successful in these efforts is obvious by reports on these lectures.

Bibliography
Primary

CHEMISTRY: "Chemical Reactions Produced by Very High Light Intensities," *Nature*, vol. 164, 1949 (with R. Norrish); "The Application of Flash Techniques to the Study of Fast Reactions," *Discussions of the Faraday Society*, vol. 17, 1954 (with R. Norrish); *Chemistry for the Modern World*, 1962; *Progress in Reaction Kinetics*, 1965 (editor); "Initiation of the Hydrogen-chlorine Reaction by Red Laser Light," *Nature*, vol. 215, 1967; "Flash Photolysis," *Photochemistry and Reaction Kinetics*, 1967; "Nanosecond Flash Photolysis and the Absorption Spectra of Excited Singlet States," *Nature*, vol. 220, 1968 (with M. R. Topp); "Flash Photolysis and Some of Its Applications," *Science*, vol. 160, 1968; "Inexpensive Flash Kinetic Spectrophotometer," *Educational Chemistry*, vol. 7, 1970 (with M. A. West); "Oxygen Quenching of Singlet and Triplet States," *Chemical Physics Letters*, vol. 7, 1970 (with L. K. Patterson and M. R. Topp); "Lasers in Photochemical Kinetics," *Chemistry in Britain*, vol. 6, 1970 (with L. Patterson); "Nanosecond Flash Photolysis," *Proceedings of the Royal Society of London*, series A, vol. 315, 1970 (with M. R. Topp); *Molecules to Man*, 1972 (with R. J. Harrison, P. R. Ehrlich, D. Phillips, G. V. J. Nossal, and C. Pincher); "Oxygen Quenching of Aromatic Triplet States in Solution. I," *Journal of the Chemical Society, Faraday Transactions 2*, vol. 69, 1973 (with O. L. J. Gijzeman and F. Kaufman); "Molecules in Microtime," *Proceedings of the Royal Institute of Great Britain*, vol. 47, 1974; "Fluorescence Lifetime in the Photosynthetic Unit," *Nature*, vol. 258, 1975 (with G. S. Beddard, C. J. Tredwell, and J. Barber); "Laser Flash Photolysis and Photobiology," *Annuals Academy Bras. Cienc.*, vol. 45, 1975; "Concentration Quenching in Chlorophyll," *Nature*, vol. 260, 1976 (with G. S. Beddard); "Chemistry in Microtime," *Highlights in British Science*, 1978 (with M. A. West); "Pure and Applied Photochemistry," *Pure and Applied Chemistry*, vol. 50, 1978; "Detection of Small Quantities of Photochemically Produced Oxygen by Reaction with Alkaline Pyrogallol," *Analytical Chemistry*, vol. 51, 1979 (with I. A. Duncan and A. Harriman); "Picosecond Time-Resolved Fluorescence Study of Chlorophyll Organization and Excitation Energy Distribution in Chloroplasts for Wild-Type Barley and a Mutant Lacking Chlorophyll B," *Biochimica Biophysica Acta*, vol. 545, 1979 (with G. F. W. Searle, C. J. Tredwell, and J. Barber); "Viscosity-Dependent Internal Rotation in Polymethine Dyes Measured by Picosecond Fluorescence Spectroscopy," *Springer Series in Chemical Physics (Picosecond Phenomena)*, vol. 23, 1982 (with A. C. Winkworth and A. D. Osborne); "Design, Preparation, and Characterization of Ruthenium Dioxide/Titanium Dioxide Catalytic Surfaces Active in Photooxidation of Water," *Journal of Physical Chemistry*, vol. 87, 1983 (with G. Blondeel, A. Harriman, D. Urwin, and J. Kiwi); "Forty Years of Photochemistry," *Journal of the Chemical Society, Faraday Transactions II*, vol. 82, 1986; "The Design of a Picosecond Flash Spectroscope and Its Application to Photosynthesis," *Journal of the Chemical Society, Faraday Transactions II*, vol. 82, 1986 (with B. L. Gore, T. A. M. Doust,

L. B. Giorgi, D. R. Klug, J. P. Idle, and B. Crystall); "Photosynthesis—the First Nanosecond," *Pure and Applied Chemistry*, vol. 58, 1986.

Secondary

Finlayson-Pitts, Barbara J., and James N. Pitts. *Atmospheric Chemistry: Fundamentals and Experimental Techniques*. New York: John Wiley & Sons, 1986. This book gives examples of the use of flash photolysis and other fast-reaction techniques as applied in atmospheric measurements.

Herzberg, Gerhard. *The Spectra and Structures of Simple Free Radicals*. Ithaca, N.Y.: Cornell University Press, 1971. This book puts the use of flash photolysis experiments into the context of the measurement of the spectra, and thus the determination of the molecular shapes of free radicals. Flash photolysis is exceptionally useful because it provides a technique for creating short-lived radicals.

Moore, J. W., and R. G. Pearson. *Kinetics and Mechanism*. 3d ed. New York: John Wiley & Sons, 1981. Another brief introduction to the ideas of flash photolysis is given in the discussions on experimental methods. This text puts the study of fast-reaction kinetics into the perspective of the whole of chemical kinesis.

Richard W. Schwenz

1968

Chemistry
Lars Onsager, Norway and United States

Physics
Luis W. Alvarez, United States

Physiology or Medicine
Robert W. Holley, United States
H. Gobind Khorana, United States
Marshall W. Nirenberg, United States

Literature
Yasunari Kawabata, Japan

Peace
René Cassin, France

LARS ONSAGER
1968

Born: Kristiania (modern Oslo), Norway; November 27, 1903
Died: Coral Gables, Florida; October 5, 1976
Nationality: Norwegian; after 1945, American
Areas of concentration: Irreversible thermodynamics and electrolyte theory

Onsager extended the applicability of thermodynamic principles to irreversible systems through his formulations of reciprocal relations. His work in the theory of electrolyte solutions has had important consequences in fields as diverse as electrochemistry and the biochemistry of cell membranes

The Award

Presentation

Lars Onsager was presented to King Gustav VI Adolf by Stig Clæsson, of the University of Uppsala, during ceremonies held at the Stockholm Concert Hall on the afternoon of December 10, 1968, the anniversary of the death of Alfred Nobel. Professor Clæsson represented the Royal Swedish Academy of Sciences, of which he was a member. He began by stating that the award was being made to Onsager for the development of the reciprocal relations, which he termed "a universal natural law."

Clæsson pointed out two unusual features of the award to Onsager. First, the reciprocal relations were totally contained in two papers published in the *Physical Review*. The first paper was twenty-two pages in length, while the second was only fifteen pages. This total made them the "smallest work" ever to be honored with a Nobel Prize. Second, these papers had been published in 1931, thirty-seven years before the conferral of the award. This long time period was allowed under a special provision of the rules of the Nobel Foundation that work done in the past may be awarded a prize only if its significance had only recently been fully realized. That this was clearly the case was demonstrated by Clæsson as he outlined the fact that the reciprocal relations attracted little attention when published because Onsager "was far ahead of his time."

Citing examples of natural processes, Clæsson showed that most are irreversible in that they cannot, of themselves, go backward. As a result, attempts to treat their energy changes by the principles of classical thermodynamics, which had been developed during the nineteenth century, failed. Classical thermodynamics treats unchanging, or static, states, as well as systems in equilibrium, and is contained in three laws. The laws deal with the conservation of energy and considerations of entropy. Clæsson proposed Onsager's reciprocal relations as a fourth law, since they allow the extension of the principles of thermodynamics to irreversible systems. He explained that the meaning of the reciprocal relations may be seen in the simple case of sugar dissolving in hot tea. The transport of the mass of the sugar and the heat flow demonstrate that the temperature difference causes a mass flow as well as a thermal flow. Onsager showed that the equations that express these flows are related. The coefficients of certain terms in the equations may be connected; the reciprocal relations are the connections.

Clæsson concluded his presentation by noting that Onsager's career included many important contributions to theoretical chemistry and that the reciprocal relations occupy a special place among them: "It represents one of the greatest advances in science during this century."

Nobel lecture

Lars Onsager presented his Nobel lecture on the afternoon of December 11, 1968. He entitled his talk "The Motion of Ions: Principles and Concepts," and it was intended to present the significance of the governing principles of irreversible thermodynamics. To begin, he summarized the work that led to the theory of electrolytes that was presented to him as a beginning chemistry student in 1920. By 1860, Joseph-Louis Gay-Lussac had stated the law of combining volumes. Avogadro's principle, that equal volumes of gases contain equal numbers of molecules, had been accepted, resting on the experimental evidence provided by Stanislao Cannizzaro. The study of thermodynamics saw its beginnings at that time, with contributions from James Maxwell and Ludwig Boltzmann dealing with energy distributions and the foundations of the kinetic theory of gases.

With the statement of the mass action law by Cato Guldberg and Peter Waage, and Jacobus van't Hoff's recognition of the analogy of gases and liquids, advances were made in the study of solutions. The theory of the dissociation of electrolytes was put forth by Svante Arrhenius and, combined with the work of Wilhelm Ostwald and Walther Nernst, accounted for the general idealized theory of electrolytes known in the early years of the twentieth century. Studies of solutions, however, revealed several anomalies in the behavior of electrolytes. The theory of Peter Debye and Walter Hückel accounted for these by considering the effects of the charged ions on one another, and they applied their theory to the conductivity of strong electrolytes.

Onsager showed how his own studies in 1923 demonstrated the limitations of the Debye-Hückel theory, which he corrected by applying the principle of superposition to the charged area surrounding a pair of ions in solution. He showed that since one constant force field is acting on every ion, the gradients of the forces involved in the electrical conductivity are equivalent. He then explained how his application of Brownian motion (random thermal motion) to classical electrolyte theory, if treated in a statistical manner, along with his application of the principle of microscopic reversibility, provided a connection to thermodynamics. The reciprocal relations resulted from the proper mathematical manipulation of the resulting equations.

Onsager then focused on the applications of the reciprocal relations to the solution of other anomalies, especially those dealing with the effects of long-range interactions on ion transport and, therefore, on electrical conductivity. He also considered electrolyte conductance in solids, focusing on the behavior of ice. To conclude his lecture, Onsager referred to ion transport through cell membranes, as in the mechanism of poisoning, also being controlled by the general principles of extended electrolyte theory and irreversible thermodynamics.

Critical reception

Lars Onsager was attending a seminar of the National Academy of Sciences at the California Institute of Technology when word reached him of the award. He stated that it was "a bit of a surprise." His wife, Margarethe, took the award in stride, asking only whether the award was in chemistry or physics. Her question reflects the mathematical and theoretical nature of her husband's work. In fact, it was stated that the applicability of the work to processes in living systems, such as membrane transport phenomena, placed the award in chemistry rather than in physics.

The abstract nature of the work resulted in comparatively brief comment in the press. *Newsweek* of November 11, 1968, described his work as "so rarefied that few scientists appreciated its value until after World War II." This sentiment was echoed by Professor Erik Rudberg, the permanent secretary of the Royal Swedish Academy of Sciences, who said in announcing the award that "science had not grasped the depth" of Onsager's work earlier. In *The New York Times* of October 31, 1968, he called the reciprocal relations "profound and uncommon." The paper also called Onsager's work "the fourth law of thermodynamics," because of its general applicability. Professor Stig Clæsson, who was to make the presentation speech at the Nobel ceremonies, responded to interviewers that Onsager gave science an expression of one of its most fundamental natural laws.

The award to Onsager completed an American sweep of the science Nobel Prizes for 1968, the first since 1946. At the presentation ceremonies, Dr. Onsager was overshadowed by the very popular physics laureate, Luis Alvarez, who (according to *The New York Times* of December 11, 1968) was "the most popular American" with the press. Onsager was described as "a more introspective man."

Writing in *Science* of November 8, 1968, Raymond M. Fuoss, an important collaborator of Onsager, was one of several in the scientific community to comment on the fact that Onsager was the Josiah Willard Gibbs Professor of Theoretical Chemistry at Yale University. Gibbs, while himself a professor of theoretical chemistry at Yale from 1871 to 1903, had been instrumental in the establishment of the thermodynamics of reversible processes. Fuoss stated that Onsager was as important to irreversible thermodynamics as Gibbs had been to the classical theory. *The New York Times* echoed this assessment by calling Onsager a worthy successor to Gibbs, as he had added a new dimension to the theory of thermodynamics.

The announcement of the award in *Nature* of November 9, 1968, described Onsager as a distinguished teacher as well as an accomplished theoretician. *Nature* also commented that Onsager's work was as "dry and economical" as that of Gibbs had been. The similarity to Gibbs was later mentioned in Onsager's obituary in *Physics Today* of February, 1977, when it stated that Onsager's appointment to the

Gibbs Chair recognized him as a "natural follower of the Gibbs tradition."

Ilya Prigogine, the winner of the 1977 Nobel Prize in Chemistry for his own contributions in the field of nonequilibrium thermodynamics, credited Onsager with the discovery of the first general relations in irreversible thermodynamics. Writing in *Order Out of Chaos*, he states that the reciprocal relations were the first work published in nonequilibrium thermodynamics to indicate that the field was "not some ill-defined no man's land but a worthwhile subject of study." He describes Onsager's Nobel work as a critical point in the transition from the classical equilibrium thermodynamics of the nineteenth century to the work in nonequilibrium thermodynamics that characterizes the twentieth century. In his book *From Being to Becoming: Time and Complexity in the Physical Sciences* (1980), Prigogine goes even further in his praise of Onsager's work, describing the reciprocal relations as "a turning point in the history of thermodynamics."

Biography

Lars Onsager was born in Kristiania (modern Oslo), Norway, on November 27, 1903. His father, Erling, was a barrister of the Supreme Court of Norway. Onsager's early education was varied. He spent several years with the Platous', well-known Oslo educators, and a year at a private school; he was also tutored by his mother, Ingrid. Despite these changes, he received a sound foundation, for when he entered the Frogner School in Oslo, he skipped a grade, and upon his graduation in 1920 was admitted to the Norges Tekniske Høgskole. He received his degree in chemical engineering in 1925.

After touring Denmark, Germany, and Switzerland, Onsager worked in Zurich in the laboratory of Peter Debye until 1928, when he arrived in the United States to serve as an associate in chemistry at The Johns Hopkins University. Onsager then moved to Brown University, where he was an instructor for five years.

The year 1933 was of major importance to Onsager: He received the Sterling Fellowship and moved to Yale University, where he was to remain for almost forty years. Also that year, while touring European laboratories, he was hospitalized for appendicitis. While recovering, he was introduced to Margarethe Arledter, an Austrian whose father was noted in Europe as a pioneer in papermaking, whom he married. Returning to the United States, Onsager rose quickly at Yale, becoming Josiah Willard Gibbs Professor of Theoretical Chemistry in 1945, the same year that he became a naturalized American citizen.

Lars and Margarethe Onsager were the parents of four children, sons Erling Frederick, Hans Tanberg, and Christian Carl, and a daughter, Inger Marie. Besides their home in Hamden, Connecticut, they owned an eighty-acre farm in Sanbornton, New Hampshire, where Dr. Onsager relaxed by growing vegetables. After his retirement from Yale in 1972, Onsager accepted an appointment as a Distinguished University Professor at the University of Miami Center for Theoretical Studies in Coral Gables, Florida, where he remained until his death on October 5, 1976.

Scientific Career
Although Lars Onsager began his career as a student of chemical engineering, the theoretical aspects of basic chemical phenomena became the main focus of his work. While a student at the Norwegian Technical Institute, he became intrigued with analytical problems and solved most of the examples in the classic textbook of the day, *Modern Analysis*, by Edmund Taylor Whittaker. He also mastered the principles of the newly published Debye-Hückel electrolyte theory. This work on the behavior of solutions of electrolytes, species which conduct an electric current in solution, was the subject of his first publication, written while he was still an undergraduate. In it, he applied the principles of random (or Brownian) motion to the behavior of ions in solution, thus clarifying some aspects of the original theory.

At the institute, Onsager was a member of a productive department that was characterized by the excellent quality of its students. He was greatly influenced by two of his professors, O. O. Collenberg and B. Holtsmark. Following his graduation in 1925, he toured Denmark and Germany with Holtsmark and was introduced to Peter Debye, who invited him to his laboratory in Zurich. Onsager's first stay with Debye lasted several months. He then returned to Zurich, where he worked for two years organizing his extensions of the theory of electrolytes for publication.

Following this work on classical electrolyte theory, Onsager came to the United States, where he served as an associate in chemistry at The Johns Hopkins University in Baltimore, Maryland, for the spring term of 1928. The appointment was not renewed, and Onsager accepted the invitation of C. A. Krauss to become an instructor at Brown University in Providence, Rhode Island. During his five years on the faculty of Brown, Onsager lectured on statistical mechanics and did the basic theoretical work on the extension of classical equilibrium thermodynamics to irreversible systems. This resulted in the publication in 1931 of the work that would later win for him the Nobel Prize. These two papers in the *Physical Review* ("Reciprocal Relations in Irreversible Thermodynamic Properties, I and II") contain the mathematical exposition of the first generalized relations in nonequilibrium thermodynamics.

Onsager demonstrated that in cases where two forces are operating simultaneously and the first force may influence the second, it is to be expected that the second force will also influence the first. The most important example of this that he gave involved the two forces of heat flow, as in a temperature gradient, and mass diffusion, as in a concentration gradient. By writing the proper equations, known as phenomenological equations, to express these flows, Onsager was able to show that the temperature gradient causes a mass diffusion to occur. He also demonstrated that the existence of a concentration gradient will result in a heat flow in the same system. The reciprocal relations are the equations that relate the coefficients of the terms in each of these equations and establish the equivalence of the two forces. The importance of these reciprocal relations lies in the fact that they are general in their nature. They apply to the behavior of systems of all three states of matter: solids, liquids, and gases. They allowed the principles of classical thermodynamics to be applied successfully to systems not in equilibrium and therefore to irreversible chemical processes.

The work attracted little, if any, immediate attention from the scientific community. This was most likely because of its abstract nature and the difficulty of the mathematical arguments Onsager employed in its proof. It was his earlier work on the theory of solutions of electrolytes that attracted the attention of the chemistry faculty at Yale University in New Haven, Connecticut, and prompted them, in 1933, to offer Onsager the prestigious Sterling Fellowship. It was only after his arrival at Yale that the faculty discovered that their new Fellow did not hold a doctoral degree. This considerable problem was solved by allowing Onsager to present for consideration work that he had completed earlier. His work on the mathematical background allowing the interpretation of observed deviations from Ohm's law in solutions of weak electrolytes was awarded a Yale doctorate in 1935. Onsager had already accepted a faculty position at Yale as an assistant professor in 1934.

His first work at Yale focused on what is known as the second Wien effect—the prediction that there would be a linear increase in the conductivity of electrolyte solutions with increasing strength of the applied electrical field. Onsager supplied the needed calculations to demonstrate the predicted effect. He also studied the effects of high fields on mixtures of electrolytes, determining the results on electrophoresis, a technique using differing electrical conductivities to separate mixtures of compounds. The technique rests on the first Wien effect, where the conductance is seen as proportional to the square of the field strength. This complete investigation of the Wien effect is contained in the Onsager-Wilson-Kim theory.

Continuing his work on electrolyte solutions, Onsager then described the behavior of ion pairs, intimate associations of negatively and positively charged species. He recognized that a dipolar molecule, one with both positively and negatively charged regions, generates its own local electrical field. This enabled an understanding of the behavior of polar liquids such as water.

In 1939, Onsager attended a meeting of the American Physical Society and participated in a discussion on the possibility of scientists creating an enormously destructive explosion by bombardment of a uranium isotope with slow neutrons. This was the nuclear fission chain reaction that had been postulated by many early workers in the field of nuclear physics, notably Frédéric Joliot and Enrico Fermi. Since the fissionable isotope of uranium with a mass of 235 atomic mass units constituted only 1 percent of all naturally occurring uranium, many scientists believed that it would be difficult, perhaps impossible, to separate enough of the 235 isotope to cause a sizable chain reaction.

Dr. Onsager explained that by his calculations, based on the reciprocal relations, it would be possible to separate the isotopes in the gas phase by passing them through tubes heated on one side and cooled on the other. While those assembled at that meeting argued about the feasibility of this process and its expense, the prediction was verified in a pilot plant later built at Oak Ridge, Tennessee. This method for gaseous isotope diffusion supplied the needed amounts of fissionable uranium for use in research and the production of the atomic bomb in World War II.

After the war, Onsager turned his attentions again to the solutions of difficult theoretical problems. He published an interpretation of the properties of the Ising lattice, which is a theoretical treatment of the two-dimensional arrangement of points representing forces, such as magnetic molecules, capable of interacting with one another. This provided the basis for studies of order-disorder transitions, which was to become the focus of the work of others in the field of non-equilibrium thermodynamics, including 1977 Nobel laureate Ilya Prigogine.

As irreversible thermodynamics became a more widely studied field, the value of Onsager's early contributions was rapidly appreciated. This recognition resulted in numerous awards from scientific societies in the United States and Europe and several honorary doctorates from universities here and abroad during the late 1950's and 1960's. He received eight major awards before the Nobel Prize.

The quality of Onsager's theoretical work and his publications is reflected in his rise through the ranks as a Yale faculty member. Before the receipt of his doctorate, he had been offered an appointment as an assistant professor in 1934. In 1940, he was promoted to the rank of associate professor. In recognition of his work on thermodynamic applications, he was appointed Josiah Willard Gibbs Professor of Theoretical Chemistry in 1945.

Onsager used his sabbatical leaves from Yale to investigate new areas of research. He spent 1951-1952 as a Fulbright Scholar at the Mond Laboratory in Cambridge, England, and served as a visiting professor at the University of California at San Diego during 1961. During the 1967-1968 academic year, he worked at Rockefeller University and served as the Gauss Professor at the University of Göttingen.

In 1972, Onsager ended his forty-year association with Yale University with his retirement. He accepted an appointment as a Distinguished University Professor at the University of Miami Center for Theoretical Studies in Coral Gables, Florida. Toward the end of his career, Onsager was interested in work as diverse as low-temperature physics (where he made theoretical predictions on the behavior of liquid helium) and problems in the electrical conductivity of ice. To those who knew him, Dr. Onsager was a source of distinctively clear and lively explanations of the most difficult concepts. He was known as a distinguished teacher as well as a brilliant theoretician, and Onsager's work changed the direction of chemical research with his extension of the principles of thermodynamics to irreversible processes.

Bibliography

Primary

CHEMISTRY: "Theory of Electrolytes I," *Physik Zeitschrift*, vol. 27, 1926; "Theory of Electrolytes II," *Physik Zeitschrift*, vol. 28, 1927; "Reciprocal Relations in Irreversible Processes I," *Physical Review*, vol. 37, 1931; "Reciprocal Relations in Irreversible Processes II," *Physical Review*, vol. 38, 1931; "Irreversible Processes in Electrolytes: Diffusion, Conductance, and Viscous Flow in Arbitrary Mixtures of Strong Electrolytes," *Journal of Chemical Physics*, vol. 36, 1932 (with Raymond M. Fuoss); "Theories of Concentrated Electrolytes," *Chemical Reviews*, vol. 13, 1933; "Separation of Gas (Isotope) Mixtures of Irreversible Processes," *Physical Review*, vol. 55, 1938; "Separation of Isotopes by Thermal Diffusion," *Physical Review*, vol. 57, 1940; "Crystal Statistics I: A Two-Dimensional Model with an Order-Disorder Transition," *Physical Review*, vol. 65, 1944; "Fluctuations and Irreversible Processes," *Physical Review*, vol. 91, 1953 (with S. Machlup); "Electrolyte Properties of Ice," *Electrolytes, Proceedings of the International Symposium, Trieste, Yugloslavia*, 1959; "Ferroelectricity of Ice," *Ferroelectricity, Proceedings of the Symposium*, 1966; "Possible Mechanisms of Ion Transit," *Principles of Biological Membranes, Proceedings of the Coral Gables Conference*, 1968.

Secondary

Ihde, Aaron J. *The Development of Modern Chemistry*. New York: Harper & Row, 1964. Reprint. Mineola, N.Y.: Dover, 1983. This comprehensive history of chemistry contains a discussion of the theory of electrolyte solutions and its place in the development of modern thought in chemistry. It considers Onsager's extension of the theory of Debye-Hückel in its historical perspective. It also contains a discussion of the classical foundations of reversible thermodynamics.

Prigogine, Ilya. *From Being to Becoming: Time and Complexity in the Physical Sciences*. San Francisco: W. H. Freeman, 1980. This work is a fairly technical account of the meaning of the work in nonequilibrium thermodynamics, showing how order develops from disorder. The irreversibility of time is a major theme. The chapter on thermodynamics contains a presentation of the meaning and importance of Onsager's reciprocal relations. The work contains an index and bibliography and requires some knowledge of physical chemistry to be of maximum value.

Prigogine, Ilya, and Isabelle Stengers. *Order Out of Chaos: Man's New Dialogue with Nature*. New York: Bantam Books, 1984. This work deals with the development of the field of nonequilibrium thermodynamics and its implications for the nature and meaning of reality. Includes an assessment of the seminal work of Onsager and details the advances that have been made since his initial publications. The book is indexed and contains a bibliography and notes for each chapter.

Rhodes, Richard. *The Making of the Atomic Bomb*. New York: Simon & Schuster, 1986. This account of the development of the atomic bomb begins with the experimental work on the structure of the atom in the early part of the twentieth century and continues through the Manhattan Project. It places Onsager's work on uranium isotope separation in its historical perspective in terms of the early work on the Manhattan Project. The book is indexed and contains an extensive bibliography.

Trudy A. Dickneider